GENERAL VIEW OF THE AGRICULTURE OF LINCOLNSHIRE

GENERAL VIEW of the AGRICULTURE of LINCOLNSHIRE

A Reprint of the Work Drawn up for the Consideration of the Board of Agriculture and Internal Improvement

by

ARTHUR YOUNG

Secretary of the Board

AUGUSTUS M. KELLEY, PUBLISHERS
NEW YORK 1970

SBN 678 05681 1
Library of Congress No 78-100414

This book was first published in 1813

This edition published in 1970

Published in the United States of America by
Augustus M. Kelley, Publishers, New York

Printed in Great Britain by
Clarke Doble & Brendon Limited Plymouth

GENERAL VIEW

OF THE

AGRICULTURE

OF

LINCOLNSHIRE.

DRAWN UP FOR THE CONSIDERATION OF

THE BOARD OF AGRICULTURE

AND INTERNAL IMPROVEMENT.

BY

THE SECRETARY OF THE BOARD.

SECOND EDITION.

LONDON:

PRINTED FOR SHERWOOD, NEELY, AND JONES,
PATERNOSTER-ROW:

SOLD BY G. AND W. NICOL, PALL-MALL; MOZELEY, GAINSBOROUGH;
NEWCOMB, AND DRAKARD, STAMFORD; DREWRY, AND
BROOKE, LINCOLN; AND RIDGE, NEWARK.

1813.

[*Price Twelve Shillings in Boards.*]

ADVERTISEMENT.

THE desire that has been generally expressed, to have the AGRICULTURAL SURVEYS of the KINGDOM reprinted, with the additional Communications which have been received since the ORIGINAL REPORTS were circulated, has induced the BOARD OF AGRICULTURE to come to a resolution to reprint such as appear on the whole fit for publication.

It is proper at the same time to add, that the Board does not consider itself responsible for every statement contained in the Reports thus reprinted, and that it will thankfully acknowledge any additional information which may still be communicated.

N. B. *Letters to the Board, may be addressed to Sir* JOHN SINCLAIR, *Bart. M. P. the President, No.* 32, *Sackville-Street, Piccadilly, London.*

CONTENTS.

CHAP. I. GEOGRAPHICAL STATE AND CIRCUMSTANCES.

CHAP. II. PROPERTY, ... 19

CHAP. III. BUILDINGS.

CHAP. IV. OCCUPATION.

4. Wheat,

Long

AGRICULTURAL SURVEY

OF

LINCOLNSHIRE.

CHAP. I.

GEOGRAPHICAL STATE AND CIRCUMSTANCES.

SECT. I.—EXTENT.

THERE is great difficulty in ascertaining, with any tolerable degree of accuracy, the extent of a county, when the maps of it are suspected to be inaccurate. I have no better source of information, than that of the last Survey by Mr. Armstrong: having employed a map engraver, on whom I could depend, for measuring that Map of the County of Lincoln, the result is,

	Square Miles.
That the Wolds, as marked in the map annexed to this Report, contain	367
The Heath north and south of Lincoln	185
The Lowland tracts	1214
The remainder, or miscellaneous tract	1122
	2888

The

	Acres.
The Wolds	234,880
The Heath	118,400
Lowland	776,960
Miscellaneous	718,080
Total	1,848,320

SECT. II.—DIVISIONS, AND FACE OF THE COUNTRY.

THE discriminating features of the county of Lincoln are strongly marked by Nature. Contiguous to the sea, in the southern part, there spreads a great extent of low land, much of which was once marsh and fen; but now become, by the gradual exertions of above 150 years, one of the richest tracts in the kingdom. These great works are not yet finished, but from the noble spirit which has animated this county, promise speedily to be effected. It is a region of fertility without beauty, in a climate not salubrious to the human constitution. Advancing north on the sea-coast, this rich tract becomes narrow, but reaches to the Humber, and there contracts to a mere edging of marsh land, cut off by the cliffs which rise on the Trent mouth, from a nearly similar tract, which fills all the part of the county on the left side of that great river. The heaths north and south of Lincoln and the Wolds, as marked in the map, are calcareous hills, which from their brows command many fine views over the lower regions: the rest of the county is not equally discriminated either by fertility or elevation, and, except certain spots more favoured by Nature than the

the rest, do not exhibit a country that classes among the more beautiful features of the kingdom. Upon the whole, however, it is a better country than general ideas have permitted some to esteem it.

I viewed specimens, which ought to retrieve the county from the condemnations I have heard. About Belton, there are fine views from the tower on Belmont: Lynn, and the Norfolk cliffs are visible, Nottingham castle, the Vale of Belvoir, &c. And in going by the Cliff-towns to Lincoln, there are many fine views. From Fullbeck to Leadenham, especially at the latter place, there is a most rich prospect over the Vale of the Trent, to the distant lands that bound it. These views over an extensive vale are striking, and of the same features are those from the Cliff road to the north of Lincoln, to Kirton, where is a great view both east and west to the Wolds, and also to Nottinghamshire. Near Gainsborough there are very agreeable scenes: from the plantation of H. Dalton, Esq. at Knaith, and from the Chateau battery of Mr. Hutton, at Burton, the view of the windings of the Trent, and the rich level plain of meadow, all alive with great herds of cattle, bounded by distant hills of cultivation, are features of an agreeable country. But still more beautiful is that about Trent Fall; from Sir John Sheffield's hanging wood, and the Rev. Mr. Sheffield's ornamented walk, following the Cliff to Alkborough, where Mr. Goulton's beautiful grounds command a great view of the three rivers: as the soil is dry, the woods lofty, and the country various, this must be esteemed a noble scenery, and a perfect contrast to what Lincolnshire is often represented, by those who have seen only the parts of it that are very different. The whole line of the Humber

ber hence to Grimsby, when viewed from the higher Wolds, presents an object that must be interesting to all. This, with the very great plantations of Lord Yarborough, are seen to much advantage from that most beautiful building, the mausoleum at Brocklesby.

There is a considerable inequality of surface in the Wolds about Louth, and particularly at Tathwell, &c. and being well ornamented with wood, parts of it are pleasing.

One of the finest parts of Lincolnshire I have seen, and it would be reckoned fine in any county, is from the hill above Dalby to Spilsby; from that hill the view of rich enclosures, spreading over a varied vale, and the opposite hill, with Partney church and village rising on a knoll amidst some wood, with the grounds about Mr. Bourne's, altogether form a very pleasing scenery.

From the Welton mill near Spilsby, the view is extensive: the Norfolk coast is commanded over a reach of low country, with Boston steeple, bounded by the sea.

Some very beautiful scenes are to be observed at Thurgunby, Stainton, &c. The former is the ancient seat of the Willoughbys (Lord Middleton); the house is situated high, and commads the vale to Swinop; there is some old timber about it, which gives a feature rare upon the Wolds. The ground behind varies finely, falling to a narrow vale, through which runs a trout stream, capable of giving any thing that water can confer; the surrounding hills are bold, and if planted with judgment, would render this one of the most beautiful spots I have seen in Lincolnshire. Indeed it is so at present, while left by the owner in the hands and neglect of a tenant. Here are some of the

largest

largest alders I have any where remarked. What a scenery would the lake at Croxby be, if surrounded by plantations, the pond tail dug out (rich manure), and the water carried, where it has been, to the grove of timber!

There are some delicious hills and vales at Stainton; Mr. Angerstein, I am told, intends planting two or three hundred acres; he will make it a region of beauty, and a place that would figure in the finest counties of England: there is a boundless command of water, the springs being exuberant.

SECT. III.—CLIMATE.

It is a curious circumstance, that immediately after the Witham drainage, the climate of the lowland district was rendered more aguish than before; but upon the drains being completed, this effect disappeared, and it became much healthier than it had ever been. Still, however, the people are subject to inveterate agues occasionally. The north-east winds, in the spring, also are more sharp and prevalent than further inland.

Minute of the Weather at Knaith, near Gainsborough, in 1797.

January, rain on .... 8 days,
(on one of them a little snow)
February, rain on 1
March, rain on 8
April, rain on 17

The rains from the beginning of January to this time

time had been very slight, on some days of not many minutes continuance; on the whole a very small quantity fell. The Trent was very low, the water at dry summer marks in March.

May, ...	rain on	18 days,
June, ...	rain on	25
July, ...	rain on	15
Aug. to 27, incl.	rain on	18

From the 1st of May to the 18th of June, inclusive, rain 7.$\frac{60}{100}$ inches.

From the 18th of June to the 27th of August, rain 4.$\frac{18}{100}$ inches.

In the very fine mild weather of the early spring, the thermometer never observed above 50.

Greatest height of thermometer, July 27, 81$\frac{1}{2}$.

Least height of thermometer, before sunrise, Jan. 16, 25$\frac{1}{2}$.

Much of the rain in summer from the northern and eastern quarters.

There is an extraordinary circumstance in the north-west corner of the county. Agues were formerly commonly known upon the Trent and Humber side; at present they are rare; and nothing has been effected on the Lincoln side of the Humber, to which it can be attributed; but there was a coincidence of time with the draining Wallin fen in Yorkshire, and this effect: that country is now full of new built houses, and highly improved, and must have occasioned this remarkable change.

About Barton, &c. the east wind in the months of March, April, and May, are very cold and cutting; and all along on the low land by the Humber, snow remains very little. At the equinoxes, especially the autumnal,

autumnal, very high westerly winds prevail; the trees do not turn their heads from the sea, but from those west winds.

Upon the whole, there is nothing very peculiar in the climate of this county, or at least nothing noted which has come to my knowledge, though it was an inquiry I every where made. The most singular circumstance is, the very general improvement which has taken place in it gradually, by the vast tracts which have been drained and cultivated, a work still going on, and which has rendered a district that extends many miles, incomparably more healthy than before. In proportion, also, as the country in general becomes more and better cultivated, and fuller of industrious population, the same effect must have, in other districts, taken place, though not in an equal degree. The bleak wolds and heaths being almost all enclosed and planted within twenty or thirty years, is a circumstance that has probably had a similar effect.

SECT. IV.—SOIL.

In attempting to give a general idea of the soil of this very extensive county, I must premise, that no one can be named which contains a greater variety; for it may truly be said to include all the sorts of land that are to be found in the whole kingdom. There are few exceptions, but granite, schistus, the white surface of the Hertfordshise chalks, and the pure blowing sand of Suffolk. If soils are divided, as may be, relative to practice, into 1. clay, 2. sand, 3. loam, 4. chalk, 5. peat, they are all to be found in large districts,

tricts, under many variations. Harsh, churlish, tenacious, infertile clays. Sands poor and of admirable fertility. Loams of every possible description, and some that rival the best in the kingdom. The calcareous class in chalk, limestone, and gypsum. Peat of many sorts, from a wretched thin covering of bad sands, to the deep treasures of ponderous bog.

On entering the county from Wisbeach to Long Sutton, every one must be struck with the richness of the soil. It is one of the finest tracts I have seen—a brown dark loam, of admirable texture. The district continues, with some variation of peat near Spalding, quite to the sea at Freestone, beyond Boston.

In boring at the bottom of a well at Boston twenty-seven feet deep, they came very soon to a stratum of blue marl, colour of Westmoreland slate, which continued for upwards of one hundred and fifty yards, with exceptions only of a few inches, amounting to not more in the whole, than three feet.

Mr. Cartwright found at Wintringham, and also at Great Cotes near Grimsby, the warp land equally calcareous. Proportion calcar. 106½ parts to 110½. In the hilly parts at Wintringham, limestone 206 calcar. to 11 of soil. The Great Cotes 38½ calcar. to 201½ of soil, and also 40½ to 199½. Query, if this soil does not extend all along the low land on the coast?

At Scot Willoughby, Osburnby, and the neighbourhood of Folkingham, there are three soils; strong clay, on a mortary bottom, stiff and churlish, difficult to work. A *creech*, loam on stone, dirty in winter; call it watery creech, because wet; lames sheep by feeding turnips on it. Rich hazel loam.

At Kirkby, near Sleaford, there is a tract of beautiful pasture land, dry enough for sheep, and rich enough for

for bullocks: Mr. Fisher's eligible farm is a fine specimen of it.

I was particularly pleased with the tract of reddish sand (by the way, that colour is always a good sign) at Belton, and which holds for several miles along the vale to Normanton, &c. it is very deep at Belton, and gives vast crops of oats; fine turnips, and large trees, beech, lime, ash, &c. Most profitable land for the alternate husbandry of grass and arable, as managed in Lord Brownlow's park.

The reddish sands upon the heath, open field arable at Blankney, are excellent for barley; and extend too far into tracts under rabbits—not equally good, but too good for that application.

The heath new enclosures north of Lincoln, to and about Hackthorne, are on limestone.

In a ride with Mr. Harrisson from Norton Place, going by the Roman road, and returning by the cliff, I had an opportunity of seeing, at a distance, a great tract of country, from the Wolds on one side, to the Nottinghamshire rising grounds on the other, and of having the nature of the country explained to me. The variations of soil are nearly all longitudinal in the direction of north and south. The heath, now all enclosed, is a tract of high country, a sort of back bone to the whole, in which the soil is a good sandy loam, but with clay enough in it to be slippery with wet, and tenacious under bad management; but excellent turnip and barley land, on a bed of limestone, at various depths, from six inches to several feet, commonly nine inches to eighteen. This hill slopes sharply to the west; the declivity of the same nature, but generally good; and this extends some distance in the flat vale, for the first line of villages (built also as the soil lies

lies in a longitudinal direction north and south); the soil is rich loam, containing much pasturage. Beyond this tract there is a line of strong wet clay, harsh, difficult, unprofitable land, which no art has yet been found sufficient to convert to good permanent grass, and will demand a man's life to do it. Beyond this comes the immediate line of the Trent, which, like the borders of most rivers that pass a flat country, is a very rich warp loam of various description. Returning to the Heath hill, and looking eastward, there is no cliff, but the country slopes gradually into a vale, of soils too various for description, but not good in its general feature. Half way to the Wolds, but in a line not regular, there is a rising tract of good land, that is narrow, on which the villages are built. This sinks again into another part of the various soiled vale to the Wolds; thus forming, between the Heath and the Wolds, first the narrow ridge on which the villages are built, lett at about sixteen shillings; then the Ancholm flat at fourteen shillings; the ridge of pasture at sixteen shillings; a flat of moor very bad; and then the Wolds.

About Gainsborough there is the same disposition observed in the country, for the soils to be found in north and south longitudinal direction. Between Gainsborough and Newark, for twenty-five miles, all is sand, with a flat marsh tract on the river, sometimes very narrow indeed; whereas on the Nottinghamshire sides, it spreads into wide commons. This is the case at Knaith. Behind the sand, which is good and in tillage, is a tract of cold wet clay. At Martin the sand is very rich, and letts at thirty shillings.

The soil of the isle of Axholm, is among the finest in England; they have black sandy loams; they have

warp

warp land; they have brown sands; and they have rich loams, soapy and tenacious; the under stratum at Haxey, Belton, &c. is, in many places, an imperfect plaster stone.

The space from Tilby to Scunthorp, four miles long, north and south, and three miles broad, east and west, chiefly light sand; but producing good turnips, barley, and rye. From Scunthorp to Messingham, part sand, part cold clay, and much open field. Winterton, good channelly loam, on a limestone substratum; Wintringham, very rich; Alkborough, mixed sand; Halton, good arable; Roxby, part sand, good barley, and turnip, and some wheat; Coalby, good wheat and beans, excellent loam. These form the nook south of the Humber. Under the whole country, generally speaking, stone is to be found at various depths. No plaster.

But the finest estate I have seen of some time for soil, is the lordship of Wintringham; it consists of three descriptions of land: marsh, called here warp and *grove;* strong loam under the bean husbandry; and dry loam for turnips. All three are excellent. The marsh is a tract of alluvion of the Humber, deposited to the depth of six feet, and apparently as good at bottom as at top. The bean land is not a strong loam; but a friable sandy loam, with clay enough in it to give it rather too adhesive a tenacity for turnips. The turnip land is a reddish, friable, rich loam, dry, but putrid; a finer soil can scarcely be seen, adapted to every crop that could be put into it.

Various good soils through Whitton and Halton.

Barton field, of 6000 acres, is a good turnip dry loam, on chalk of various depths, dry at bottom, yet moist enough on the surface from texture to it fit for all

all common crops, and does well both for sainfoin and wheat.

It would be loss of time to attempt many distinctions in the soils of the great tract of the Wolds; all I saw or heard of, is a sandy loam, on a chalk bottom; the quality very various, from poor sand producing heath *(erica vulgaris)* to rich, deep, fertile loams, that yield capital crops of barley and wheat, and some even beans.

Between the boundary of the Wolds (see the map) and the sea, there is the tract called the Marsh and Middle Marsh; the former is a rich tract of salt marsh, the soil therefore well known; the latter is a line of strong soil, called *the clays*, and it is stiff; but from Belesby towards Grimsby consists of a strong brown loam, much superior to a real clay.

To the west of Caistor there is a bad moor for some miles extent, which was reported to me so bad as not to be worth cultivating: on examining it I found it miserably pared for fuel: it is not good; but would pay well for enclosing and cultivating. It belongs to Sereby, Grasby, Clixby, Audleby, Hundon, and Caistor; the soil is a peaty sand, on a hungry reddish sand stone.

Going from Brocklesby to Cadney, I had an opportunity of viewing from a contrary point of high lands, that series of ridges of country, running longitudinally north and south, which I viewed from the heath at Norton Place, and found Mr. Harrisson's observations confirmed. The line of pasture at Cadney, &c. is here rushy and rough, and letts at not more than fifteen shillings. The soil is strong, and almost impassable in winter.

There is some very rich pasture in front of the new parsonage

parsonage at Bigby, a very deep, reddish, brown, strong loam. The verdure luxuriant.

At Belesby the soil changes from dry wold land to stronger and richer, and soon, in descending, becomes clay; it is chiefly pasture; but every one has some arable.

In digging Grimsby haven, they cut twenty feet deep in a bed of stiff, blue, clayey warp, with many micaceous particles.

In that part of the marsh district which I viewed at Humberstone, and to Tetney, the soil is a strong, fertile, clayey loam, but with much sand in it and mica; which looks as if the whole had been once an alluvion of the sea, resembling an argillaceous warp—no sand, no gravel, no chalk, no rock; with rain it is greasy, and with successive sunshine, hardens into brick. Nearly the same quality of land, but, with slight variations, holds all the way thence till the hilly lands near to Louth.

The wold land about Louth, to the west and south west, is good, very generally a dry friable, loamy sand on a flinty loam, and under that, chalk every where: this is the soil on the warrens between Gayton and Tathwell, which I passed, and I was much hurt at seeing such land so applied. I exclaimed to Mr. Clough on seeing it; he replied, *Oh! it is good for nothing but rabbits: what would you do with such poor land two or three miles from the farms?* When men have long been accustomed to see rabbits on such deserts, and heard only that they are good for nothing else, they come to think with their neighbours, let the absurdity be what it may. But here are no leases, and therefore can be few or no effective improvements.

These

These silver grey rabbits answered better when their skins sold high. The friable surface loam is various. There is much excellent, and also some rich pasture and upland meadow on it, and of all degrees of quality; and on the sides of the hills, great spaces covered with rushes, from springs, but not a draining idea, except of paltry grips that are all vain. But to drain well, demands leases.

From Louth to Saltfleet, Sutton, and then to Alford and Spilsby, a considerable tract of the Marsh and Middle Marsh is viewed. The soil of the Marsh is rich, adhesive, marine clay and loam; and the Middle Marsh resembles it; but is of inferior fertility, much in open arable fields detestably managed: fertility very great, indeed, on the Marsh, as is noted under the article Grass Lands.

From Spilsby to Boothby, in the Middle Marsh, much excellent soil; and, in the vale of Partney, the broken banks of the river make a rich and deep display of a fine mellow reddish loam, apparently an alluvion of the river. Towards Boothby there are lanes which have a tendency to *mook* and *blather*.

The hundred of Skirbeck is in general extremely various: in the part near Boston, and some others, the surface is a rich loam, upon clay first to some depth, and then the silt, which is found at a certain level in general: this silt is a porous sea sand, which has been deposited ages ago, becomes firm with rain, but is not fertile; near the sea there is a thin covering upon clay; and Mr. Linton has observed, that by ploughing into it no damage has been sustained; however, it is a general observation, that the soil is best where there is none near it. Near the fen there is an infertile very stiff

stiff blue clay upon the surface; grass almost always mown: the very richest pastures are a black mould, or mass of vegetable particles.

The sandy soil, which prevails from Spilsby to Reevesby, extends very much in the following parishes: Tattershal, Tattenshal, Thorpe, Kirkby, Roughton, Coningsby, Tumby, Tofthill, part of Mareham and Reevesby, East Kirkby, Hagnaby; much in East and West Keal; Spilsby, Haulton, High Tointon, Partney, Hundleby, part of Langton, all Asgarby, Harrington, part of Agworthingham, Somersby, Enderby, Salmonby, Ashby Puerorum; part of Greetham; part of Tetford, Belsford, Goulsby, Asgarby, Scamblesby, Stennigate, Hainton, Willingham, and the Raisins, Market Raisin all sand. The other soils in the vicinity of Reevesby, are white marl or blue clay, the latter of which makes the best pasture. The fen lands consist of a heavy, deep, sandy loam, which makes very rich breeding pasture for sheep, but not for feeding; another part of a rich soapy blue clay, and another of black peat, consisting of decayed vegetables, and when drained, is deemed by the inhabitants to be of all others proportioned to rent the best for arable.

The tract of Wold north of Louth, by Elkington, Ormesby, Wyham, Binbrook, Swinop, Thoresby, &c. exhibits a great variety of excellent soil, all calcareous, friable, sandy loams on a chalk bottom, dry enough to feed turnips where they grow, and much good enough for wheat. The red chalks are particularly good, being almost without exception excellent for turnips and barley. At Thoresby Warren the vales are red, and nettles are among the spontaneous growth. Nettles and rabbits together!

Very

Very good loamy land from Hainton to Lincoln, of various qualities.

About Claypool the soil is very strong and excellent; a fat clay, but much of it subject to floods: fine bean land, and some parts do very well for seeds, but they soon wear out on the inferior lands; the better fields run well to white clover; and Mr. Hebb gave me an instance of a seedsman sowing very ill, and not joining his casts, yet in three years no distinction, all run equally to white clover.

Five or six miles round Grunsthorn, at Grimsthorp, Tromestead, Edenham, Swayfield, Bytham, Witham, &c. the soil is sand, creech, or clay; the creech the best for arable; the sand whitish, or light red; some of the clay good, much of it cold, wet, and poor.

There is fen below Bourn and Marton, which joins the great tract to the Isle and to Boston.

SECT. V.—WATER.

In the low districts the water is almost every where brackish.

At Horbling there are very fine springs of water, and at Billingborough: Mr. Fydel of Boston sends his cart seventeen miles for this water.

On the heath to the north of Spittal, there are brooks almost in every valley.

At Haxey, in the isle of Axholm, the water is uncommonly hard; impossible to wash with: mixed with milk, it turns it in boiling to a curd; the under-stratum an imperfect gypseous stone. They have here and there wells of better water.

Upon

Upon the Wolds near Brocklesby they make artificial ponds for their sheep; by a layer of clay of six inches, well beaten and trodden by sheep, &c. and then covered with flints, to keep the feet of cattle from piercing the clay.

In the parishes of Tetney, Fulstow, and that vicinity, blow-wells, which are deep flowing pits of clear water, which flow in considerable streams; the depth said to be unfathomable; but Sir Joseph Banks found the bottom without difficulty at thirty feet. The same thing as at Bourne, where a spring turns a mill almost as soon as out of the earth, near the flat country, and from the chalk-hills.

There are sometimes in very dry seasons a want of water in the rich marshes of Skirbeck hundred, and about Boston; no springs or ponds are made for cattle, as they fail: the *sock* or *soak* among the silt is sometimes brackish.

In the sandy parishes that reach from Spilsby to Tattershal there is every where plenty of water, which breaks out of the hills in springs, and if not cut off, find their way into the fens below.

Mr. Loft, at Marsh-chapel, bored for water, and with great success: it yields a constant stream from the depth of above 100 feet; runs equally every year, and in all seasons, enough for 100 head of cattle: but it is apt to silt up: to prevent which he tried a tin pipe, but it rusted and spoiled: has since put down a copper one to the depth of eighty-one feet.

There is at Louth a spring, which always runs in summer, and never in winter.

At Binbrook I remarked several very powerful springs; and the Rev. Mr. Allington shewed me, at Stainton, some other beautiful ones. These all run into the

the sea near Tetney, and I conclude that hereabout is the highest point of the Wolds, for afterwards going from Kirmond to Tealby, I found the streams running to the west.

The navigation of the county is treated of under another head, where the Trent will be mentioned.

There is nothing in the other rivers which demand particular attention, unless it be the circumstance, that the whole course of the Witham, from the spring to the sea, is within the county.

CHAP. II.

PROPERTY.

AS to property, I know nothing more singular respecting it, than its great division in the isle of Axholm. In most of the towns there, for it is not quite general, there is much resemblance of some rich parts of France and Flanders. The inhabitants are collected in villages and hamlets; and almost every house you see, except very poor cottages on the borders of commons, is inhabited by a farmer, the proprietor of his farm, of from four or five, and even fewer, to twenty, forty, and more acres, scattered about the open fields, and cultivated with all that minutiæ of care and anxiety, by the hands of the family, which are found abroad, in the countries mentioned. They are very poor, respecting money, but very happy respecting their mode of existence. Contrivance, mutual assistance, by barter and hire, enable them to manage these little farms, though they break all the rules of rural proportion. A man will keep a pair of horses that has but three or four acres, by means of vast commons, and working for hire.

The enclosure of those commons will lessen their numbers, and vastly increase the quantity of products at market. Their cultivated land being of uncommon fertility, a farm of twenty acres supports a family very well, as they have, generally speaking, no fallows, but an endless succession of corn, potatoes,

toes, hemp, flax, beans, &c. They do nearly all their work themselves; and are passionately fond of buying a bit of land. Though I have said they are happy, yet I should note that it was remarked to me, that the *little* proprietors work like negroes, and do not live so well as the inhabitants of the poor-house; but all is made amends for by *possessing* land.

In the angle of country in the north-west of the county, the land is possessed by half a dozen persons. The coast from Ferraby Sluice to Gun-house inclusive, nearly all belongs to Lord Carrington, Sir John Sheffield, and Mr. Goulton.

SECT. I.—ESTATES, AND THEIR MANAGEMENT.

In this immense county there are found, as in all such extensive districts, estates of every size: my list, without pretending to correctness, contains one of 25,000*l.* a year; one of 14,000*l.*; one of 11,000*l.*; six of 10,000*l.*; one of 8000*l.*; one of 7500*l.*; two of 7000*l.*; one of 6000*l.*; one of 4500*l.*; one of 4000*l.*; seven of 3000*l.*; five of 2500*l.*; one of 2100*l.*; six of 2000*l.*: but from the situation of these properties, not spreading into some large districts, I have reason to believe that the catalogue is very incomplete; that it must be incorrect, the nature of such inquiries ensures to a certain degree.

Upon enclosing Kirton, it was found there were 146 proprietors in 5000 acres, two of them possessing 1500 acres.

On the enclosure of Barton there were above 120 proprie-

proprietors. About a third of the parish possessed by the two Mr. Grayburns. Some owners have one to three hundred a year; and abundance of small proprietors, themselves the occupiers.

Lord Yarborough's property is very extensive around Brocklesby; he has the lordships of Brocklesby, Immingham, Hayborough, Great and Little Limber, Audleby, Cayburn, Swallow, Kerrington, Croxton, and Melton, all contiguous, besides abundance more scattered.

Laceby is, I think, one of the prettiest villages in the county, containing a great number of very well-built houses, with much air of comfort, and several of a more considerable appearance, and being on a slope of country, and very well wooded, with a fine clear stream through it, the aspect is on the whole very pleasing. I inquired the cause, and found it inhabited by freeholders; each man lives on his own.

At Wintringham, Lord Carrington has a man employed, whose only business is to be constantly walking over every part of the estate in succession, in order to see if the fences are in order: if a post or rail is wanting and the quick exposed, he gives notice to the farmer, and attends again to see if the defect is remedied. This, upon a tract of land large enough to bear the expense, is an excellent system.

There is nothing in the state of property, in Lincolnshire, that pleased me more than to find on the Wolds, and especially about Louth, men possessed of estates of three, four, five, and even six or seven hundred a year, and yet remaining farmers, occupying other farms hired, and some of them living merely on their own, but keeping entirely to the

manners

manners and the appearance of farmers; consequently thriving, independent, and wealthy, and the result of all, as happy as their personal merit, their moral virtue, and dependence on, and attention to, their religious duties permit them to be. Such a spectacle is not only pleasing to an individual, but highly beneficial to the community; such men are able to cultivate their land well, and to make exertions not in the power of weaker efforts; and would do much more if it was the custom of the county to give leases; but unfortunately it is not.

In the vicinity of Reevesby, freeholds, in Sir Joseph Banks's time, have upon the whole diminished; but in South Holland it is said that they have increased much.

A fifth part of all this neighbourhood is small freeholds, but in the Fen parishes half are so.

In the hundred of Skirbeck property is very much divided, and freeholds numerous. In the parish of Frieston, containing about 3000 acres, there is not one plot of more than 48 acres together, belonging to one person; some late purchases have raised it to 60 acres.

In the management of a great estate, I remarked a circumstance at Reevesby, the use of which I experienced in a multitude of instances. The liberality of Sir Joseph Banks opened every document for my inspection; and admiring the singular facility with which he laid his hand on papers, whatever the subject might be, I could not but remark the method that proved of such sovereign efficacy to prevent confusion. His office, of two rooms, is contained in the space of thirty feet by sixteen; there is a brick partition between, with an iron plated door, so that the

room

room in which a fire is always burning, might be burnt down without affecting the inner one; where he has 156 drawers of the size of an ordinary conveyance, the inside being thirteen inches wide by ten broad, and five and a half deep, all numbered. There is a catalogue of names and subjects, and a list of every paper in every drawer; so that whether the inquiry concerned a man, or a drainage, or an enclosure, or a farm, or a wood, the request was scarcely named before a mass of information was in a moment before me. Fixed tables are before the windows (to the south), on which are spread maps, plans, &c. commodiously, and these labelled, are arranged against the wall. The first room contains desks, tables, and bookcase, with measures, levels, &c. and a wooden case, which when open forms a bookcase, and joining in the centre by hinges, when closed forms a package ready for a carrier's waggon, containing forty folio paper-cases in the form of books; a repository of such papers as are wanted equally in town and country. Such an apartment, and such an apparatus, must be of incomparable use in the management of any great estate: or, indeed, of any considerable business.

SECT. II.—TENURES.

At Ferraby, Sir John Nelthorpe has a right to turn in horses on the common meadows saved for hay; and it is preserved to the present time.

Tenures in this country are much copyhold in the low country, but not much in the higher land; and a consi-

considerable quantity in church-leases: lett some for three lives, and others for twenty-one years, renewable every seven: and many crown lands lett for years.

Lord Exeter has property on the Lincoln side of Stamford, that seems held by some tenure of ancient custom among the farmers, resembling the *rundale* of Ireland. The tenants divide and plough up the commons, and then lay them down to become common again; and shift the open fields from hand to hand in such a manner, that no man has the same land two years together; which has made such confusion, that were it not for ancient surveys, it would now be impossible to ascertain the property.

CHAP

CHAP. III.

BUILDINGS.

SECT I.—SEATS AND HOUSES OF PROPRIETORS.

THIS is a subject of considerable consequence to men of small fortune, who are under the necessity of building, to contrive a house that shall be convenient, well adapted to the mode of living of the proprietor, and capable of being executed at as moderate an expense as may be, is an object worthy of attention. In such an inquiry nothing more is to be expected from a hasty survey, than to omit no opportunity of noting the practices which seem effective, and may not be generally known; such scattered remarks, when the whole kingdom is reported, may probably afford much useful intelligence.

Observing at Brothertoft, that Mr. Cartwright's stucco was remarkably hard, and not discoloured, I inquired the process; he favoured me with the following very interesting particulars.

The Materials used, and the mode of preparation, in making and applying the Stucco, with which the House at Brothertoft Farm is fronted.

"It is to be observed, that stucco for ceilings, which is not exposed to the weather, and which is required to be elastic, that it may not crack with the vibration of the

the floor above, is properly made with effete lime, in which the cementing principle is become weak. It is apprehended also, that the workmen, not making the necessary distinctions, have been accustomed to carry into practice the same mode of making their stucco for the walls of rooms, staircases, &c. where it should seem a strong cement would be preferable to a weak one; and in general carried away by the notion of its being necessary to have stucco *elastic*, and *tough*, instead of perfectly hard, and consequently brittle like stone; they have even for the most part prepared stuccos for the outsides of houses on the same principle as for ceilings. Mr. Cartwright thinking this a gross error, and that an external stucco ought, if possible, to have all the properties of the hardest stone, determined to proceed accordingly.

Agreeing with Anderson respecting the properties of lime as a cement*, Mr. Cartwright imagined the whole business to lie in the purity of the lime and the sand, in the lime being as fresh from the kiln as possible, in the proportions adopted in the mixture, and in the care observed in forming it; and he therefore proceeded as follows:

1. River sand was obtained, of which the stony particles in general were about half the size of white clover seed†; some of them larger. After using a common bricklayer's riddle to clear the sand of gross impurities, it was well washed in six successive waters; putting into the tub at a time a small quantity of sand

---

* See his Essays on Agriculture and Rural Affairs, vol. i. Essay on Quicklime.

† It is not imagined the size of sand is material, except it be in an extreme either way. The reason for avoiding extremes in this particular, will be seen in what respects the mixing the materials.

to

to a large quantity of water. This number of washings perfectly freed the sand from all earthy particles, so that it would not soil a white handkerchief; which is the point to be secured, whether it require less washing or more.

2. The lime came from Warmsworth, near Doncaster, as fresh from the kiln as the length of the navigation would admit. In slacking it, no more water was used than absolutely necessary to reduce it to powder, and the operation was performed on a clean flag pavement laid on purpose. Without waiting for the whole being pulverized, the fine part was separated by a fine riddle from the coarse. The fine part was again immediately passed through the finest sieve used for dressing flour for French rolls, pastry, &c.

3. The materials being thus purified, and in readiness, they were mixed in the proportions of six parts of sand to one of lime, and the greatest care taken to make the mixture as intimate as possible before any water was put to it. *Lime-water* was then put to it in very small quantities at a time, working the sand and lime together with the greatest attention, and without sparing labour. This operation was also performed on a clean flag pavement, and a spade used in preference to the common wooden beater. The action of the spade was much the same as applied by the bricklayer's labourer, when preparing mortar for immediate use; but of course in preparing this cement, abundantly more pains were bestowed upon the operation.

It being the intention of this operation, first to bring particles of the water into contact with every particle of the lime, now reduced to an impalpable powder; and then to spread this moistened lime over every face and every angle of each particle of stone of which the sand is is composed; it is evident that too much nicety cannot be bestowed upon it, and that the labour ought not to cease until the end be obtained. As in the water there is no cementing principle, there ought to be no more used than sufficient for moistening all the particles of the lime. And as, in this moistened state, it is the property of caustic lime, coming in contact with flints and other stony particles, to crystallize, with a powerful adhesion to such particles, it should seem that the quantity of such moistened lime should only be sufficient for merely filling up the interstices between the particles of sand.

Hence it is very probable, that the stucco here particularly spoken of might even have been improved by a larger proportion of sand than was used; although indeed it is apparently perfect in a very high degree. But the proportion of sand should ever be regulated by the quality of the lime made use of; for as lime (not affecting to speak with the utmost chemical accuracy) is nothing more than calcareous matter united with sand; so if the limestone itself contain a large proportion of sand, a smaller proportion will of course be required to form a good cement. It was therefore on a presumption, that Warmsworth lime, which is in esteem for making good mortar, contained a considerable proportion of sand in its own composition, that Mr. Cartwright adopted the proportion of river sand he used in his stucco.

4. As only one steady careful workman ought to be employed about the cement (unless a very large work were in hand), and as it is disposed to crystalize very rapidly, no more should be made at a time than the plasterer or plasterers can lay on at once; and all that may be spared at night, should be thrown to the common

mon mortar heap, and fresh stucco made in the morning.

In preparing the stucco for his house, Mr. Cartwright attended personally for the greater part of the time; but there are small variations of colour in some parts, which he considers as proofs, that in his occasional short absences the materials were not always mixed with all the attention required for a perfect work.

5. Prior to laying on the stucco, the wall is to be washed with a brush and *lime-water;* and as the making of lime-water is attended with neither trouble nor expense, it is recommended even to use it in slacking the lime, that the lime first used may correct any possible quality in the water unfavourable to the cementing principle.

If an *old* wall is to be stuccoed, all moss or other vegetation must previously be removed. The face of the house at Brothertoft farm was so much covered with green moss, that it was thought necessary to dress it over with a mallet and chisel, and then to scrub it with a hard brush, constantly dipped in lime-water.

The stucco has now stood four winters, with every appearance of hardening with time; and, in consequence of the agreeable colour of the sand made use of, the composition has a tint, a shade or two darker than Portland stone, but much more uniform in colour. That stone, when nearly inspected, has a spotted appearance; whereas this stucco, carefully made, will always resemble a stone of one uniform grain; and is extremely well adapted to buildings of elegance.

From considering the simplicity of the composition, and the extreme stony hardness of the stucco, Mr. Cartwright is strongly persuaded that in this very composition we have the whole secret of the cement of the

the ancient Romans, consisting of nothing but lime and sand in purity, and knowing how to make use of them. Particles of brick are frequently found in their mortars, and may be no bad substitute for good sand. If a recovery of the fixed air, expelled by burning limestone, be necessary to great hardness, and the perfection of cement, we must not expect new made stucco or mortar to rival that which has been made two thousand years; but so far as a judgment can be formed from examining the stucco now spoken of, by the stroke of iron tools, without absolutely breaking into it, its present hardness is equal to that of excellent stone, and it bids fair to endure as long as the best.

It is not consistent with the design of this work to describe seats; but as I find an article in the arrangement of chapters and sections with this title, there are one or two notes I took which I venture to introduce. The creation Mr. Harrisson has formed at Norton deserves to be mentioned, because for 22 years it is really surprising. What is now Norton-place was, 23 years ago, an open field, under the barbarity of the common field system: there is now an excellent house, with offices complete, a large lawn, a water half a mile long, a very handsome bridge over it; a garden walled, with the appurtenances, and shrubberies planted with taste, and kept in beautiful order, and the whole surrounded with flourishing plantations, that have attained for their age a very fine growth. There is upon the whole, turn which way you will, a finished air; it is complete, and an extraordinary place for 22 years to have effected.

Thirty years ago I was at Summer-castle, Sir Cecil Wray's, and my surprise at viewing it again was very great; the plantations are of such extent as to fill the eye on every side, and the lawn so great with the castle boldly seated on the highest ground, looks down on the woodland vale, where the water appears to advantage. What a scene of wood, &c. to be raised for miles together, in such a space of time!

Those who are fond of mild snug retreats, where taste is more indulged than grandeur, and an execution in a difficult line free from affectation, will approve Knaith, the ornamented cottage of Mr. Dalton: it is very pretty, on the Trent, sheltered with hills and woods, and the house in a style that must please every one: the drawing-room opens into the green-house, which is planted like a conservatory, and not benches of pots and tubs, in the common formal order. If this sort of pleasing luxury is connected with a house, something of a walk, or shrubbery of exotics, disposed as in a decorated garden, only covered with glass, is far preferable to green-houses; which are so absolutely artificial to the eye without any circumstance to take off the effect, that one views the proudest assemblage of plants with comparative indifference.

Of Lord Yarborough's immense plantations, I speak in another place.

Grimsthorpe-park is one of the most exensive in the kingdom; there are three ridings in it, each four miles in the straight line, and not in the same direction. Magnificence resulting from the extent of the space under lawn, from the happy position of the woods, and the situation of the castle, commanding on one side the park and water, and on the other a large extent of cultivation, is the character of the scene: there is more variety, than strangers who pass it quickly would conceive; the rough forest scene near the Black quarry, and May's-hill, are very different from

from the rest; and if the vale beneath had been floated, as was once intended, there would have been few water scenes more beautiful in the kingdom.

SECT. II.—FARM-HOUSES.

MR. HOYTE, at Osbornby, having built a new and very convenient farm-house, which I thought remarkably cheap, I requested the elevation, plan, and estimate of it.

The sum Total of the Estimate of Mr. Hoyte's House, Osbornby, Lincolnshire; all the Materials, Carriage, and every Article complete, for the sum of 919l. 18s. 11½d.

James Norbury, Billingborough—Carpenter's Work.

Cube ft.	in.		£.	s.	d.
87	0	oak to bottom floor, and labour, at 3*s*. 6*d*.	15	5	4½
9	6	oak-wrought rabited, and in door and window, at 4*s*. 6*d*.	2	2	9
757	6	fir to roof, floor bond timber, and labour, at 3*s*.	113	12	6
77	0	ridge roller to roof, run at 3*d*.	0	19	3
679	0	superficial clean batten floor, and dowled, at 80*s*.	27	3	6
1175	0	white deal floor, superficial, at 37*s*. 6*d*.	22	0	7½
421	0	sashes and glass, weights, lines, and complete, at 3*s*.	63	12	0
22	0	sash to skylight, at 2*s*. 4*d*.	2	11	4
			103	6	clean

Cube ft.	in.		£.	s.	d.
103	6	clean deal stairs, at 1*s*. 6*d*.	7	15	3
87	0	ramp and kneed hand rail, mahogany and deal banisters, at 1*s*. 9*d*.	7	12	3
205	6	inch deal backs and elbows, at 5½*d*.	4	13	11
288	0	inch deal grounds to doors and windows, at 6*d*.	7	4	0
354	0	double architraves to doors and windows, at 10*d*.	14	15	0
161	0	single architraves, at 8*d*.	5	0	8
Two chimney-pieces, ornamented, at 3*l*. 10*s*.			7	0	0
Two chimney-pieces, at 18*s*.			1	16	0
One chimney-piece, at 9*s*.			0	9	0
366	0	window shutters quirk, ogee and astragal inch ¼ and 2 heights and 4 panels, at 12*d*.	18	6	0
163	6	framed jambs to door, soffits, quirk, ogee astragal in 2 and 3 panels, at 11*d*.	7	9	5
652	0	narrow grounds to mouldings, at 2*d*.	5	8	8
151	6	superficial base and surbase mouldings, at 10*d*.	6	12	6
45	0	base moulding and dust board, at 9*d*.	1	13	9
170	0	of ¾ deal dust board, at 4*d*.	2	16	8
225	9	of ¾ deal wash-board, moulded edge, at 5*d*.	4	5	1
31	0	of ½ inch deal capping to backs and elbows, at 2*d*.	0	5	2
125	0	of narrow capping to surbase, at 1*d*.	0	10	5
			431	0	inch

M^r. HOYTE's HOUSE.

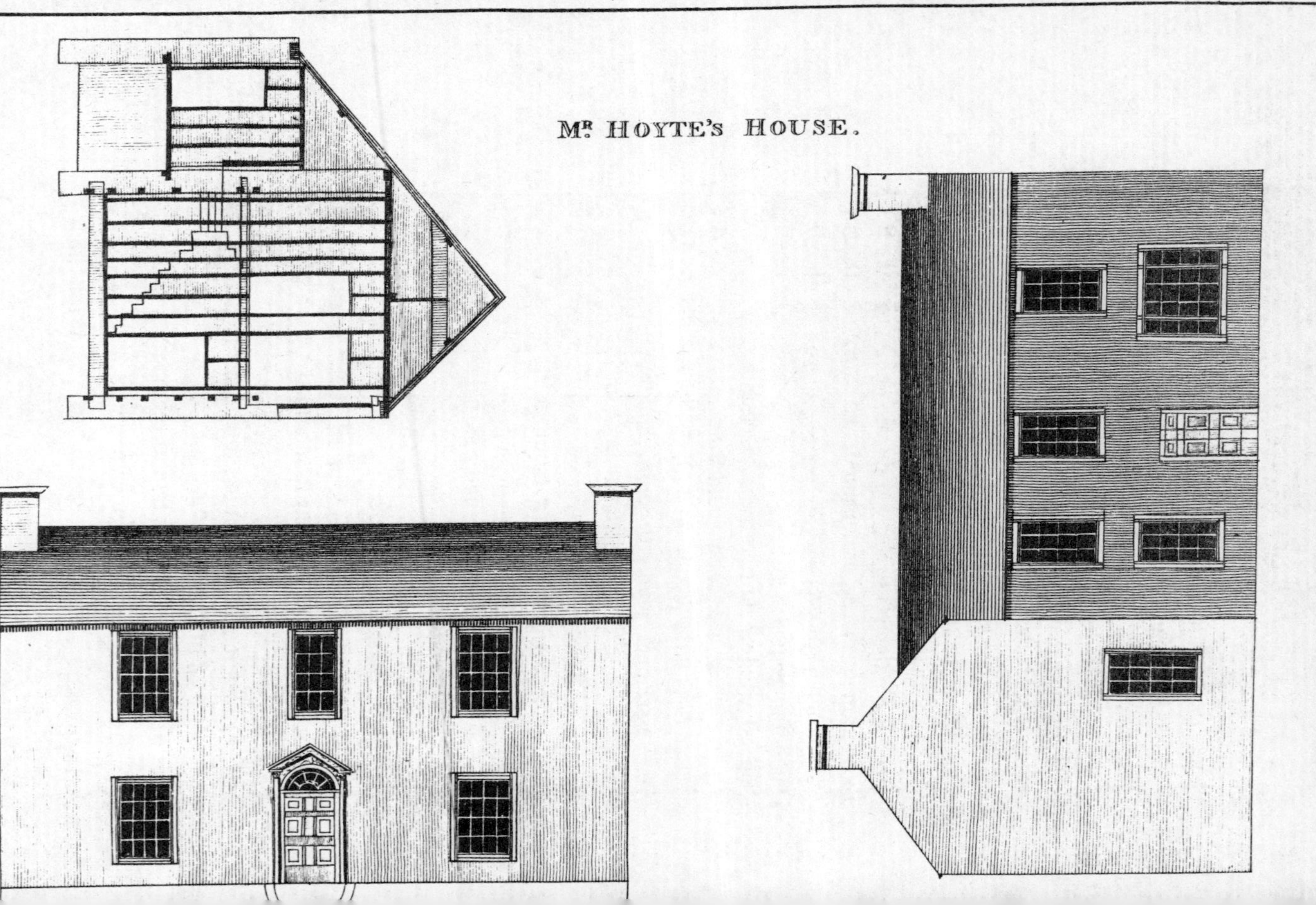

Neele sc. Strand

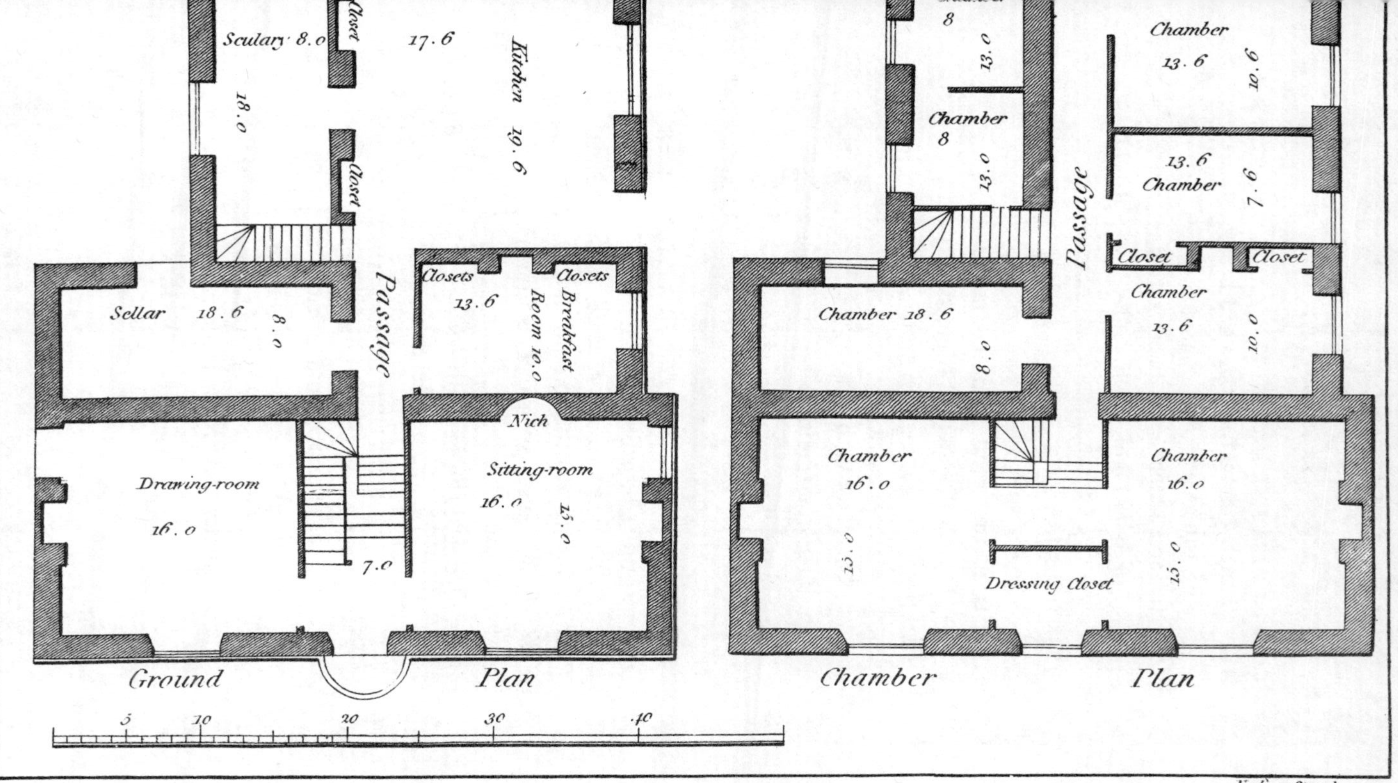

Neele sc. Strand.

Cube fts	in.		£.	s.	d.
431	0	inch ¾ moulding ogee and bead run at 2*d*.	5	6	9
158	6	inch ¾ door, six panel quirk, ogee astragal, both sides, at 1*s*. 4*d*.	10	11	4
158	0	double rabited inch ½ door-cases, at 8*d*.	5	4	3
14	0	of inch and ¼ deal window-board, moulded edge, at 7*d*.	0	13	3
24	6	of 2½ inch 6-panel work, both sides, quirk, &c. at 1*s*. 6*d*.	1	16	9
		Frontispiece to door	3	15	6
		To iron fanlight top of front door	2	2	6
123	1	cornice to front of house, &c. at 1*s*. 6*d*.	9	4	7½
123	0	battening to walls, at 7*d*.	4	6	4
48	0	gutter boarding, at 3*d*.	0	12	0
		Two coat painting, at 6*d*.	0	10	0
543	0	sound-boarding, at 16*s*. 6*d*.	4	9	8
32	0	two inch six-panel bead and flush, at 1*s*.	1	12	4
48	0	¾ deal shutters, at 6½*d*.	1	6	0
51	9	inch ½ deal 6-panel door, quirk, &c. at 1*s*.	2	11	8
124	6	inch ½ deal 6-panel door quirk, ogee and moulded back, at 1*s*. 2*d*.	7	5	2
13	3	pilasters to niche, at 12*d*.	0	13	3
138	0	inch deal framed shutters to cupboards fronts, at 11*d*.	6	5	11½

150 3 inch

Cube ft. in.		£.	s.	d.
150	3 inch deal shelves, cut edges, to cupboards, at 7s.	4	7	6½
31	0 inch ¼ deal pegs to hang clothes in closets, at 7d.	0	18	4
102	9 inch deal back stairs, at 9d.	3	17	0
204	0 framed closet fronts, at 12d.	10	4	11
	To 2 chimney-pieces, at 3l. 10s.	7	0	0
19	0 inch deal door, at 6½d.	0	10	3½
18	0 ¼ deal doors, at 6d.	0	9	0
15	3 inch ¼ deal bead and butt four-panel doors, at 10d.	0	12	8½
39	0 angle beads to jambs, at 3d.	0	9	9
76	0 ditto ditto ditto, at 3d.	0	19	0
To 22	spring window bars, at 3s.	3	3	0
72	pair of butt joints and screws, 1s. 2d.	4	4	0
48	strong brass drops, at 8d.	1	12	0
7	iron-rimmed locks, brass handles, at 7s.	2	9	0
32	pair of butt joints and screws, at 2s. 4d.	3	14	8
46	ditto ditto ditto, at 1s. 6d.	3	9	0
10	fine warded locks, at 7s. 6d.	3	15	0
18	glass bars, at 6d.	0	9	0
7	cupboard locks, at 2s.	0	14	0
8	chimney bars to chimney, at 6s.	1	10	0
2	strong iron bolts, at 2s. 6d.	0	5	0
7	thumb latches, at 2s.	0	14	0
40	ridge roll irons, at 6d.	1	0	0
16	feet of green glass, at 1s.	0	16	0
10	cwt. of lead, at 28s.	12	14	0
4	cwt. of mill lead, at 30s.	6	15	0

rain

	£.	s.	d.
rain water pipe head	1	0	0
6 yards of pipe to ditto, at 9*s*.	2	14	0
Bill ditto, day's work, putting nails, &c.	3	2	7
Total	£.502	16	2½

The Bricklayer's, Slater's, and Plasterer's Work, to Mr. Hoyte's House.

	£.	s.	d.
To 105 yards of gage chopped stone wall, on front, clean arches to ditto, at 3*s*. 3*d*.	17	1	3
518 yards of chopped stone walling, and clean arches, at 2*s*. 6*d*.	64	15	0
34 yards of rough stone walling foundation, at 1*s*. 6*d*.	2	10	0
36 yards of nine inch brick wall, at 6*s*. 6*d*.	11	14	0
46½ yards of brick wall, at 17*d*.	3	5	2
building chimnies	7	2	0
bricks to ditto	2	10	0
120 feet of water-tabling, at 6*d*.	3	0	0
83 feet of stone sills to sashes, at 1*s*.	4	3	0
37 feet of astragal stone steps to front, at 22*d*.	3	7	10
36 feet of plain stone to passage, at 1*s*.	1	16	0
7 feet of stone sill to kitchen, at 1*s*.	0	7	0
77 feet of stone chimney-pieces, at 1*s*.	3	17	0
477 feet of stone floor, at 7*d*.	13	18	3
182 feet of ditto, at 7*d*.	5	6	2
34¼ feet of brick pavement, at 17*d*.	2	9	7

To

	£	s.	d.
To 62 yards of plaster floor, at 2s. 6d.	7	15	0
404 yards on the walls, at 6d.	10	2	0
32 feet of , at 1s.	1	12	0
63 feet of enriched cornice, at 20d.	5	5	0
258 feet of cornice, at 8d.	9	10	0
63 feet of plain cornice, at 8d.	2	2	0
346 yards of three coat-plaster ceiling, at 16d.	23	1	4
201 yards of three-coat plaster on walls, at 1s.	15	3	0
54 feet of stone coping to chimnies, at 1s. 6d.	4	0	0
12 yards of composition to chimnies, at 18d.	0	18	0
258 yards of two-coat drawing on reed, at 10d.	10	15	5
29¾ square of blue slating, &c. at 15s.	22	6	3
scaffolding to ditto	5	0	0
niche in dining-room	2	12	6
2 ovals, &c.	1	1	0
220 load of stone carriage, at 5s. 6d.	60	10	0
40 chaldron of lime, at 14s.	28	0	0
carriage of lime, 20 load, at 4s.	4	0	0
11½ ton of slate, at Boston, portage 4s. 6d. at 83s.	47	19	0
20 miles carriage of ditto	8	8	0
Total .... £	417	2	9

Mr. Gregory, of Humberstone, near Grantham, has great merit in building new houses and offices for his tenants to a remarkable degree, under the direction of Mr. N. Stubbins, of Pierrepont, near Nottingham.

About

About Norton, and all along the heath tract, repairs are done, if considerable, by the landlord, and smaller by the tenant: 500*l.* will raise all the buildings, house included, for an arable farm of four hundred acres. Mr. Harrisson has, at Kirton, raised a new house and farm offices, including complete bullock stalls, and yards for thirty-six bullocks, which, had he had no old materials, would have cost him 800*l.*; the farm 400 acres.

Mr. Thorpe, at Owersby, has built a pigeon-house over the thrashing-floor of the barn, which he recommended me to observe, as he thought it a proper place for it. I am inclined to think, that thrashing-floors will so soon be entirely discarded, that it is not worth thinking what should be put over them.

Upon Sir John Sheffield's estate, on occasion of repairs upon a large scale, such as additions, the rent is raised 7½ per cent. upon the money expended. Repairs are done by the tenants.

At Winterton, there is a famous windmill, that cost 2000*l.* building. It has five sails, 30 feet long, of wood, in cross boards, no sail-cloth, space between, and they open and shut at pleasure: the great axletree is of iron, and took twenty-two oxen to draw it.

At Wintringham, Lord Carrington has built several new farm-houses, barns, &c. with conveniences for new farms, and at a rate which shews the cheapness of such works in this country.

Mr. Lloyd, of Belesby, who has built various conveniences, among the rest a good barn, by contract with his landlord, remarked that for tiling, the laths should be laid over first with a regular cast of mortar, like plastering a house, and then the tiles laid on; his on the new barn are pantiles; they last thus as long again.

At

At Gayton, near Louth, the farmers do all repairs, and buy timber for them; such circumstances should be noted, for without them the rent of land cannot be properly judged.

About Revesby, the farm-houses built of late years, are of brick and tile; and for a farm of 100*l.* a year, a dwelling will cost about 250*l.* the stables 50*l.* the cart-house, cow-house, hog-sties, &c. 50*l.*; the barns will cost 80*l.* and 50*l.* The old buildings are of timber, walled with clay, called stud and mud, and covered with reed; some with wheat and rye straw, which when new, will cost one third less than brick and tile.

Mr. Ellisson, at Sudbrook, has built farm-houses complete; one cost 370*l.* every thing included except leading, for a farm of 280*l.* a year, being 478 acres. For another for 235 acres, 290*l.*

The dairy at Grimsthorpe is one of the best contrived that I have seen; coolness is secured by its being sunk in the side of a hill, and from shade unpierced by the sun; air in every direction, and a double roof. The management seems as good as the building.

SECT. III.—COTTAGES.

In the low rich country they are commonly built of what is called *stud and mud;* the stud-pieces as large as a man's arm.

At Brothertoft, 29 cottages of brick and slate have been built in one regular front by Mr. Cartwright

8 of which, the rooms are 12 feet square.

8 ———————— ditto 12 by 14.

8 ———————— ditto 12 by 16.

4, 12 feet by 12.

One

One centre one, of three rooms on a floor, two of 12 feet square, and one of 12 by 18, besides the bow.

All have a pantry six feet wide, and a necessary and pig-sty, with a small back yard for coals and wood, and a small garden in front. The whole cost building 2538*l*. 15*s*. 2*d*.: would lett for, free from the manufacture of woad, 3*l*. each, on an average.

There has been around Folkingham, many new enclosures made by act of parliament, upon which occasion a proper attention has been paid to assigning to every cottage at least three acres of land, including a garden, upon which, for the most part, they keep a cow, and are much better labourers for it. In that of Osbornby I saw these plots.

They will, at Frieston, build a cottage of stud and mud for 30*l*. Mr. Linton shewed me four he had built, two-and-two: one set of stud and mud, and thatch; the other of brick and tile; the two former cost 40*l*. the two latter, 60*l*.

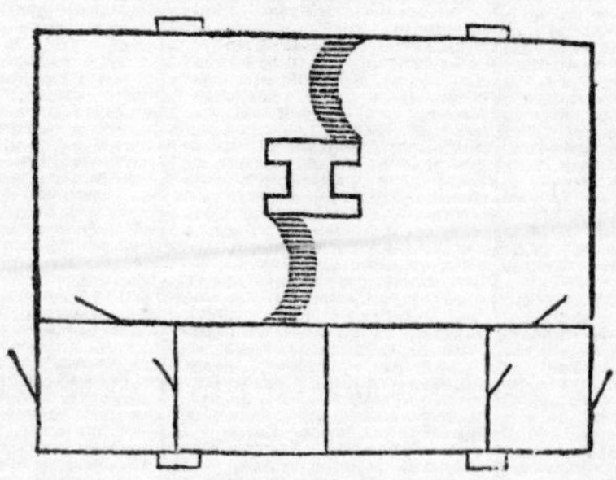

Each cottage consists of a room below, and a room above; the entrance is into a small room for washing, a sort of common open store-room; by this means, the keeping room is much warmer than if the house door opened directly into it; the other room is a little

little dairy, in which also the beer is kept. By the staircase being reversed, as in the plan, each cottage has a closet under his neighbour's staircase.

At Reevesby, &c. a brick cottage for two families will cost 80 guineas; and the smaller sort, for one family, will cost 50*l*. Of stud and mud, one third less. There are many new cottages built, and especially in the new enclosed fens; sometimes land is leased on contract for building them.

CHAP. IV.

OCCUPATION.

SECT. I.—FARMS AND FARMERS.

IN the Holland fen, from 100 to 400 acres the large class; but many very small.

About Folkingham they are from 100 to 400 acres, the general size.

On Lincoln-heath side, along the cliff, and across to the fen on the other side, they vary much, but in general are moderate; 400*l.* a year, very large.

About Hackthorne, for some miles in the new enclosed lands, from 40*l.* to about 200*l.* but some much larger; at Riseholm one of 1600 acres, a beautiful one, well managed by Mr. Moody.

At West Keal, near Spilsby, about 60 tenants pay 1330*l.*; but said to be worth much more.

North of Lincoln, on the heath, the variation from 50*l.* to 200*l.* and 300*l.* and some few much larger.

About Gainsborough and Knaith they are small; 200*l.* a year is large.

In the north-east angle, on the east of the Trent, they are in general large; from 200*l.* to 500*l.* Some small, and too small in the opinion of well-informed men; as the farmers now can scarcely bring up their families.

At Wintringham, on one of the richest soils in England, farms rise from 200*l.* to 600*l.* a year.

On the Wolds, farms are in general large; from the nature of the country they can hardly be small. From 500 to 1000 acres, about Brocklesby.

About

About Louth the same; but Mr. Grant rises much higher, and is said to have paid near 3000*l*. a year rent for many years.

About Spilsby farms are from 100 to 500*l*.

In the manor of Reevesby, all enclosed, there are 62 farms for the rental of 1397*l* being the rent of 3401 acres. This vast division of farms arises from a determination in Sir Joseph Banks, not to distress the people by throwing them together, by which he loses much in rental, and sees a property ill cultivated; and which must be the case, till by deaths he can gradually, but very slowly, improve it. In the following estates, also belonging to him, the same humanity operates. In Marum, 399 acres of old enclosures, and 82 of field land, 481 in all, rent 276*l*. from 29 tenants. In Horncastle, 497 acres, 765*l*. from 52 tenants. Fulstow, 378*l*. from 14 tenants. Marsh-chapel, 701*l*. from 13 tenants; in this estate one of 319*l*.

By taking the acres and rental of a part of the estate of Sir Joseph Banks in Lincolnshire, being something more than the half of his property in that county, I found that 268 tenants of land pay 5721*l*. per ann. which is something under 22*l*. each, on an average. The largest farm on the whole estate is 319*l*.

The farms adjoining the Fens are generally small, the largest not more than 200*l*.; but with some exceptions a few of 300*l*.; the greatest part from 30*l*. to 100*l* The Wold farms, part white marly clay, and part chalk, are from 200*l*. to 500*l*. a year; there is a necessity for those hills being in much larger occupations than the lower county. When it was lett in smaller farms they could not manure those hills so well, and the turnip culture has thriven only in the hands of the larger ones.

In

In the hundred of Skirbeck they are very small, but few exceeding 100*l.* a year. Several lands are occupied by Wold farmers, for the purpose of maintaining the stock bred upon the hills, for which purpose they will give higher rents than others.

Farms about Sudbrook, enclosed in 1766, from 50 or 60 acres, to 400 or 500. At some distance, larger Mr. Moody's at Riseholm, one of the largest in the country, 1400 or 1500.

Upon the size of farms in general in Lincolnshire, it may be very safely asserted, that they are moderate. The number of large ones bears no sort of proportion to those which are very small. And where both extremes are excluded, the size will be found much under what is common in many other counties. Farms of 20*l.* or 30*l.* a year, though a few may be useful in some cases, as spurs to the industry of saving labourers; yet these instances will occur much more seldom than is commonly supposed. Upon a great estate minutely divided, Sir Joseph Banks would have very rarely an opportunity of placing such a labourer in a farm, without turning out some widow or son of a deceased tenant; so that in districts where these little farms greatly abound, they do not operate in this respect in any thing like the degree that has been stated by various writers. And it should further be considered, that as the occupiers of them are incomparably less at their ease, yet working much harder than labourers, it is much to be questioned, whether the mass of human happiness is not considerably lessened by such occupations. As to the effect of them on the cultivation of the kingdom, no doubt can be entertained of its evil tendency; and I have had very many opportunities of remarking it in the course of my journey through this county.

As

As to the character of the farmers who have occupations sufficiently large to be met with at the most respectable ordinaries, or whose exertions had occasioned their being named to me as men proper to call upon, I can dispatch my account of them in very few words: I have not seen a set more liberal in any part of the kingdom. Industrious, active, enlightened, free from all foolish and expensive show, or pretence to emulate the gentry; they live comfortably and hospitably, as good farmers ought to live; and in my opinion are remarkably void of those rooted prejudices which sometimes are reasonably objected to this race of men. I met with many who had mounted their nags, and quitted their homes purposely to examine other parts of the kingdom; had done it with enlarged views, and to the benefit of their own cultivation. And the great energy at present exerted in consequence of the introduction of the New Leicester sheep, by some to spread that breed, and by others to improve their old race, will not only have excellent effects, but has set them to think upon all other sorts of stock. It has diffused an activity and a vigour, which will shew itself gradually in many other objects. The rapidity with which the culture of turnips has spread, and the manner in which they are cultivated; and the immense drainages, which having opened new fields of wealth to landlords, have given opportunities to the tenantry neither lost nor neglected, are proofs also of the vigour with which these men have conducted their business. But without descending to particulars, and viewing only the general rise of rent in the county, we may be convinced that such a spectacle could not have taken place, but with a tenantry such as I have described.

SECT. II.—RENT.

In this article it would conduce to clearness, were the notes easily arranged under the same heads as the acreable contents of the country, respecting soil and situation; but much intelligence having been procured from the same persons relative to very different districts, to divide such articles would not only occasion many repetitions, but the reader would lose the authority in many cases; a point in such Reports as the present, of the first consequence. My authority personally cannot be what the reader wishes; but that of persons who, from long residence and extent of knowledge, must be acquainted with facts, stands in a very different predicament—it is easy to trace every article to its source; a satisfaction of much more consequence than an arrangement somewhat more agreeable.

From Wisbeach to Spalding, average rent 30*s*. an acre. Long Sutton Common, lately enclosed, 30*s*. to 50*s*. About the latter, more low and fenny, but much rich, and where corn, &c. good. Commissioners' valuation of Moulton, the whole parish 18*s*. to 20*s*. an acre. From Spalding to Boston 30*s*. In fifty years, rent and tithes have been doubled, on some estates trebled.

In Holbeach, Sir Joseph Banks has 1478 acres, rent 967*l*.; tithe 135*l*. and dikegrave's rates 49*l*. deducted; net rent 804*l*.; but greatly improvable. In Fleet, he has also 678 acres, rent 498*l*.; tithes 56*l*. and dikegrave 22*l*. deducted; net rent 419*l*. In Whaplode, 836 acres, rent 500*l*. tithe 50*l*. and dikegrave 27*l*. deducted; net rent 422*l*. In Moulton, 130 acres, rent 73*l*. tithe 10*l*. and dikegrave 14*l*. deducted; net 58*l*.

Seven-

Seventeen acres in Wiberton, enclosed under the Holland fen act, that never had been either ploughed or pared, sold lately for 1200 guineas, more than 70 guineas an acre.

Mr. Senderson sold four acres of copyhold, at the will of the lord, for 80*l*. an acre.

The 17th December, 1793, the following farms were lett by auction in Wildmore fen.

Acres.		Old Rent.				New Rent.		Per Acre.		
		£.	*s.*	*d.*		£.		£.	*s.*	*d.*
100	....	70	0	0	....	165	....	1	13	0
67	....	30	3	0	....	94	....	1	8	0
100	....	80	0	0	....	165	....	1	13	0
119	....	95	4	0	....	175	....	1	9	4
28.2	....	19	19	0	...	26	....	0	18	5
101.2	....	53	8	9	....	145	....	1	8	8
98.2	....	61	11	3	....	160	....	1	12	7
244	....	190	0	0	....	430	....	1	15	4
56	....	81	4	0	....	100	....	1	15	8
50	....	46	5	0	....	86	....	1	14	4
100 }	....	86	5	0	.... {	160	....	1	12	0
50 }						75	....	1	10	0
100	....	100	0	0	....	170	....	1	14	0
1214	....	914	0	0	....	1951	....	1	10	2½
		0	15	0 per acre						

No tax, tithe, or rates, to pay.

Lett under the Witham act of drainage for a great tract, including Holland fen, in 1762; tax 1*s*. an acre on Wildmore fen, if enclosed; 4*d*. if not; these 1200 acres enclosed and lett to pay that 4*d*. over the whole.

The eleven parishes of Holland fen contain 22,000 acres, and lett for about 27*s*. an acre, tithe free, but pay

pay a drainage tax. Before the drainage and enclosure, it was worth not more than East, West, or Wildmore fens, at present, that is nothing at all.

In nine years the rent of land in the low land district has been raised 6*s*. 6*d*. an acre, except in some instances, in which proprietors have not taken the same advantages as others have done: all might have been so.

The parish of Ewerby is an extraordinary instance how little the value of land was known some years ago in this county: Mr. Tyndal purchased 1300 acres, much of it very rich grazing pastures, for 13*l*. an acre, and has been offered 40*l*. an acre for large tracts of it; the whole would sell now probably for above 30*l*.

Around Folkingham, for five miles every way, the average 18*s*.; that is, from 25*s*. down to 12*s*.

For five miles round Sleaford, 20*s*. an acre.

Seventy-five acres of land in Ancaster Valley, with a house that wants such repairs as to reduce that consideration to a matter of no great importance, sold lately for 7000*l*. Suppose the land worth 40*s*. an acre, and the price thirty years' purchase, it would be only 4500*l*.; what it was that occasioned apparently so enormous a price, I could not learn.

Rent, five miles round Belton, town enclosures at Grantham for convenience excluded, 18*s*. an acre.

From Folkingham to Grantham, 16*s*. an acre; heath part, 7*s*. and 8*s*.

At Leadenham, the heath land, the only arable, as below the hill all is grass, at 20*s*.; the rent is 10*s*. Quadrupled in 20 years every where about Leadenham. An estate of 900*l*. a year become 4000*l*. Dr. Ellis's father lett a farm for 13*l*. a year, which is now 100*l*.

About

About Blankney, &c. land sells at thirty years' purchase; some has been sold at 50; and at Nainby at 40.

Rent of all that was Lincoln heath, 10*s*. an acre on the average. Rent of all the Wolds in the north-eastern part of the county, 8*s*.

West Keal 1800 acres, arable 682; grass, 1021, besides the rector's glebe; above 200 lett at 1330*l*. but worth more.

Hackthorne and vicinity, for some miles new enclosures, 10*s*. an acre now; the lower tracts something higher, but Hanworth is chiefly grass, and letts at 13*s*. or 14*s*. tithe free; the tenants pay land-tax; this not general.

The whole of the heath north of Lincoln, from 8*s*. to 12*s*. or 14*s*. Some higher.

About Spilsby the Wold land high, to 15*s*. and more; near Horncastle good. About Louth, low, in general from 3*s*. or 4*s*. to 10*s*. An estate of 2000 acres in the Wolds, 6*s*. 8*d*. an acre, but there is a warren.

About Norton, &c. land now sells at 28 years' purchase; it was before the American war upwards of 30; but land-tax deducted before calculation.

The lime sand which extends twenty-five miles from Gainsborough to Newark, letts at 15*s*. an acre in many places; in some more, in others less; and the tract of flat land below it, on the Trent, whether grass or arable, at 20*s*. to 30*s*.; but the average nearer 20*s*. Behind the sand is a tract of cold wet clay, on which much open field; this letts at 10*s*. or 12*s*. an acre. It lies longitudinally between the sand and the good land below the heath.

At Haxey, in Axholm, 45*l*. to 50*l*. an acre, open field;

field; but a close is worth 10*l.* an acre more than the same quality open.

At Butterwick in the Isle, the land is very fine and fertile; the best letts from 30*s.* to 40*s.* and sells up to 80*l.* the chain acre.

At Garthorpe, fresh land is lett by Mr. Curtis in large quantities to break up, at 3*l.* 15*s.* an acre, for fourteen years. Land in general here sells from 40*l.* to 70*l.* an acre.

About Normanby, Burton, and the parishes named in the article, *Soil*, the sand letts at from 6*s.* to 12*s.*; in some cases tithe free, in others not; but more at 6*s.* average perhaps 8*s.*; there is some so low as 3*s.*; the best 15*s.* tithe free. Winterton, arable and convertible, 18*s.* to 21*s.* Roxby is worth 15*s.* All down to Messingham very low rents, and yet the farmers very poor; horridly managed! At Burton a farm that was 90*l.* a year, and little made by it, is now 300*l.* in the hands of a man that is growing rich. Rise of rent in 20 years has been the half of the old rent, the third of the present. Average of all flats on rivers, from Ancholm to Birmingham-ferry, 22*s.* or 23*s.*; of this, Wintringham the best by far. Flat of the Ancholm to Brig, 21*s.*

Rents in some few estates fell in the American war, but not general.

Alkborough, all through, 15*s.* tithe free, Mr. Goulton's; the rest of it 20*s.* Whitton is 14*s.* 6*d.* tithe free.

Goxhill marshes sell at 15*l.* to 30*l.* East Horton open three roods measure, 8*l.* to 10*l.* arable. Hillingholm 15*l.* to 20*l.* an acre.

Rent of Barrowfield open, 7*s.* to 12*s.* going to be enclosed.

Wintring-

Wintringham is a a lordship particularly interesting from the excellence of the land. It is at present about 4200*l*. a year. As many vague and very false reports have been circulated about the rent of this estate, it will not be improper to specify the fact, which is as follows:

120	acres of warp land, old grazing ground, allowed to be ploughed up, at 5*l*.	£.600
80	of marsh ditto, at 2*l*.	160
30	of ditto new, at 3*l*.	90
183	at 2*l*.	366
2040	at 30*s*.	3060
2453		£.4276

I may venture to assert, that this estate, under the existing circumstances of tithe and poor-rates, is well worth 40*s*. an acre, one with another, supposing prices of all products to be at a fair average rate.

It appears that the whole is at present under 35*s*.; and it is to be noted, that all is tithe free, and that poor-rates amount to a mere trifle

At Brocklesby, by means of the noble possessor of so large a tract of country, I made inquiries into rents, and was informed that the average of all the Wolds, as marked on the map, is about 5*s*. an acre. That the line of what is called *the Clays*, between the Wolds and the Marsh, is at 10*s*. 6*d*. to 12*s*. That the Marsh is from 20*s*. to 25*s*.; some at 40*s*.

In riding over Grassby open field, and observing miserable crops, and horrible management, I inquired the rent: 9*s*. or 10*s*. The land is good, and therefore such beggarly doings are terrible: the farms are small.

At Belesby, inquiring rents in general, found that the Wolds vary from 2*s*. 6*d*. to 25*s*. The Middle

Marsh,

Marsh, as it is called, that is, the line of clay, 20*s.*; the Marsh 21*s*.

It is seldom that a proper opportunity occurs of calculating, with propriety, what ought to be the rent of land; but at Humberston something of this sort did happen: I found the tenants of that lordship thought they paid too much, and desired them to prove it; how to do that they did not altogether know, except by those vague assertions which farmers, for want of regular accounts, or rather of regular ideas, are apt to be deficient in. However, I drew from them the following particulars, which are all their own. The rotation is, 1. fallow; 2. wheat; 3. beans.

Expenses.

	£.	s.	d.
Fallow, four ploughings	£.1	0	0
Manuring	0	16	0
Seed, 10 pecks wheat, at 40*s.*	0	12	0
Sowing	0	0	6
Reaping	0	10	6
Leading, stacking, and thatching	0	6	0
Thrashing 2½ qrs.	0	7	6
Carrying to Grimsby	0	2	6
Beans. One ploughing	0	5	0
Harrowing	0	2	6
Seed, 4½ bushels. at 20*s.*	0	11	3
Sowing	0	0	6
Mowing, gathering, and tying	0	7	6
Leading, &c.	0	6	0
Thrashing three quarters	0	4	6
Carrying out	0	3	0
Tolls on two crops	0	1	0
Poor-rates, three years (no tithe)	0	3	6
	£.5	19	9

Three

Three quarters of wheat, at 44*s*.	£.6 12 0
Straw, ...	0 10 0
Four quarters of beans, at 25*s*.	5 0 0
Straw, ...	0 10 0
	12 12 0
Expenses	5 19 9
Remains	6 12 3
Farmer's profit	1 16 0
Landlord's rent	4 16 3
Per acre per annum	1 12 1

The course is an execrable one.

But calculate upon, 1. fallow; 2. wheat; 3. clover; 4. beans; 5. wheat; and then see what the result will be! I can believe their beans do not produce much more than three quarters, from what I saw in a favourable year; but all broad-cast, and no hoeing, no weeding; a marvellous exhibition of every sort of luxuriant weed.

Rents about Louth on the Wolds are various; but in general, from 3*s*. 6*d*. for warrens, to 20*s*. for the better soils; in general, if an average could be drawn, it would probably be about 8*s*. or 10*s*.

To Saltfleet across the Marshes, open arable 12*s*.; grass of inferior quality 20*s*.; marshes 30*s*. to 40*s*. and the same to Sutton, and thence to Alford. The late Mr. Chaplin's marshes at Skidbrook sold up to 77*l*. an acre. Thirty-four acres at 34*l*. a year, and not worth more, sold, in September 1797, at 1160*l*.: all small parcels of land in the marshes sell at high rates; this is very near thirty-five years' purchase.

A good

A good deal of rich marsh of Burgh, Croft, Wainfleet, Winthorpe, Adlethorpe, lett at 40*s*. an acre.

For five miles round Dalby, land letts at 15*s*.; much at 18*s*.

Rent of all the Wolds from 8*s*. to 10*s*. Of the clays 14*s*. or 15*s*. Of the marsh 14*s*. to 40*s*.; average 21*s*.; tithe excluded in all.

Rent of arable in the hundred of Skirbeck,—consisting in part of ancient inferior pasture, broke up and continued in tillage for many years, rent about 26*s*. and some in open or partially enclosed fields, the rent about 19*s*.; for that of the grass, see Grass.

Sir Joseph Banks's property:

Reevesby,	3401 acres, rent	....	£. 1397
Marum,	481 ditto, ditto	....	276
	3882, or 8*s*. 6*d*. per acre		£. 1673

Rents on the Wolds, the barren parts partly under rabbits, lett at 8*s*. to 10*s*. The convertible parishes, part in arable, and in pasture, from 12*s*. to 18*s*. Between the Wolds and Lincoln-heath, and the Witham fens, a heavy clay earth, a small part of very good feeding ground for oxen and sheep, and a much larger part appropriated to breeding oxen and sheep; some meadow, and very subject to rot in wet seasons; each farm a proportion of arable for wheat and beans with fallow, as too dirty for turnips in their opinion; average of the whole 14*s*. or 15*s*. The marsh from Sutton to Wrangle, the best 36*s*. average; the second rate 26*s*.; the ings 18*s*.; and the open field arable 12*s*.; the partially enclosed 21*s*.; the open meadows, &c. 16*s*.; all Holland fen at 25*s*.; much at 21*s*.: these are the rates of the estates of great men,

men. Between Deeping fen and Lincoln-heath a tract of clay; from Sleaford to Grimsthorpe, much good soapy clay; and some red hazel earth of inferior quality, average 21*s*. Between Notts and Lincoln-heath, from Glentworth to Lincoln, including to Trent; the Cliff-Row towns, from Spital to Lincoln, average 15*s*., being four sorts; a very light weak creech stone, 6*s*.; next 12*s*.; next 21*s*.; being creech stone mixed with clay, on a rock. Next line below the hill good pasture, at 20*s*. Next, cold clay, pasture, and meadow, at 14*s*. Trent side land, part very rich, and some sand, average 20*s*. The range of Cliff towns from Lincoln to Grantham consists of three ranges of land like the above, and same rent; but the best creech land on the hill top, worth 23*s*. Lincoln-heath, in two lines east and west; the east side from Thorpe to Canwick 6*s*.; the west at 8*s*.; the heath, north of Lincoln, 6*s*. The Isle of Axholm, and the Marsh land 26*s*.; although many small freeholders, who lett to one another at from 40*s*. to 3*l*. or 4*l*. for particular crops. From Spalding to Tidd, north to the sea, south to Cambridgeshire. In all this level, the high land being chiefly rich feeding ground for sheep, and some parts beasts; but being indifferently watered, in dry seasons, is uncertain consequently for the latter; average 30*s*. The Marshes, anciently embanked, part light silt or sand, and part indifferent for breeding, suitable for wethers brought from the Wolds and the high country, fed off at three years old, gives good and much wool; average 10*s*. to 20*s*. The fen side not effectually drained; a good soapy clay, rent average 12*s*. If well drained, cheap at 21*s*.; as good as Holland fen. From Spalding to Boston, both sides, best, 36*s*. good feeding, some part indif-

indifferently watered; second rate 26*s.*; third rate, poor silt, 20*s.*; Spalding to Deeping, the embanked land well drained, 21*s.*; enclosed black peat, very rich, 21*s.* The open commons do not pay more than 2*s.* 6*d.* Thus far Mr. Parkinson.

Rents for some miles round Sudbrook, and to Wragby, 16*s.* or 17*s.* an acre. To and about Hamton, 20*s.* Mr. Ellison bought Toft and Newton in 1785; 2000 acres lett for 737*l.*; he gave 19,000*l.* and 2000*l.* in buildings, &c.; and it is now lett at 1160*l.* net rent. It therefore pays above five per cent.

Mr. Gibbeson's farm near Lincoln, twenty years ago, was 30*l.* a year; it is now 300*l.*

Mr. Jennison of Lincoln, has a farm at Ludford, which was lett at 25*l.* a year, when the tenant could not pay the rent; it is now 100*l.* and the farmer does well.

For five miles round Claypool every way, rent 20*s.* an acre; would be worth more, but they are much subject to floods, which rot many sheep.

Rent of the country west of the north road at Grantham, &c. 20*s.*

Grantham to Closterworth, hilly, 16*s.*

Rents five miles every way round Grimsthorpe, 15*s.* but some open fields at 6*s.* or 7*s.*; some grazing land worth 30*s.*: about Bourn, &c. the Fen begins.

To draw these various articles to some general result, it will be proper to divide the county, as before, into the four divisions of 1. Lowlands, 2. Wolds, 3. Heath, and 4. Miscellaneous.

Lowlands.

Lowlands.

Upon calculating the average of all the minutes, I find it amounts to 1*l.* 4*s.* per acre; but in order, by a different mode of estimating, to examine the truth, I supposed certain proportions of this tract as follow:

Acres.		*Rent per Acre.*	*Total.*
100,000	Axholm and Marsh	28*s.*	£. 140,000
150,000	Being half the maritime line from Wainfleet to the Humber	30*s.*	225,000
150,000	The other half ditto	15*s.*	112,000
80,000	The fertile district, which may be called, of Boston	40*s.*	160,000
150,000	Remainder of South Holland	25*s.*	187,500
80,000	The Witham tract	16*s.*	64,000
66,000	Fens, &c. not begun to be drained	—	—
776,000			£. 888,500

By this account the average is about 1*l.* 2*s.* 10*d.* per acre. This division of the 776,000 acres is by conjecture, as accuracy is not necessary; the result not being materially different, may justify our estimating the rent of this great and valuable tract of country at 23*s.* an acre. It is capable in most, I might say in almost every part of it, of being improved to the average of 30*s.*

The Wolds.

The average of all the minutes is 10*s.* 4*d.* per acre; but that of the general rent of the whole district is only 8*s.* 6*d.* Paying due attention to the richer parts near Louth,

Louth, &c. not, I conceive, so much in the contemplation of some of my informants as they ought to be, I am inclined to estimate the medium at 9*s*.

The Heath.

The average of all the minutes is 8*s*. 4*d*. which will not vary materially from the more general information.

The Various District.

The average of the minutes is 17*s*. an acre. The variety is so great from the rich lands of Wintringham at 40*s*. down to the worst soils in the county at 1*s*. and 1*s*. 6*d*. that accuracy is unattainable. Combining, however, the general information with the particular notes, I think this ratio too high, and shall estimate the whole at 14*s*.

RENTAL OF THE COUNTY.

The Lowlands	776,960 at	23*s*.	£. 893,504
The Wolds	234,880 at	9*s*.	105,696
The Heath	118,400 at	8*s*. 4*d*.	49,333
Miscellaneous	718,080 at	14*s*.	502,656
	1,848,320 at	16*s*. 9¼*d*.	£. 1,551,189

Thus the average rent of the whole county appears to be 16*s*. 9*d*. per acre.

Uniting the information gained under this head, concerning the rise of rent, with that which appears in the Chapter of Enclosures, there is some reason to believe this rental to have been trebled in 30 years.

SECT.

SECT. III.—TITHE.

In the new enclosures about Folkingham, exonerated by giving land.—In Osbornby one-seventh of the whole. In some one-fifth of the arable, and one-ninth of the pasturage.

All gathered at Haxey in Axholm. About Normanby, Burton, &c. some are gathered, some lett—4*s.* in the pound was not an uncommon composition.

About Spilsby they are seldom taken in kind, but the compositions high; arable land 5*s.* grass 2*s.* 6*d.* an acre, some lower; but in general 3*s.* 6*d.* or 4*s.* an acre round.

There are in the county about 660 pieces of preferment, including perpetual curacies and donatives, which are on an average about 70*l.*

In the hundred of Skirbeck tithe of pasture about 3*s.*; acre of arable 5*s.* to 6*s.*; new broken up land for a few years 10*s.* A small modus generally prevails for the tithe of hay, of 2*d.* an acre.

About Sudbrook, compounded at 2*s.* or 2*s.* 6*d.* an acre.

Mr. Parkinson—the tithe of pasture is worth one-ninth of its improved rent, which he proves thus; produce two lambs, on an average of twenty-one years, at 12*s.* or 24*s.*, two ewe fleeces at 4*s.* or 8*s.*; in all 32*s.*; deduct for loss one-eighth, remains 28*s.*; the tenth of which 2*s.* 9½*d.*; deduct for gathering one-third, remains 1*s.* 11*d.*; call it 2*s.* The tithe of meadow one-seventh, and one-eighth of inferior quality. That of rich grazing one-ninth of the rent. Of arable, the best one-fifth of the rent, and the inferior detached one-

one-sixth and one-seventh, according to circumstances. Approves of the Bishop of Lincoln's tithe; for the present mode of taking it is such an impediment to improvements, that his corn-rent is much better: the rector often cannot cultivate or stock it, and this prevents the necessity. Woods exempted, because, from a very ancient custom, all stand from 21 to 23 years.

Mr. Parkinson's Estimate.—Average tithes of the county is one-fifth; best arable one-sixth, inferior one-seventh; best meadow one-eighth, inferior one-ninth; pasture makes a mean of land one acre at 14*s*. the mean proportion one-sixth to 2*s*. 4*d*.

Ditto, 21*s*. per acre; ditto, one-sixth, 3*s*. 6*d*.

Ditto, 28*s*. per acre; ditto, one-sixth, 4*s*. 8*d*.

Ditto, 35*s*. per acre; ditto one-sixth, 5*s*. 10*d*.

I found throughout the county a very general desire that some law should pass for the commutation of tithe. The farmers here, with their brethren in every other part of the kingdom, consider this as one of the heaviest of obstacles to good husbandry. There can be no question of the fact, and it is not a fair argument, on the other hand, to recur to the vast rise of rent, in consequence of a superior husbandry, which has taken place in this country. Encouraged by great capitals, and the general liberty and happiness enjoyed by the nation, agriculture has made a vast progress; but this progress would have been much greater, had tithe been generally commuted. And it much deserves attention, that in this county enclosing and draining, which have flourished perhaps more than in any other, have established an exemption from tithe over a very considerable portion of the whole; and that conse-

quently

quently much of the prosperity and rise of rent and improvements effected, may very fairly be attributed to this very circumstance.

SECT. IV.—POOR-RATES.

In Holland fen low; in some parishes very low, even to 1*s*. and few high.—Quere, poor-rates in Northolm near Wainfleet 24*s*. in the pound, but only 14 acres in the parish; this year 50*s*.? In Swineshead 2*s*. in the pound, nominal rent. About Folkingham, on an average 1*s*. 3*d*. in the pound, real rent. The poor, church, and roads, 2*s*. 6*d*. At Hackthorne 9*s*. a week for the whole parish; but six or seven keep cows. At Kirton 2*s*. 2*d*. in the pound; at Mr. Harrisson's 1*s*.; but now more. At Gainsborough, rates 3*s*. and will, by the enclosure, be brought down to 1*s*. 6*d*. At Knaith, &c. 1*s*. 6*d*. At Haxey in Axholm 2*s*. 6*d*.; 15 years ago 6*d*. to 8*d*. In 1795, total in this parish 223*l*., land-tax 267*l*. At Alkborough 9*d*. At Normanby and Burton 1*s*. 10*d*.

At Wintringham about 9*d*. or 10*d*. in the pound, and much less, were only the poor reckoned: on a rental of 5*l*. 10*s*. it appears in the article of *Grass-Lands*, all amounts only to 3*s*.; but they reckon by the acre.

About Spilsby, on an average, about 2*s*. to 3*s*. in the pound. Skirbeck hundred, see *Grass-Land*.

About Reevesby, &c. &c. they come to 5*s*. in the pound, including all town charges, through 11 parishes on the real rent. They are the lowest on the Wolds, where

where they do not exceed 3*s*. In the Fens pretty high, from persons ruined by commonage speculations.

In the hundred of Skirbeck all sorts of town charges 3*s*. 3*d*. in the pound; poor-rate only 2*s*.

At Sudbrook all rates about 4*s*. in the pound; but the poor only, on an average, 7*d*. At Lincoln, 4*s*.

Uniting these notes with other general information, I am inclined to calculate all sorts of parochial rates at 2*s*. in the pound, *real* rent, over the whole county. There is no possibility of coming to any thing like accuracy in such an estimation; as in some parishes where the assessments are said to be on the real rent, it is not so in fact; and alterations constantly taking place that are unknown. It is much to be regretted that returns are not made to the Board of Agriculture, or the Privy Council, by authority of Parliament, from every county in the kingdom, of the annual amount of rates, especially those for the poor. When first the Minister undertook the great object of the poor, had he proposed a Bill simply for the purpose of gaining information (a part of his scheme), it would have been at this moment in full operation, and a great basis gained, on which to erect any edifice his great talents might devise: and whenever he may think proper to resume the business, *this* will be the best first step in a work that can only be well executed by gradual advances.

SECT. V.—LEASES.

VERY few leases in Holland fen. None at all about Folkingham, except part of the lordship of Pointon, where

where twenty-one years, under covenants of improvement; and in consequence of these leases the tenants have wrought very considerable improvements, in converting old bad pasturage into arable, by means of draining; subdividing, and quicking large fields: in liming the sandy ground.

No leases on Sir J. Sheffield or Mr. Gouldon's.—Leases on Mr. Eleve's; but the general practice not to grant them.

No leases on Lord Carrington's estate at Wintringham; but though the tenants have not this circumstance, they are under covenants of cropping as much as if they had them. On the stronger arable lands they are bound to 1. fallow; 2, wheat; 3. beans. And on Sir J. Sheffield's, 1. turnips; 2. barley; 3. turnips; 4. barley; with seeds broken up for turnips again.

Lord Yarborough does not give leases; but with much candour made the observation, that the principal culture of sainfoin on the Wolds, was by men who either have leases, or farm their own land.

Very few about Spilsby.

In the hundred of Skirbeck they are very unusual.

Mr. Parkinson observes upon this subject, that upon barren lands which demand marl, or that want lime, it is necessary to grant leases, in order to make estates productive. Lord Fortescue grants them on poor weak soils for 21 years, on condition that the farmer puts three chaldron of lime, or 40 loads of marl or good clay, on each acre. In circumstances where no expense of this sort, he does not think them necessary.

Sir Joseph Banks has no objection to granting leases; but he is never asked for them. Seeing a tenant of his improving his land by hollow-draining, he gave him a lease of 21 years, as a reward and an encouragement.

The

The idea is an excellent one; and if they were thus given only to such as merited reward, they would prove a powerful instigation to good husbandry.

Mr. Smith, of South Elkington, shewing me two new cottages he had built, his landlord, Mr. James Greenville, finding timber; and mentioning some other improvements he had made, observed he would do much greater things if he had a lease. The same remark has often been made to me in this county.

Very few leases about Sudbrook.

Respecting the county in general, the fact is, that leases are very rare.

Upon the subject of leases, as I wish to avoid all disquisitions which concern the kingdom at large, as much as the county of Lincoln in particular, it will be necessary only to remark, that great as have been improvements in it, I have not the least doubt they would have been much greater and more rapid, had the custom of granting leases been as common here as it is in Norfolk and Suffolk. I had particular conversations with some hundreds of farmers on this subject, and the universal opinion was, that if leases were granted, they would occasion exertions which are not found at present. Upon soils so rich that there is nothing to do, the want of them cannot be material; but upon all others, where liming, marling, draining, fencing, &c. are demanded, the want of a lease will often be the want of the improvement: and the *principle* will pervade the whole conduct of the business; nothing will be so well done upon an uncertain tenure, as with security. Confidence in a landlord attaches to himself only, and not at all to his successor; and the various instances that have occurred of estates being considerably raised, must act as warnings to others. Granting

leases

leases would, in this respect of raising rents, ease a landlord greatly; when there is no lease, there is no more reason for raising at one period than another, and when it has been done in Lincolnshire it has usually raised a great clamour. But if leases of 21 years were granted, the farmers would, in the first instance, very readily pay an advanced rent, as the price of the lease; and they might be given to understand, that at the expiration the rent would be raised again. Then a rise would be looked for as a matter of course, and no clamour would attend it. Should any landlord be inclined to make this very valuable experiment, I would caution him upon one point; not to lease the farms of an estate at one time; but give them so in succession, that some might expire every year, when they begin to fall in; which might be easily done by making it a work of five or six years, with a little variation in the duration of the leases. When a few farms in a great estate fall every year, and there is no general operation of *tasting* and valuing,—there will be no outcry; the business will be regular, and the effect smooth and quiet. The landlord will have his fair share in the progress of national prosperity, and his tenants will be secure and active.

As to covenants, a landlord would not sign leases without consulting some person upon this head, on whom he could well rely.

SECT. VI.—EXPENSES AND PROFIT.

The rich land of Holland fen I found so interesting and so fertile a district, that it was natural to wish to ascertain how far the advantages and disadvantages balanced each other, and what was the profit of cultivation, upon comparison with other districts of similar fertility. To calculate this, let us take the course of crops at present practised by that very attentive cultivator, Mr. Cartwright, with no other addition than that of a crop of wheat after the clover, to bring Lincoln and Suffolk a little nearer in system. The course will then stand thus: 1. cole; 2. oats; 3. beans; 4. wheat; 5. clover; 6. wheat.

Expenses.—1. Cole.

	£.	s.	d.
Rent and taxes	1	16	0
Four ploughings, at 5*s*.	1	0	0
Harrowing and rolling	0	12	0
Clearing twitch	0	5	0
Seed and sowing	0	1	6
Gripping	0	1	6
Manure	2	0	0
Incidents	0	5	0
	£6	1	0

	£.	s.	d.
Expenses	6	1	0
Produce	2	10	0
Loss	£.3	11	0

2. *Oats.*

2. *Oats.*

Rent, &c.				£.1	16	0
One ploughing				0	5	0
Seed and sowing				0	14	0
Harrowing, &c.				0	2	6
Gripping				0	1	6
Weeding				0	7	6
Harvesting reaping	£.0	12	0			
——— carrying	0	6	0			
				0	18	0
Thrashing and dressing 8 qrs.				0	6	8
Carrying out				0	2	6
Agency				0	2	0
Incidents				0	5	0
				£.5	0	8

Produce.

8 qrs. at 18*s*.	£.7	4	0
3 acres feed a beast for 20 weeks; straw, at 1*s*.	1	0	0
	£.8	4	0
Expenses	5	0	8
Profit	£.3	3	4

3. *Beans.*

Rent, &c.	£.1	16	0
Ploughing twice	0	10	0
Harrowing	0	1	0
Gripping	0	1	6
Seed, two strike	0	6	0
Drilling	0	0	9
Horse and hand-hoeing and weeding	0	16	0
Carry forward	£.3	5	3

Reaping

Brought forward				£.3	5	3
Reaping	£.0	10	0			
Bands	0	2	0			
Carrying	0	6	0			
				0	18	0
Stack and thatch				0	3	0
Carting to barn				0	2	0
Thrashing				0	5	0
Carrying out				0	1	6
Agency				0	1	0
Incidents				0	5	0
				£5	6	9

Produce.

5 qrs. at 24*s*.	£.6	0	0
Straw	0	5	0
	£.6	5	0
Produce	5	6	9
Profit	£.0	18	3

4. *Wheat.*

Rent, &c.	£.1	16	0
Scuffle, rake, and burn	0	10	0
Ploughing	0	5	0
Harrow and roll	0	3	0
Seed, two strike, 6*s*.	0	12	0
Drilling	0	0	9
Gripping	0	2	0
Hoeing twice	0	4	0
Weeding	0	2	6
Carry forward	£.3	15	3

Reaping

Brought forward			£.3	15	3
Reaping	£.0 12 0				
Carrying	0 6 0				
Thatch and stack	0 3 0				
			1	1	0
Carting to barn			0	1	6
Thrashing 4½ qrs. 3*s*.			0	13	6
Carrying out			0	1	6
Agency			0	1	0
Incidents			0	5	0
			£.5	18	9

Produce.

4½ qrs. at 5*s*. 6*d*.	£.9	18	0
Straw	1	1	0
	£.10	19	0
Expenses	5	18	9
Profit	£.5	0	3

5. *Clover.*

Rent, &c.	£.1	16	0
Seed, 14 lb.	0	10	0
Sowing	0	0	3
Two pecks ray	0	2	0
Mowing	0	3	0
Making	0	3	6
Carting	0	6	0
Stacking and thatching	0	3	0
Incidents	0	5	0
	£.3	8	9

Produce.

Produce.

2½ tons, at 40*s*.	£.5	0	0
After-grass	0	15	0
	£.5	15	0
Expenses	3	8	9
Profit	£.2	6	3

6. *Wheat.*

Rent, &c.	£.1	16	0
Ploughing	0	5	0
Harrow and roll	0	3	6
Seed	0	12	0
Drilling	0	0	9
Gripping	0	2	0
Hoeing and weeding	0	6	6
Reaping, &c.	1	1	0
Carting	0	1	6
Thrashing 4 qrs.	0	12	0
Carrying out	0	1	6
Agency	0	1	0
Incidents	0	5	0
	£.5	7	9

Produce.

4 qrs. at 44*s*.	£.8	16	0
Straw	0	16	0
	£.9	12	0
Expenses	5	7	9
Profit	£.4	4	3

Reco-

Recapitulation.

Cole, loss				£.3	11	0
Oats, profit	£.3	3	4			
Beans, ditto	0	18	3			
Wheat, ditto	5	0	3			
Clover, ditto	2	6	3			
Wheat, ditto	4	4	3			
	£.15	12	4			
	3	11	0			
	6)12	1	4			
Profit per acre, per ann.	£.2	0	2			

In discourse at Louth with some considerable farmers, upon their extraordinary course of crops, of, 1. turnips; 2. barley; and urging that a more profitable system might be pursued, they defended it; and asserting the benefit, I desired to calculate it, which we did thus:

Expenses.

Three or four ploughings for turnips	£.1	0	0
Manuring 12 waggon-loads once in four years, the half	1	0	0
Harrowing	0	2	6
Seed and sowing	0	2	0
Hoeing	0	5	0
Herdling, herdles, &c.	0	5	0
Ploughing twice for barley	0	10	0
Harrowing	0	1	0
Carry forward	£.3	5	6

Seed

	£.	s.	d.
Brought forward	£.3	5	6
Seed barley four bushels, at 24s.	0	12	0
Sowing	0	0	6
Weeding	0	1	0
Harvesting	0	7	0
Thrashing 4 qrs.	0	6	0
Leading out	0	2	0
Two years rent, tithe free	1	10	0
——— rates	0	3	0
	£.6	7	0

Produce.

	£.	s.	d.
Turnips, on an average	£.3	0	0
Barley, 4 qrs. 24s.	4	16	0
Straw	0	10	0
	£.8	6	0
Expense	6	7	0
Profit	£.1	19	0
Per annum	£.0	19	6

This they thought would do; but some observed, that expenses would generally run higher than any such calculation could include; and that worse land was always a drawback.

The expenses of farming near Louth are great; labour is very high: and though there is a navigation to that town, yet such is the state of trade upon it, that it generally answers, on account of difference of price, to carry twenty miles to Lincoln by land carriage, where they go with only ten quarters of barley with four horses: leave home at eight at night, and return at at eight the next night; the price is sometimes 3s. to 5s. a quarter lower Louth.

In hiring and stocking farms, Mr. Parkinson observes, that upon such a farm as is usual in Lincolnshire, to wit, part grass and part arable, so much should be the latter, that the fallow part shall raise turnips, rape, &c. to support the lamb hogs that the farmer breeds, and fatten the two shears; upon such a farm, for each 100*l*. a year he should have a capital of 750*l*. Upon a farm of 300*l*. a year, if a man has not above 2000*l*. he will soon want money.

Under the heads of *Rent*, and *Grass Lands*, the reader will find some other estimates of expenses and profit. There are circumstances very favourable to the county in this respect, and there are others extremely adverse. Of the latter complexion is the price of labour, the price of corn, the distance from Smithfield, and the custom of giving no leases. Labour is much higher in Lincolnshire, on the average, than in most other counties of the kingdom; in the Fen district, to a degree that is uncommon; and marks how very much improvements of all other kinds, have exceeded that equally necessary one of building cottages. The price of corn is considerably below the general average, and there is the further disadvantage of a heavy land carriage in many parts of the county. The distance from Smithfield, the rich grazing lands of this county suffer in common with those of Somersetshire; but the West Riding of York is probably as good a market here, as Plymouth, Bath, and Bristol, are to the former: compared with other grazing districts on a large scale, Lincolnshire is remote. The want of leases is a deficiency which is remediable; and probably a better system respecting the management of landed

landed property, will improve that point. The circumstances favourable are, first, the soil, which must, on the whole, be reckoned among the first in the kingdom; and extremely bad land is rarely found in the county. To Lincoln eyes, this is not a fact; but they are so accustomed to seeing very good land, that indifferent soils are apt to be undervalued. Another very great advantage, is so large a part of the county being, by acts of parliament, exempted from tithe. A third, is the very low burthen of poor-rates, compared with many other counties. These three essential points will be found to have a considerable effect in influencing the profits of the farmer.

CHAP. V.

IMPLEMENTS.

ON Mr. Cartwright's farm at Brothertoft, there are a great variety of implements of considerable merit. The plough is the common one of the Fen tract, and a most excellent tool it is; the mould-board of a good sweep; the throat, a segment of an ellipsis; and the form of the share of great merit, always well steeled and sharpened with files; the coulter, a sharpened steel wheel. It much resembles the Dutch paring plough of the Cambridgeshire fens; deserves attention, and ought to be in the collection of the Board *. To this plough

* The sort of plough here sketched, is almost universally used in the fens between Boston and Croyland, its wheel-coulter being much better adapted for ploughing amongst stubble and twitch-grass, than the sword one; they turn all their land over with two horses, double or parallel to each other, and in this business many of them are very clever, and will make their furrow as straight as a line; and by laying your head so low on the bottom of it, that your sight is confined by the sides, you may see down it to the further end, which is in some not less than a quarter of a mile in length. This extraordinary regularity is done by training their horses in this manner: they fix a piece of wood (pointed at both ends) between the horses, in an horizontal direction, of about two feet in length, by which means they are kept at such a distance, that the ploughman can see between them to the further end of the land he is about to plough, and is thereby enabled (by fixing his eye upon some object that is stationary) to make his furrow as above-mentioned. The points of the stick, when the horses are inclined to move too near each other, remind them of their misdoings.—*MS. of the Board.*

Mr.

Mr. Cartwright has affixed a bean drill of great simplicity, for drilling upon the centre of the preceding furrow, while the next is turning; it answers well, and drills every year a great extent of land, nor does it require previous tillage upon a stubble.

A twitch drag of his own construction, for tearing out twitch, he finds of great use; he took the hint from one used near Rotherham; when first he made it, he had a turnip fallow which his bailiff had prepared, and thought clean enough to sow: sending in the drag to try its effect, he got seven cart-loads of twitch by this tool, and it is always found, for this use, very effective.

Drilling-machines have been tried largely by Mr. Cartwright: he had two of Cook's; but prefers the improvement of Mr. Amos, his bailiff, who claims the original invention, which he now uses. This plough is described with a plate, in Mr. Amos's Treatise on the Drill Husbandry. Another tool, which is found in the same work, and Mr. Cartwright finds very useful and effective, is the expanding horse-hoe for all breadths; used constantly here for beans, cabbages, potatoes, &c.

In carriage, Mr. Cartwright uses one-horse carts for much of his work, and has invented a waggon-cart, which he calls a *cartoon*, the body of which tilts up, and delivers the load like a cart; it is lighter in weight than two carts, and made to contain the same bulk of load: clear width, four feet; height, one yard nine inches; length, eight feet. Scufflers also are in use at Brothertoft, and found very effective. Mr. Cartwright has long been making experiments on forming a reaping-machine, and has been at a great expense in executing them: difficulties have, however, occurred hitherto,

hitherto, which have prevented success. His bailiff, Mr. Amos, has varied the application of the scythes, from being pushed forward by horses, with their heads to the machine, to drawing it laterally. I saw it tried with lucern, but it would not do: and indeed this object, though infinitely desirable, will be found so difficult to carry into execution, that many experiments will probably be made, before success is attained. A machine for weighing cattle and sheep alive, Mr. Cartwright erected while he pursued grazing, and found it a very useful tool.

Mr. Cook's chaff-cutter is employed at Brothertoft: a man and a little boy cut 100 quarters in a week.

A sward-dresser has been found very useful upon the meadows and pastures of Brothertoft. It includes a scarificator, with a bush of thorns, and cuts deeper or shallower at pleasure; two horses draw it, carrying the breadth of five feet.

Vigilance in the lambing season, prevents much of the danger in bad weather; and a provision against the loss of lambs in the ditches of the breeding pastures, has here been made at a small expense, by means of lamb-hurdles, according to the annexed drawing.

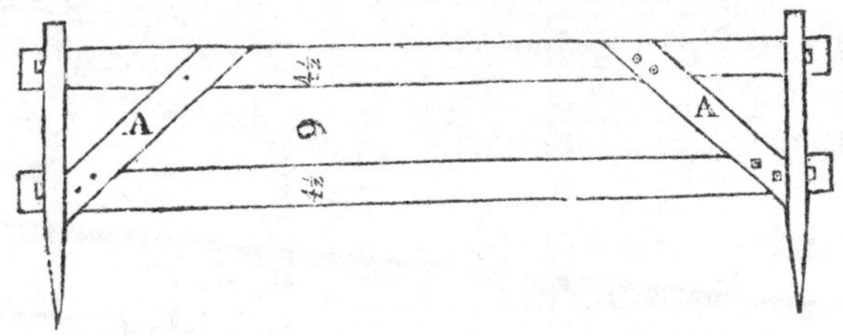

The space between the rails to be closed with tarpaulin, whereby the hurdle, when the lower rail touches the

the ground, is a perfect defence against the wind, and of sufficient height to prevent the lambs driving before a storm into the ditches; so that it answers two good purposes. At other seasons, also, these hurdles may come into use for guarding the brows of banks against sheep.

As the tarpaulin would require many nails, and canvas is a dear article, perhaps the space between the two rails may be better filled by a slit deal, held in its place by having braces, AA, on both sides, one of which might be moveable, and fix with nuts on the rivets; by which means the board might be put in only occasionally when wanted.

Covering Corn-Stacks.

DEAR SIR,

A scarcity of time will not allow me to make you at present so complete a set of drawings for explaining my contrivance for covering corn-stacks, as I could have wished; but together with the drawings I gave you, I flatter myself a moderate degree of attention will enable any one to understand it.

JOHN CARTWRIGHT.

Fig. I.—An end view, or more properly, a section of a stack, secured under an oiled canvas covering.

	I.	*I.*	*Ft.*	*In.*
A, an oak post, of which four feet is in the ground			7	0
B, a fir post, fastened to the oak post with two bolts, its bottom even with the surface of the ground	6 × 6	—	18	6
C C, moveable spars, hanging on pins fixed in the post	4 × 1½	—	12	0

	I.	I.	Ft.	In.
D, a fixed roof, for covering an interval between the two canvasses, which interval is left to carry off the damp.				
K K, sections of the upper rods, to which the canvasses are nailed. These rods are bolted to the posts, but can be taken down at pleasure	4 × 2	—	26	11
F F, sections of the lower rods, to which the bottom edges of the canvasses are nailed	4 × 2	—	26	11
G G, stretching cords; fastened to the lower rods F; and which pass through a dead sheave towards the end of the spar (see fig. 7.) By these cords the canvasses are held tight down, being fastened to				
H H, stakes which are run into the stack directly under each spar. To the heads of these stakes the cords are brought down, and there well fastened.				
Stack, wide at the base from *c* to *d*			14	6
Ditto, the eaves, from *a* to *a*			18	6
Ditto, high at the eaves, from *a* to *b*			14	6
Q Q, the two canvasses extended, being deep 11 feet, and long			27	3

Fig. II.—Exhibits a plan, on which is represented the fir posts; the spars, single and double; and the connecting rails: but omitting the oak or ground posts; the canvas rods; and the roof.

As

As this plan is adapted to a long stack of three joints, or smaller stacks, it shews where you are to place double spars, viz. at the beginning and the ending of every joint invariably (the intermediate spaces being occupied by single spars), which double spars are constructed on the principle of spouts.

To every joint, two canvasses are required; one for each side of the stack; which canvasses must all be of the same dimensions.

As the posts keep the upper rods four inches asunder, as may be seen in fig. 5, that interval forms a vent for the damps of the stack; but the interval is defended from rain by the roof D, and the damps escape sideways between the upper canvas rod and the roof.

On the same principle as here exhibited, a stack may consist of any number of joints, less or more than three, at pleasure.

N.B. The span of the spars, when in their position for covering a stack, will not exceed 22 feet six inches; whereas in this plan (in which they are represented as if horizontally extended), the span is nearly 24 feet.

	I.	*I.*	*Ft.*	*In.*
BBB, &c. are the posts, 9 feet asunder from centre to centre	6 ×	6	— 18	6 long.
CCC, &c. spars	4 ×	$1\frac{1}{2}$	— 12	0
CCCC, &c. double spars, or spouts, of which the sides are	4 ×	1	— 12	0
The bottoms	6 ×	1	— 11	6
The oblique lining boards ...... See fig. 8.		$\frac{3}{4}$		

a a a a,

	I.	*I.*	*Ft.*	*In.*
a a a a, &c. checks, making lodgments for the connecting rails, and having in them dead sheaves; through which pass the stretching cords G (see fig. 1 and 7.)	4 ×	$1\frac{1}{2}$ —	0	6
I I I, &c. connecting rails, some	4 ×	1 —	3	$10\frac{1}{2}$
Others	4 ×	1 —	8	3

In joint No. 1. on the side A B, the connecting rails are represented, as finally placed for steadying the spars; but on the side C D, they are turned up and lying against the spars, to which they are attached by hinges at *f*. When so turned up for being stowed away, they are fastened by means of a staple, *g*, fixed in the spar, and long enough to pass through an aperture in the rail, and receive the point of a hook, *h*, which is fastened to the rail itself by another staple, as seen in joint No. 3, of this plan; and upon a larger scale in fig. 3.

When these rails are let down, and lodged against the cheeks at right angles with the spars, as on the side A B, then the hook *h* enters a corresponding staple fixed in the cheek to receive it. See fig. 3.

By means of these connecting rails the spars are kept steady, parallel to each other, and vertical, forming air-vents from the eaves to the ridge of the stack on each side of every spar.

In joint No. 2, on the side D F, the connecting rails are omitted, in order to shew more distinctly the cheeks, *a*, with their staples, *g*.

In joint No. 3, on the side F H, the connecting rails, turning on their hinges, *f*, and furnished with their hooks, are seen in an intermediate position, between their two different situations, when laid by, and when in use:

Fig. III.—C, a spar, with its own connecting rail I, attached to it by the hinge *f*.

a, its cheek pierced with the hole through which is to pass the stretching cord G (see fig. 1 and 7).

I 2, the other connecting rail, in its proper lodgement for use, and fastened by its hook *h*.

Fig IV.—Plan of a post, B, six inches square, with its round pin O, one inch diameter, and 12 inches long; and shewing the manner in which the double spars or spouts, C C and C C, must be fixed where they are required. For fixing these spouts, the pin O must be loose enough to drive easily in and out, and require no cotter. Where only single spars are to hang on the pins, there must be cotters, as expressed in fig. 5 and 6; and the pins are then to be fast in the posts. In these cases the cotters are to act as wedges against the spars, for keeping them perfectly vertical and steady.

Fig. V. (same scale).—B, a post and its accompaniments, as seen when you are opposite the *end* of the stack. See fig. 1.

It is now seen, that the post is somewhat reduced in substance at the sides, where the upper rods K K, are fixed; whereby the interval along the ridge of the stack, between post and post, is reduced to the width of four inches; whereby it is better protected by the roof D; and the end lining piece *r s*, within the spout, gets better placed for keeping out rain. The top of the post terminates at *i*.

K K,

K K, sections of the upper rods. And on the left hand side, is also seen

Q, the canvas sheet or covering, which at a short distance from the rod will, when stretched out, touch, and rest upon

C, the spar. The dotted lines on this spar shew the positions of the bottom, and of the end lining of a double spar.

L, a board nailed across the head of the post, for carrying

M M, the boards which form the fixed roof D.

O, the pin on which the spar hangs.

Fig. VI. (same scale).—B a post and its accompaniments, as seen when you are opposite the *side* of the stack.

K K, two upper rods bolted to the post, but not meeting by one inch.

L L, the cross boards, to which

M, the roof board is nailed.

O, the pin with wedge cotters.

Fig. VII.—Exhibits a section of part of the stack, with C, the lower end of the spar, of which the upper end was shewn in fig. 5. It is 4 × 1½ inches, and 12 feet long in the whole, as before expressed; *a a a a*, is the cheek, six inches long, and 1½ thick. *k*, shews the manner of cutting the dead sheave in the cheek before it is nailed on.

G, the stretching cord.

H, the stake.

F, the lower rod, to which is nailed the bottom edge of Q, the canvas, which, when stretched out, will not touch the spar in the part immediately above that rail.

l, is the place where the connecting rail finds its lodgement

ment against the square end of the cheek, and abutting against the spar C.

m, is the crown of the staple, for receiving the hook of the connecting rail.

n, a knot, for stopping the stretching cord when drawn tight; and by which, where the canvas is to be rolled up, the cord may be drawn out, that it may not injure the rolled canvas.

Perhaps experience may shew, that weights at the ends of the stretching cords may answer better than stakes; by keeping the canvas always equally stretched, whether the weather be wet or dry.

Fig. VIII.—Is a section of a double spar, or spout marked with its dimensions.—It is here seen, how all the edges of the canvasses are secured by small cords sewed to the canvas, and fastened to staples in the bottom of the spout; so that no wet can get to the stack; either at the ends or the joinings; nor can the wind find an entrance.

For a farther explanation respecting these spouts, see the subjoined instructions for building and covering a stack supposed to consist of more joints than one, each joint being covered with a distinct canvas.

Instructions.—On this occasion it is necessary to distinguish the posts into *end* posts and *joint* posts; the former being those only which stand at the extreme ends of the whole stack, whatever be the number of joints; and the latter those posts which stand at the junction of two joints of corn.

1. In building the first joint of corn, let the ends of the bottom sheaves be laid even with the *inside* face of the *end* post; and as you ascend, project the ends of the sheaves rather outwards, but very little at a time, so that

that at the top of the stack they shall not project above five or six inches beyond the *outside* face of this *end* post. Thus you will obtain a firm lodgement for the double spar, or spout which belongs to this post (see fig. 2). When the stack is finished, you cut off all the ends of the straw which project beyond the outer side of the spout, and by trimming the whole end of the stack with the cutting knife, the upper part will have a slight projection, inclining gradually outwards from bottom to top, so that no wet can lodge. The lower end of the end-spout being well secured by a cord and stake, neither rain nor wind can make any impression at the extremity of the stack.

2. At the other end of this joint of corn, a different mode is to be observed, because of the union at this joint with the succeeding joint. Here let all the sheaves project about an inch or two beyond that which, while building this joint, is the *outer* face of the joint post, and carry up this end of the joint as perpendicularly as possible. Thus again you get a firm lodgement for the spout which belongs to this post. Here it would be a waste of time to trim with the cutting knife.

3. When your joint or stack is built to your dimensions, level the eaves as neatly as you can; hang on your spars, extend and hook fast your connecting rails; having your covering canvasses tightly rolled upon the lower rods, raise them to their places, and bolt the upper rods to the posts; then extend the canvasses, insert the stretching cords through the lower rods, reeve them through the dead sheaves in the cheeks of the spars, and fasten them down to the stakes, which should by this time be firmly thrust into the stack. Secure the edges of the canvas to the staples in the two spouts, and then your stack is perfectly safe. These

operations,

operations, when the servants were used to them, could scarcely require half an hour. But as it is to be recollected, that the distance between spar and spar will be about nine feet, perhaps it may be advisable to have one or two intermediate stretching cords, which might be tightened to the connecting rail.

The cutting knife need not be used at the end or sides of the stack till a time of leisure, when the stretching cords might be tightened, and the stack left for the winter.

N. B. If the weather be precarious the canvas rods might be bolted on, prior to building the stack, and the canvasses rolled tight upon the lower rods might be suspended to the fixed roof, in readiness for securing the stack at a moment's warning, during the progress of building it.

P. S. Whenever a joint of corn is taken in, it seems advisable not to trust the canvas to mere rolling up, and suspending to their proper posts, because of mischievous people, or of such as are ignorant and inquisitive, who might damage them. But it is recommended to every one adopting this invention, to appropriate a secure place for depositing each pair of canvasses, with the apparatus belonging to them; and to have all the spars properly marked and numbered for going to the proper places without error or confusion.

4. In building a second joint of corn to unite with the first, at the end of the junction let the butt-ends of the sheaves be forcibly thrust against the butt-ends of the former joint. At the other end, accordingly as it is to be a mere joining with a subsequent joint, or a final end of the stack, the same directions as already given in either of those cases respectively, is again to be observed.

It

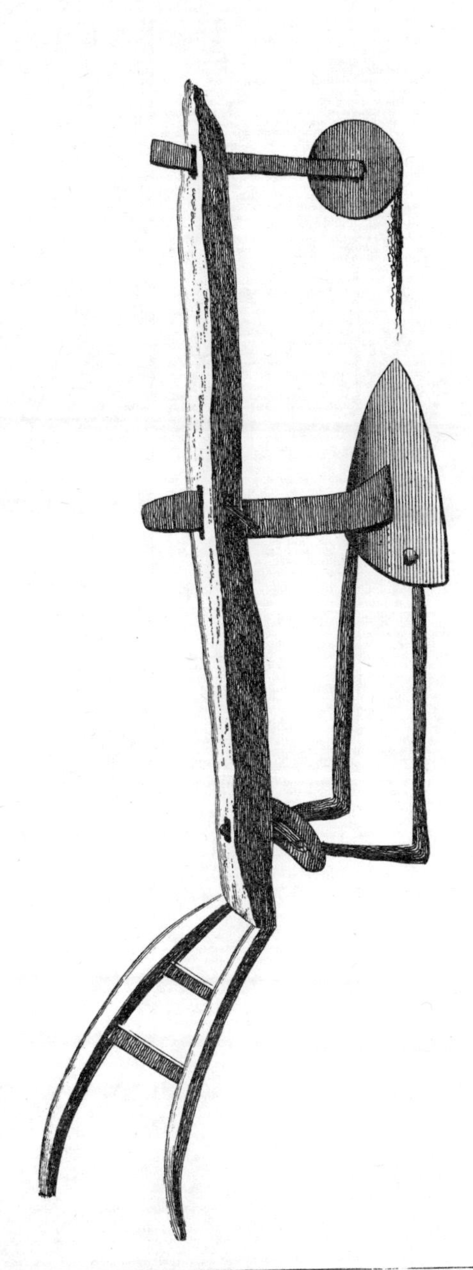

COVERING CORN STACKS

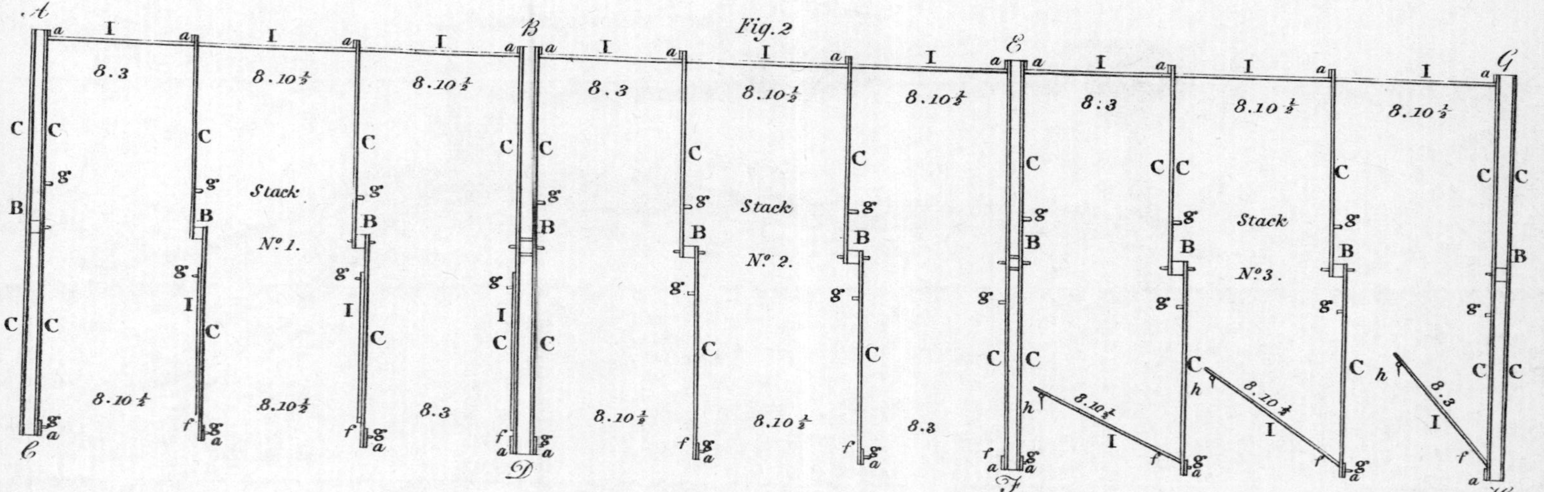

It is presumed that, from a stack thus covered, all damps must find a vent upwards, and escape at the ridge, as the vertical position of the spars must form as it were a flue on each side of every spar, from the eaves upwards. Supposing hay to be thus covered, and that the damp by these means should not at some particular times be carried off with sufficient velocity, the canvas could be occasionally rolled up in dry whether, and secured again before night; but it remains a question, whether it could be necessary at any time, unless the hay were stacked in very bad condition.

If a side wind should be found to entei at the eaves, and agitate the canvas, an insertion of a little loose straw would cure that inconvenience.

Preparing the Canvas.

Extract of a Letter to J. Cartwright from Charles Gower, Esq.

"*Edmonton, Sept. 4th,* 1797.

" Your scheme is certainly practicable in the fullest sense of your expressions, viz. *water-proof*, *supple*, *free from cracking*, or *sticking together*, and *as cheap as may be*. I will just relate to you the mode practised in China for oiling silks, cottons, linens &c. (which mode is *imitated* here in the materials for umbrellas, but not so closely as to equal the Chinese), and from this relation we may fairly argue by analogy, that a coarser sort of stuff, such as sail-cloth or tilting-cloth, may be manufactured after a similar method.

" A quantity of *very old* seed-oil, linseed-oil for instance, is to be put into an iron (not a *copper*) caldron, which must be large enough to contain full twice as much as is put into it, lest it boil over, and ruin the process; a fire is to be kept *briskly* burning under it, with

COVERING CORN STACKS

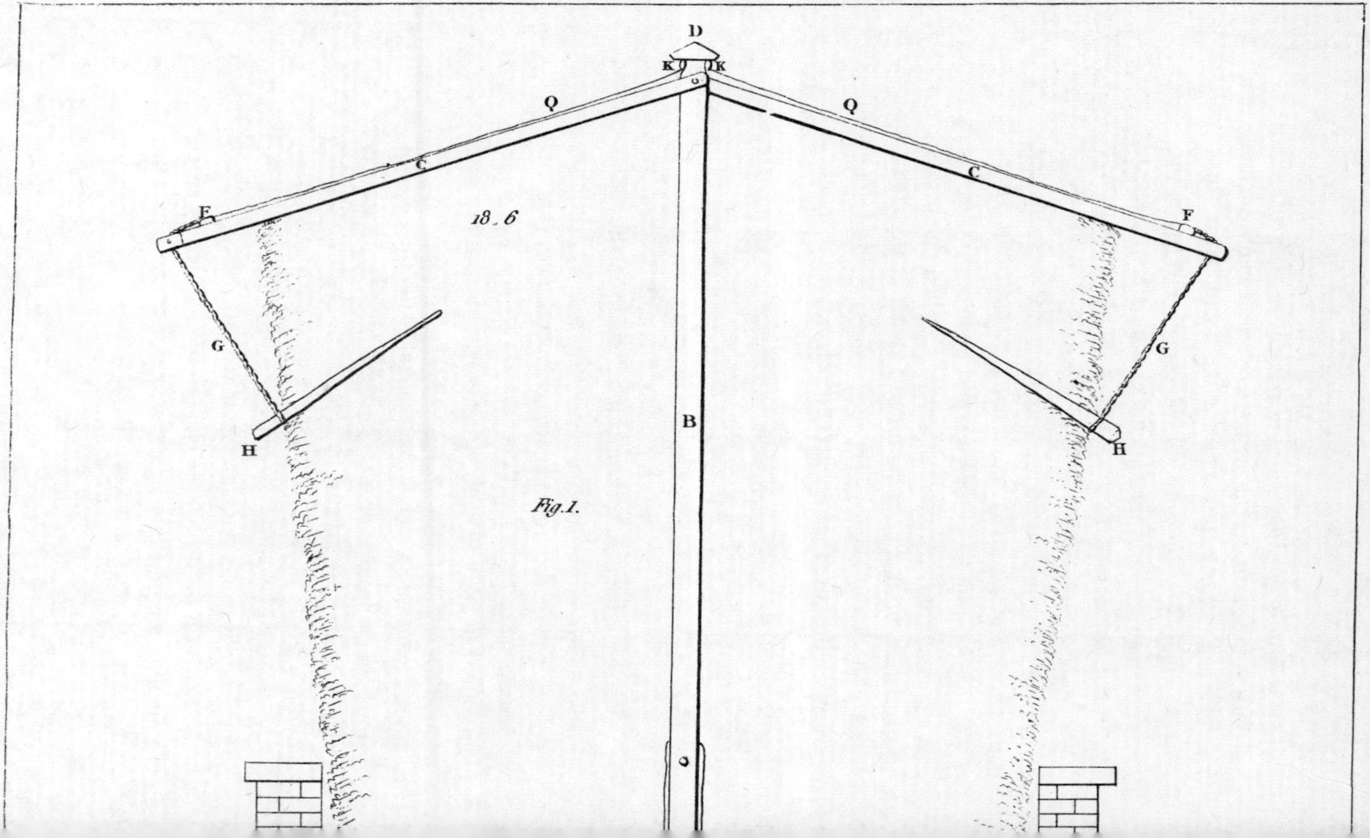

D
K K
Q Q
C C
F F
18_6
G G
H H
B
Fig.1.

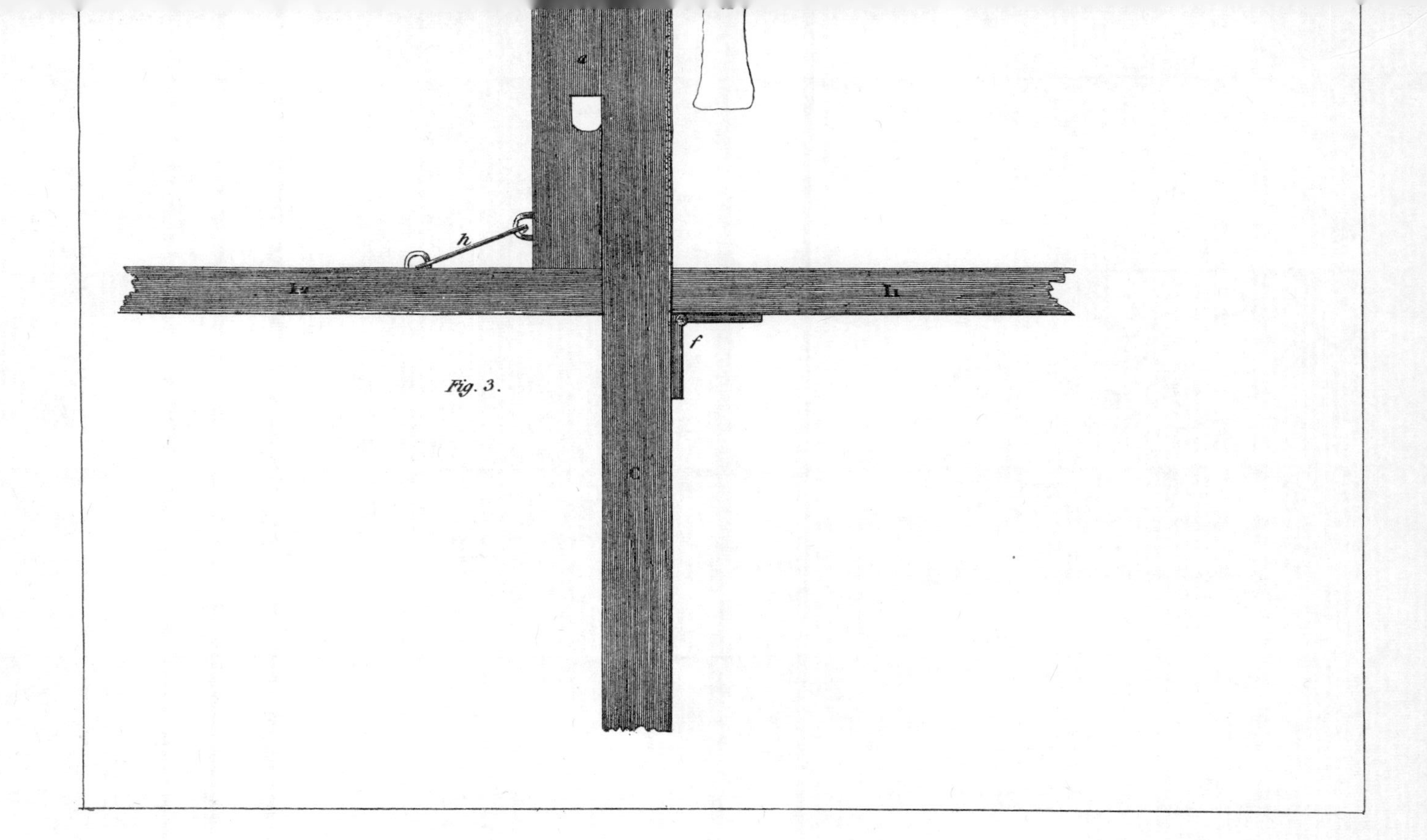

Fig. 3.

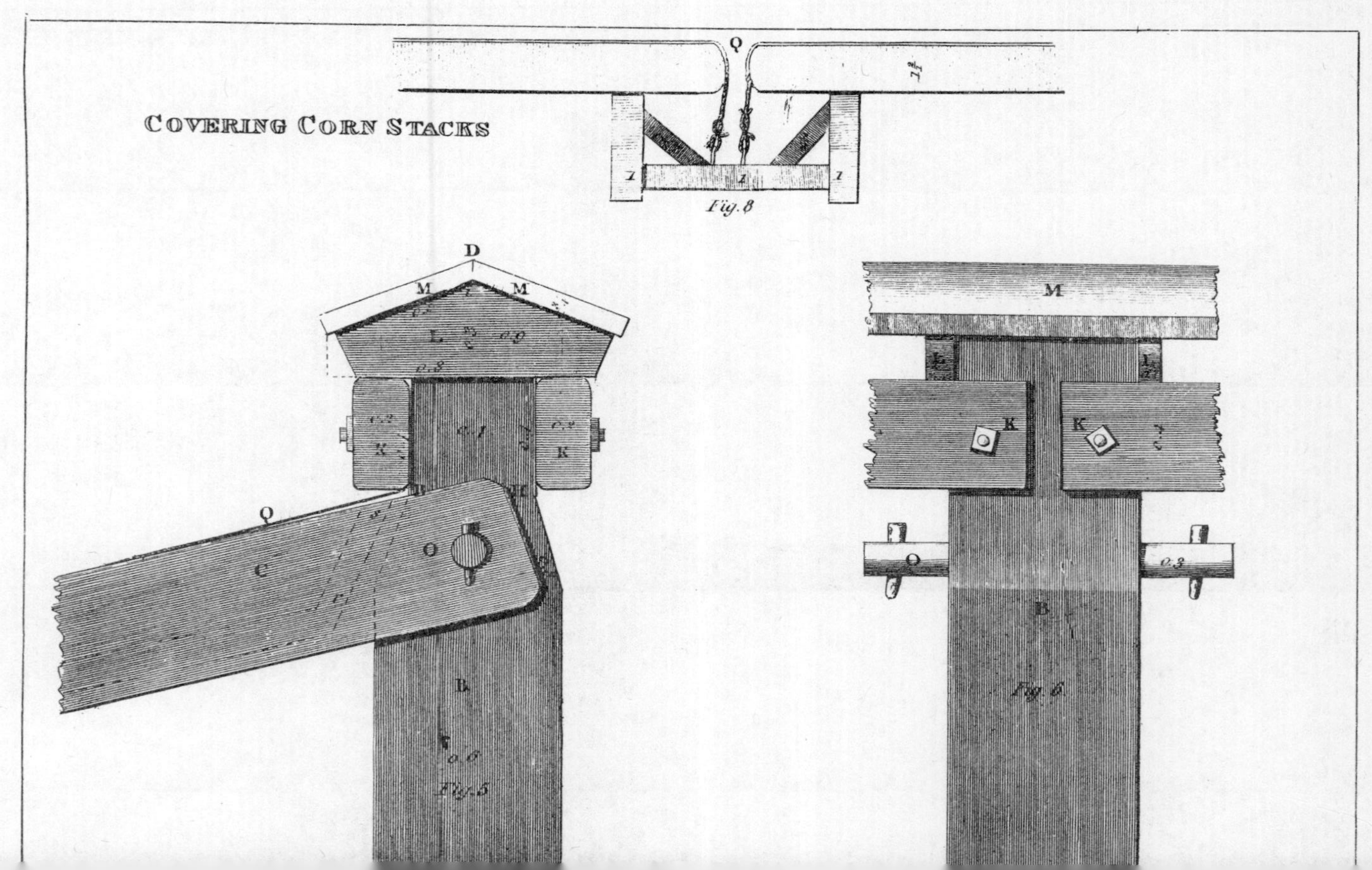
COVERING CORN STACKS
Q
Fig. 8
D
M
M
L
K
K
Q
O
C
B
Fig. 5
M
L
L
K
K
O
B
Fig. 6

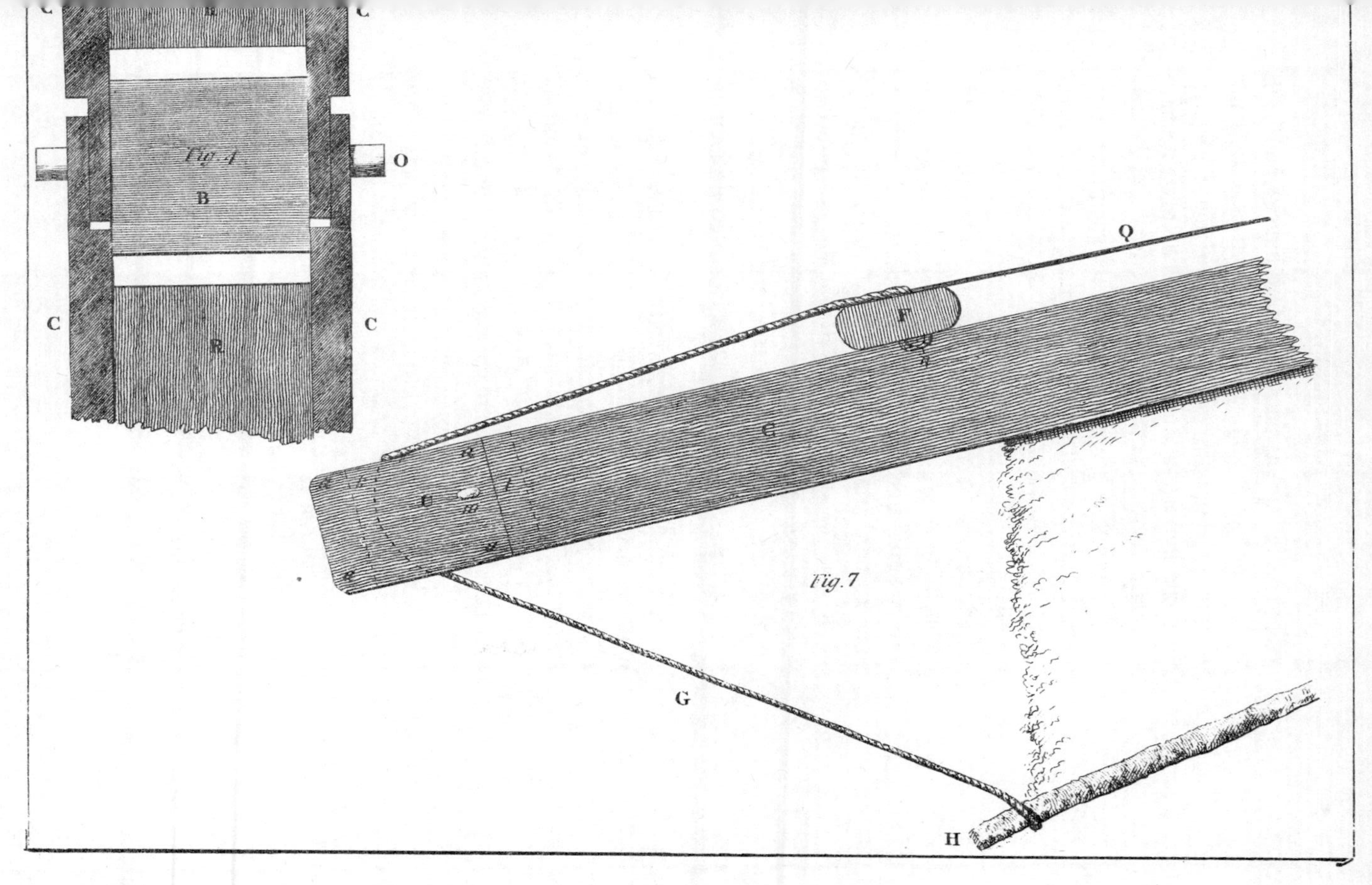
Fig. 4
O
B
C
C
R
Q
F
G
Fig. 7
G
H

with as little flame as possible, till it boils (which will be three or four hours), and when it has boiled long enough to catch fire by the introduction of a red hot poker into it, it is to be permitted to blaze for half an hour at least. At the end of this process it will be tacky, and of a green colour, and is completely rendered a drying varnish, of a supple quality, though somewhat slower in drying than varnishes of other materials.

" A material secret remains behind as to the application of this varnish, viz. the stuffs, &c. on which it is to be applied are to be previously wetted with water, so as to be thoroughly and equally *damp*, but not a single *drop* of superfluous water adhering (just that difference which laundresses make between wet linen on the lines, and linen again artificially *damped* throughout, called sprinkling and folding, fit for ironing).

" The stuff may be now payed over with varnish, or wrung out with it, as linens are done in starch, and this latter mode is preferable, if the quantity of stuff be not too great to prevent it. I saw a silk handkerchief, previously *damped*, dipped into a similar varnish (but made of a more curious and costly oil, viz. nut-oil), and afterwards wrung out, which when dry, might be crumpled up in the pocket, and expanded again without crack or injury. Remember! *very old oil* is necessary, because *no* artificial *dryers*, such as umber, red lead, sugar of lead, litharge, &c. &c. are admissible here; for though they hasten the drying, they make the varnish friable and cracky. Now, *very old oil*, like *very old wine*, is completely homogeneous, and its component parts are *intimately assimilated*, which raw and newly crushed oils are not, as they

they contain much *mucilage*, which is *floating* in them, and must be *deposited* ere they be fit for the above purpose.

"Pray be highly cautious in performing the process, it is so dangerous a one; for in burning the oil, it will blaze full 15 feet perpendicular, and send forth a suffocating stench. Let, therefore, a lid or cover be closely fitted to the pot, and when you want to stop the process and put out the flames, let the cover be put closely on, and coarse cloths, which have been wrung out in water, be placed round the crevices, to exclude the air. (N. B. If the cloths are not wrung out, and a *single drop of water* should find its way into the *hot oil*, the pot will explode with the noise of a cannon. In short, act thus:

"Place your caldron in the middle of a field, at a distance from any house; let your fuel be *coke*, which bears the bellows to *brisken* the fire, without raising a *flame*; and let your lid be suspended on a *long pole*, whereby the operator may be able to press it down hard, without injury to himself. All this process I myself have performed on 60 gallons of old oil, at different times (10 gallons at a time) with success.

"When your cloths are varnished, suspend them on tenter-hooks at their corners, on the beams of an empty barn, free from dust, with a current of fresh air. Wait PATIENTLY (for weeks if necessary), and you will succeed.

"The expense of varnishing such a cloth must depend in a great measure on the nature of the stuff to be varnished, for the measurement of the *superficies*, as in common house painting, will not do; the cloth is *soaked*, and of course admits varnish through its whole texture. Your linseed-oil, in plentiful times, may be had

had for 4*s*. per gallon, and the process will reduce it one-fourth at least, which adds to your expense in that proportion, without a word of *fuel* or *workmanship*; but as these *two* are upon 10 gallons at a time, one-tenth of the expense is to be allotted to each gallon.

" I do not think it would *invite* the mice to eat it, because I know from experience their *aversion* from it; but they will eat through papered canvas in parlours, whence I infer they may perhaps penetrate through this, if *they want an outlet*, for the air soon deprives the varnish of its *smell*.

" The *durability* of the varnish is *great*, for having no friable materials admixed with it, it will not chip off in rolling, as a painted cloth would do; moreover, when the oil is impoverished by wear and tear, in *paint*, the several cracks not only let in wet, &c. but the edges of the *chips* of *paint* act as a knife to cut the fibres of the cloth."

It is for consideration, and perhaps for the decision of experiment, whether a light canvas or a strong linen would be the cheapest and most durable.

Supposing the covering to be duly taken care of, it should seem to be liable to so little friction, or wear and tear of any kind, as to be likely to last for a great number of years; and if the wood work of the posts, the roof, and the lower ends of the spars and the spouts, as well as the inside of the latter, be well painted, all these articles should seem calculated to last equally long.

If snow should be likely to drift under the sides of the wooden roof, that might be prevented by stuffing in a little straw; but if the ridge of the stack were topped up on the first building, with fine straw or stubble, any such stuffing might be unnecessary.

With regard to the comparative expense with that of

of annually thatching, I am not yet able to ascertain it; but if the mode practised by Sir James Wright, in covering his hay at Ray-house, in Essex, with a combination of many pendent slate frames, so connected together as to constitute a complete roof, can answer, I should incline to think the present mode must answer in a superior degree. For the very great advantage of the artificial slate frames, see his pamphlet.

This system of covering wheat stacks seems to require an adoption of the walled brandrith, or enclosure, such as I use; which if well coped, is a perfect security against rats, provided no lumber be left against the wall, nor any thing reared against the stack, to serve the vermin as bridge or ladder. The wall below the coping is   in height.

My experimental purse being for the present drained, I must hope to hear of some other farmer carrying my plan into execution before me.

Boat for conveying Sheep.

Fearing I may not have leisure for some time, to make a new drawing of my boat, contrived for carrying sheep, I send you the original

Explanation. Fig. I.—B B B, plan of the boat without its hatches.

	Ft.	In.
Extreme length	52	0
Extreme width	12	0
From centre of beam A to centre of B	40	0

E E, fixed gangways, the outer plank of which, forming the gunwale, is of oak.

C D, fixed beams; *a a a a a a* moveable beams.

F F, these dotted lines shew the width of the middle hatches, which, when there are sheep in the hold, are to be inlaid, in order to give air below.

G, hatch-

G, hatchway into the cuddy, which must be raised, as expressed in fig. 3.

H, chimney.

The dots along the gunwale shew the positions of the timbers. Those which receive the shanks of the stanchions should be four inches square at top.

Fig. II.—A, oak beam, rising considerably in the middle, which rising may be augmented by a thickening of fir.

E E, the fixed gangways.

K, a sheep-trough the whole length of the deck, resting upon the beams.

I I, longitudinal hatches, which, together with the fixed gangways, form a deck for sheep, leaving an opening as wide as the foot of the sheep-trough, for giving air to the sheep below.

L, another sheep-trough on the vessel's bottom.

Fig. III.—A, side view of the boat with its sheep net, extended between two ropes. The bottom rope passes through eyes in the stanchions, nine inches from the gunwale; the top rope has a knot at one end; it is passed through a staple or cleat upon the gunwale, then through the upper eyes of all the stanchions, and to the gunwale again at the other end; where it is drawn tight and fastened.

When sheep are carried, cross nets at both ends of the decks will of course be wanted.

When sheep are not the cargo, by leaving at home the stanchions, nets, and troughs, the boat is adapted to any other use.

I am, dear Sir,

Very truly yours,

JOHN CARTWRIGHT.

At

At Osbornby Mr. Hoyte has introduced the Norfolk wheel plough, which is found to do well on the lighter soils; and Small's plough from Scotland, for the heavy lands; also a surface-draining plough. Mr. Sensicall of Stoke, near Grantham, has introduced a wheel plough, that goes without holding, for crossing broad high lands at an equal pitch; which is liked better before winter than either gathering up, or splitting down, by reason of every furrow being a drain from the crown to the main furrow. Mr. Hoyte and others have used Cook's drill, but now it is confined to light soils; well convinced it will not answer on stiff ones.

The double plough (price *5l. 5s.*) is in use at Belton, and does its work well on sand, with three horses; never more than four.

Mr. Webster at Bankside, has a small thrashing-mill built by Mr. Parsemore of Sheffield, which cost, the machine itself, *33l.* but complete to him, about *50l.*: it is worked by two horses, and most of the work done by women. The beating wheel is about eighteen inches in diameter, and three feet eight inches long, and moves under, and very near to, an almost semicircular coving of cast iron of three plates, fluted and shouldered, which is found to assist much in the operation. It thrashes sixty bushels of beans a day, and six bushels of wheat an hour; clears beans, wheat, and oats to his satisfaction; but barley not equally well, till he added that coving, however, well enough to induce him to use it for the little he has had.

Mr. Webster has also Mr. Cook's chaff-cutter fixed to a very large wheel, in which an ass or a galloway walks; it cuts 45 to 50 quarters a day. His steaming apparatus for turnips is very complete; a wine pipe lifts

lifts on and off with a crane, and is steamed in two hours.

Mr. Grayburn, of Barton, has had two thrashing-machines, but neither of them well made; it thrashes clean; barley exceedingly well, but beans not equally so: was for four horses: now two, and better; but in the expense no saving. Has a chaff-cutter worked by a horse, on Cook's principle; cuts seven quarters an hour. Cost, 10*l.* 10*s.* for the machine. Tried Winlaw's, but was good for little. Mr. Bourne, at Dalby, uses the double ploughs with great success; he works them with a pair of horses, doing, on an average, of all lands, upwards of two acres a day.

Mr. Linton, at Frieston, has just erected a thrashing-mill, the work done by Mr. Hume, from Scotland, recommended by the Hon. and Rev. Mr. Lindsey; it requires four horses, cost one hundred guineas; thrashes, dresses, rakes off, and cuts chaff at the same time. Mr. Linton is satisfied with what he has yet experienced of its performance; but has had it too short a time, being hardly finished, to make any particular experiments.

He has also Mr. Nailor's patent chaff-cutter: two men, before annexing it to the thrashing-mill, cut 24 bushels with it in an hour, fine enough for any stock. Price ten guineas. Has also made a twitch rake, containing a double row of teeth; those of one row against the intervals of the other: it is six feet long, and executes its work to his satisfaction. Cost 3*l.*

Mr. Linton uses a drill, and the expanding horse-hoe made by Mr. Amos, of Brothertoft, and approves them well: but for beans, rather prefers a small barrow drill, which delivers into the furrow.

An ingenious and very simple tool, in use in East Fen,

Fen, is a sledge for going on the ice; it is a small frame that slides on four horse-bones, the driver pushing himself forward with a pitchfork.

Mr. Curtis, of Ashby cum Fenby, falling very short of fodder, set up an ass-wheel chaff-cutter, and the effect of cutting was such, that it went twice as far as uncut.

The late Mr. Cod, at Ranby, seems to have been in various respects a very spirited and active farmer. I found there a complete set of Mr. Ducket's implements; and was informed that he had viewed Mr. Ducket's farm, &c. in consequence of the various accounts he had read of his management, in the Annals of Agriculture. Here are two skim-coulter ploughs, two drill-markers, turnip drills, scuffler, miner, double plough, horse-hoes, &c and a capital spike-roller, which cost 40*l.* building; also a horse dew-rake, but which had not answered. He not only procured Mr. Ducket's tools, but hiring a man for three years, sent him a twelvemonth to Esher, to be instructed in the use of them: this was doing the business effectually, and much praise is due to his memory on such accounts. In the article *Sheep*, it will be found that he was no less active in another branch.

Mr. Holdgate, at Thoresway, has erected a thrashing-mill, which is worked by water. He has, with a true spirit of exertion, formed a reservoir on the side of a hill, and conducted the water to a very large wheel, in troughs, upon trussle-posts 20 feet high, and a considerable distance: from errors in the construction, it did not perform well, and I found him taking it down for alterations. The drum wheel has eight beaters; and his workmen said they were so numerous, to remedy the defect of velocity.

Mr.

Mr. Michael Pilley, of Lincoln, has invented a water-cart, to take up a ton, by a valve; it moves on two rollers, loads itself, and he thinks that the advantage is very great upon new sown turnips, as it discharges clear of the roller, so as not to daub;—and he thinks that if manure was, for this purpose, converted into a fluid, it would, in many cases, be of considerable utility. Another idea he has,—to construct granaries with a double floor, the upper one like a malt-kiln floor; and by pipes to introduce air through the walls and chimnies to carry it off; this he thinks would tend very much to the preservation of corn.

Mr. William Naylor, at Langworth, near Sudbrook, has invented and patented a chaff-cutter, which he says will cut a strike a minute; and that two men will cut forty quarters a day, to hold it the day through, the length of a barley corn, but it may be set to that of a grain of wheat; price 10*l.* 10*s.*

Mr. Moody at Riseholm, has one of Mr. Parsemore's (of Sheffield) thrashing-mills; it cost 36*l.* 15*s.* I have seen so many of these machines, which do every thing well except barley, that I inquired particularly about that grain. I saw it in his absence, when his thrashers gave me an account of it, and they assured me that it thrashed barley cleaner than they could; and did ten quarters a day, with two horses, four men, one woman and one boy. On returning to Riseholm when Mr. Moody was at home, he confirmed this account; and informed me that he puts out all his barley to the men at 1*s.* a quarter, finding horses; but they take it from the stack, and deliver it to the sack. The circumstance upon which the good thrashing of barley depends, the iron covering under which the beating wheel, having six beaters, moves; this, in Mr. Moody's, is fixed;

fixed; but the beating wheel admits rising and lowering at pleasure; but a new improvement is, to make the iron roof moveable, and the wheel fixed. This iron is so near to the beaters, that it rubs as well as strikes the grain out.

Mr. Walker, of Woolsthorpe, has a thrashing-mill worked by four horses, to my surprise, in sight of a fine perpetual stream, large enough to work an hundred mills. It had not worked well, and he was now altering it with additions; but not that of the semicircular cast iron to close upon the beating wheel, which I advised, and hope Mr. W. will have. The beaters (six) are rounded, which I should suppose inferior to the common flat ones. It thrashed twenty-four quarters of oats in eight hours, and ten quarters of wheat.

The preceding detail is sufficient to prove, that the farmers of this county are alive to improvements, and ready to adopt any new instruments which promise utility. Indeed the general conduct of their business would give reason to suppose this; and there are, without doubt, many other tools, which will, upon a more minute survey, be found deserving attention.

CHAP. VI.

ENCLOSING.

THERE are few instances of the benefit of enclosing commons, greater than that of Long Sutton; the act passed in 1788, by which near 4000 acres of common became *several* property; the rent of it, before enclosing, was 1000*l.* a year, or 500 rights, at 40*s.* each; the whole now letts from 30*s.* to 50*s.* an acre, and about half of it is ploughed. Before this act the old enclosures were subservient to the common, but now the common is subservient to those; and if all are included in the account, there is now more live stock kept than before, and of a much better kind; though above 2000 acres have been ploughed up to yield an enormous produce.

About Folkingham, many new as well as old parliamentary enclosures, of arable, open, common fields, have taken place; the improvements by which have been very great; lands adapted to grass have been laid down; and some better for the plough have been broken up. At Osbornby the rent of 10*s.* was raised to 17*s.* 6*d.*; and several others in an equal proportion. The produce vastly more considerable: 1. fallow; 2. wheat; and 3. beans, are now changed to, 1. turnips; 2. barley; 3. clover; 4. wheat. In some of these parishes the old flocks of sheep, which were folded, and sold lean, are greatly increased in number, without folding, and sold fat.

The

The vast benefit* of enclosing can, upon inferior soils, be rarely seen in a more advantageous light than upon Lincoln-heath. I found a large range which formerly was covered with heath, gorse, &c. and yielding, in fact, little or no produce, converted, by enclosure, to profitable arable farms; lett, on an average, at 10*s*. an acre; and a very extensive country, all studded with new farm houses, barns, offices, and every appearance of thriving industry; nor is the extent small, for these heaths extend near seventy miles; and the progress is so great in twenty years, that very little remains to do.

The effect of these enclosures has been very great; for while rents have risen on the heath from nothing, in most instances, and next to nothing in the rest, to 8*s*. or 10*s*. an acre, the farmers are in much better circumstances, a great produce is created, cattle and sheep increased, and the poor employed. The rectory of Navenby, one of the Cliff towns, has become greater than the total rent of the lordship was before.

* Although it may be a received opinion with many, respecting enclosing depopulating the parishes; yet, from carefully searching the registers of many parishes in the Kesteven division of this county, and comparing the result with a similar one, made by a gentleman in Boothy-Graffoe hundred, published in the Gent. Mag. for 1782, p. 74, I find enclosures to have produced a very little variation in the number of births and burials; and it may be necessary to observe, that the places wherein I made my inquiry, have likewise had no manufacture, or other partial circumstance, to influence any increase or decrease of the people.—And that there are other causes capable of increasing the number of inhabitants in a parish besides a manufacture, I will produce *Donington* as a proof. A Mr. Cowley and others gave to that place, for charitable uses, an estate, which, by an enclosure, &c. has so improved, as to become of the yearly value of 600*l*.; notwithstanding this circumstance the poor-rates are above double what they were before the improvement of the estate; arising from the lower class of persons gaining settlements in the parish by every means in their power, merely through the expectation of benefiting by the said charity.—*Mr. Cragg, MS. of the Board.*

From

From Lincoln to Barton all was, or very nearly all, heath, but now enclosed by acts of parliament. And for five, six, or seven miles every way round Hackthorne, the same within twelve or sixteen years; and of that tract, the heath part was not more than 1*s.* 6*d.* to 2*s.* an acre; large sheep-walks, with pieces tilled alternately, now letts at about 10*s.* tithe free; and the result otherwise has been, that the tenants live much better, and shew, in every circumstance, signs of greater prosperity. The land is universally kept in tillage.

Around Norton-place, or rather longitudinally from it to Kirton, &c. open heath did lett for 2*s.* an acre, now for 8*s.* tithe free; some, however, rising to 15*s.*; and this general, except near Lincoln, where it is much higher. In Kirton, of which Mr. Harrisson has the tithes, lambs and wool paid him about 30*l.* a year, on 5000 acres; from which may be collected how favourable open fields and heaths were to rearing sheep: for in this parish, now under the plough, except the vale lands, proper for grass, the quantity of sheep is considerable; and a great culture of turnips to winter feed them.

The expense, that is, the commissioners' rate, for enclosing 5000 acres in Kirton, was about 7000*l.* including every public charge; roads came to near 1000*l.* of it.

The parish of Gainsborough is just enclosed; the old rent was 8*s.* an acre; the new 20*s.*

At Newton, the rents were 3*s.* 6*d* twenty years ago, before enclosing; now, some of it 25*s.*; much 20*s.*

In the Isle of Axholm, there is an immense enclosure on the point of beginning; the act and survey having been passed, of no less than 12,000 acres of commons,

commons, in the four parishes of Haxey, Hepworth, Belton, and Owston. I passed these commons in various quarters, and rode purposely to view some parts; they are in a wretched and unprofitable state; but valued, if enclosed, in the ideas of the islanders, at 10*s*. or 11*s*. an acre*.

			Acres.
In Haxey, claims	305	on account of	3810
Hepworth	236	———	2285
Belton	251	———	3664
Owston	229	———	4446

Cottage rights are claims; but lands without a cottage have none. It was a most barbarous omission, that when this act was procured, they resisted a clause to divide the open arable fields, subject to rights of common. But they have here by a custom, a right of enclosure which is singular; every man that pleases may enclose his own open-field land, notwithstanding the rights of common upon it, while open; and accordingly many do it, when, by purchase, they get five or six acres together, of which I saw many instances; and could not but admire their beautiful quick hedges, which are very fine, and must have been well preserved while young; but there is no clearer proof of good land, than what is afforded by whitethorn hedges.

In the angle of country, east of the Trent, and between that and Ankohlm, no new enclosures, of much consequence; one at Wintringham of 500 acres.

Barton Field is one of the greatest enclosures in Eng-

* The enclosure has taken place, and answered to an extraordinary degree. 1808.

land

land; the act passed in 1793. Before the enclosure, the quantities of land were supposed to be nearly as under in statute measure.

Barton upon Humber.

		Acres.
Open arable lands, nearly		4500
Open meadows in the *ings*, including the *growths* next the Humber, about		420
Open meadows and pastures in the Little Marshes, about		160
Open common, including the growth,	cow-pasture	250
	horse-pasture	225
Open Wold land, common, chiefly furze ground, about		270
		5825
According to the survey upon the enclosure, all the open lands and grounds were found to contain		5920
From which about 110 acres were set out in roads and drains.		
The ancient enclosure within and about the town, including the sites of the homesteads, &c. in the town,—contain, by survey		150
The Grange and Warren farm on the Wold ancient enclosure, about		170
Therefore the whole parish contains, as nearly as may be, by survey		6240

Of which, after deducting the roads, and the site of the town, there may be 6000 acres of land used in pasture and tillage.

The assessments of the commissioners, under the enclosure

closure act, amounted to about 13,180*l.* to defray the expenses of the act, fencing of tithe allotments, public and private roads, banks, jetties, cloughs, bridges, &c. &c.

The completing the public and private roads cost about 5000*l.* The Humber banks and jetties about 2000*l.*, or rather more.

The parish pays yearly to the land-tax 210*l.* 8*s.* 4*d.*

The value of these lands before the enclosure were open arable lett at from 4*s.* to 9*s.* per acre, of something less than three roods; little parcels for 10*s.* or 12*s.*; average about 6*s.* 6*d.* Part of the Marshes was lett with the arable; thus the plough land of 72 acres arable, and eight of meadow in the ings, being four ox-gangs, were lett together: all at the same rent. The common was stocked by the occupiers of common-right houses and lands; and also a part of the Marshes. The enclosure began directly, and they entered on the allotments in 1794. The amount of the commissioners' assessment was 13,000*l.* for the act, tithe fencing, roads, Humber banks, jetties to secure the shore, sluices for drainage, bridges, &c. The roads alone cost 5000*l.* Drains 700*l.* Now the arable fields lett, on an average, at 20*s.* About the town, much more; at a distance, less. The Marsh land would now sell at 70*l.* an acre, near the town; at a distance, 40*l.* Some ploughed land, one mile from town, 40*l.* to 50*l.* an acre. Old enclosures near the town, 100*l.* an acre, for convenience. The common on the Wold, 12*s.* an acre. The parish, including every thing, may now be rented at, or worth 6000*l.* a year; it was 2000*l.* and all the tenants better satisfied than before; 150 acres were given to the vicar for his small tithes; and 900 were assigned for great tithe, most conveniently for the impro-

impropriator. Many new farms, barns, &c. built, and more building.

The wheat, before enclosing, two quarters on the customary measure of three-fifth statute;—the beans not more than two quarters: these crops are now changed to 1. turnips, worth 30*s.*; 2. barley, 4½ quarters; 3. clover, mown once, two loads per acre, worth 50*s.*; and a very fine after-grass of 10*s.* an acre; 4. wheat, four quarters. There is wheat now in the field that will be five. They formerly carted their corn and manure two miles and a half.

Horton was enclosed 20 years ago, and advanced from 10*s.* to 20*s.* Winterton also from 10*s.* to 20*s.* Coalby was enclosed 40 years ago; 800 acres, lett now at 700*l.* a year, about 17*s.* 6*d.* an acre. Killingholm, enclosed about 20 years ago, was open clay arable, lett at 4*s.* or 5*s.* an acre, now 12*s.* to 13*s.* Enclosing does not answer to any great degree upon clay, as they cannot have seeds or turnips; and if laid down to grass, it is 20 years before it comes to good pasture.

By the acts for enclosing Barton, Barrow, and Goxhill, no less than 17,000 acres are rendered productive, to the infinite advantage of the community.

I was told, before I got into the Clays, as they are called, or Middle Marsh, that enclosing did not answer that, however it had succeeded on the Wolds. When I got to Humberston, I discovered the explanation: they summer fallow for wheat, and then take beans, after enclosing, exactly as before. How then can it answer? and old tracts of pasture are ploughed up in consequence, and not converted to a good system of tillage, but covered with bean crops that never see a hoe. In going from thence to Tetney, Fulstow, Covenham, &c. I passed through a large open field in the

the fallow year, which had not, in September, received its first earth; but was covered with thistles, past their blossom, high enough to hide a jackass; yet the dung was spread amongst them as if the wheat would be sowed: and the soil, thus horribly neglected, a fine rich tenacious loam, not clay, as greasy and soapy almost as a pure clay; but there is much sand in it: —a soil well worth 30*s.* an acre, or upwards, in rent, tithe, and rates. Who will be hardy enough to hazard such a folly, as that any part of the lime of Clays, I have seen or heard described, will not answer enclosing? Yet, such nonsense I have heard; no wonder, in a country where landlords, stewards, farmers, are all five centuries behind in every idea relative to strong land. They are awake and moving on turnip land; but on bean soils, are still fast asleep.

From Louth to Saltfleet, and from Sutton to Alford, open fields, with unploughed fallows, the 15th, &c. of September, covered with thistles in beautiful luxuriance, and plenty of other rubbish. But they have imbibed the same notion, I suppose, that strong land will not pay for enclosing.

The following enclosures have taken place about Spilsby, &c.; among many others, Dalby twenty-eight years ago; Driby twenty; Langton forty; Tetford twenty-five; Swayby ten; Belleau ten; Hagg three: Greetham three; Ashby Puerorum five; High Toynton fifteen; also Ashby, East and West Keal, and Fulletsby; in all which, upon an average, rents have trebled by enclosure; forty years ago very little was enclosed in all the county.

Upon the principles on which the commissioners of enclosures should conduct themselves, Mr. Elmhurst observes: "Where the town happens to be situated in, in, or pretty near the centre of the lordship, the properties (upon the enclosures) may, with great propriety, be laid contiguous, or nearly so, to the farm-houses; and as much in squares as the nature and shape, &c. of the fields will admit; but when otherwise, then the distant lands ought to be so laid out and allotted, as best to suit for occupation, as a farm or farms, on which houses, &c. may be built; having, as much as may be, an eye to water, and different sorts of land; but to have due consideration to the *whole* of the proprietors (small as well as great) so as not to injure any one, by making it *particularly* convenient to another or others. I acted as a commissioner a great many years; and was at *one time* concerned in *nine* different enclosures; and from my first being in that business (which is near 28 years), I ever have attended first to what concerned the public, respecting the laying out, forming and making the roads (at the expense of the proprietors) in the properest and most eligible situations, for the greatest conveniency of all who may travel, or do business upon them; for, I thought and said, that the Legislature could never *intend* to place such power in any set of men, as commissioners, or delegate them with such extraordinary power (as they *then* seemed to *fancy* they had) by which they should or might injure the public.—And that *mode* I ever and always pursued, so long as I continued to act. Another observation I, at the first, made, and ever after put in practice, was this, *always* to begin to line out and allot for the *smallest* proprietor *first* (whether rich or poor), in *every* parish, so as to make such allotment as proper and convenient for the occupation of such, or their tenant (as that might be) to occupy; and so on, from the smallest to the greatest: for it is for

for the advantage of the greatest and most opulent proprietors, that a Bill is presented and Act passed; and at *their* requests,—and not the small ones; and, as the little ones would have no weight by opposition, *they must submit*, was it ever so disadvantageous to them: as it *very often* happens; and, therefore, there can be no *partiality* in defending *those*, who cannot help or defend themselves; and a *little* man may as well have *nothing* allotted to him, as to have it so *far off*, or so inconvenient for him, that it is not worth his having, as it would prevent his going to his daily labour; and, wherefore,. he *must* SELL *his* property to his rich and opulent adjoining neighbour; and *that*, in some measure, decreases population."

For the following most important table, I am obliged to Mr. Parkinson of Asgarby, steward to Sir Joseph Banks, &c. It is, in every respect, a very curious paper, and shews the vast works which have been carried on successfully in this great county.

A State

A State of certain Improvements by Enclosing and Draining.

Parishes.	A.	R.	P.	Improv. Value. £.	s.	d.	Old Value. £.	s.	d.	Improvement. £.	s.	d.	Expenditure. £.	s.	d.	Interest at Five per Cent.	Net Gain to the Owners.
Donnington	1728	0	0	681	5	0	380	0	0	301	5	0	1100	0	0		
Swayby	1555	1	24	738	5	6	310	14	0	427	11	6	1967	13	0		
Belleau	649	1	14	323	8	0	274	0	0	49	8	0					
N. Rauceby	3168	0	23	1129	16	0	352	0	0	777	16	0	3399	0	0		
S. Ditto	2461	0	20	1010	18	7	347	0	0	663	18	7					
Normanby	1718	3	20	1021	18	3	480	0	0	541	18	3	1820	0	0		
Huttoft	3352	0	16	2356	2	0	1800	0	0	556	2	0	2300	0	0		
Hemswell	2581	2	20	1472	2	6	630	3	0	841	19	6	1874	0	0		
Legburn	2335	2	3	973	14	7	655	0	0	318	14	7	1663	0	0		
Canwick	2059	3	33	1437	5	0	672	12	0	764	13	0	1722	0	0		
Skendleby	1028	1	25	571	3	1	285	0	0	286	3	1	800	0	0		
Wd. Enderby	798	0	0	526	4	8	340	0	0	186	4	8	848	10	7		
Anwick-fields, &c.	954	0	0	708	19	0	385	3	0	323	16	0	1510	0	0		
Greetham	1275	0	29	763	2	6	400	0	0	363	2	6	1348	0	0		
Brigg	2383	2	13	1806	17	0	1560	0	0	246	17	0	2100	0	0		
Kirton	4583	0	0	3864	3	7	1168	0	0	2696	3	7	5267	16	9		
Nettleton	3549	2	32	1523	17	9	460	0	0	1063	17	9	2425	0	0		
Osbornby	1475	2	0	1323	7	0	662	0	0	661	7	0	2032	12	1		
Scarthe	1186	2	0	876	15	0	452	0	0	424	15	0	1447	1	6		
Quarrington	1500	0	0	1268	8	0	627	0	0	641	8	0	3669	0	0		
Sleaford and Holdingham	2321	1	20	2191	2	0	918	0	0	1273	2	0					
Dunsten heath and fields	1957	0	20	1037	1	3	641	0	0	396	1	3	1300	0	0		
Tattershall enclosure	4003	2	18	2168	1	11	1706	11	8	461	10	3	626	0	0		
Fens.—Ditto embankment	892	0	26	838	13	9	387	19	9	450	14	0	3630	0	0		
Anwick-fen	1097	0	0	703	16	0	54	17	0	648	19	0	4070	0	0		
The nine embanked fens from Tattershall to Lincoln	19,418	1	34	15,534	8	0	1941	16	0	13,592	12	0	77,672	0	0		
Holland-fen, eleven towns	22,000	0	0	25,300	0	0	3600	0	0	21,700	0	0	50,600	0	0		
Total	92,033	2	30	72,150	15	11	21,490	16	5	50,659	19	6	175,191	13	11	£. 8754 11 7	£. 41,905 8 11

"There are other parishes that I have been commissioner for, which I have not an account of, owing to my books being from home.

"Add to the improved annual value of 72,150*l.* 15*s.* 11*d.* upon a moderate estimation, the annual produce of three times the rent; making for the Fens, drained by the Witham, 127,130*l.* For the high land old enclosures 89,321*l.* 14*s.* 6*d.* together; for the whole, 216,451*l.* 14*s.* 6*d.* being the annual produce by cultivation."

Upon this animating detail, I have only to remark, that the valuation of the improved rents was that of the commissioners; but the real rents, at this time, exceed it in many instances; thus Holland fen is here reckoned at about 1*l.* 1*s.* per acre, whereas the average is now, as appears by the minutes, about 27*s.*: but even if we suppose that no further rise has taken place, than here stated, it is a noble spectacle, to see such a prodigious improvement effected. The old rent is 4*s.* 8*d.* per acre. The new rent is 15*s.* 8*d.*

Mr. Loft, of Marsh Chapel, is of opinion, that in the clay arable of the Middle Marsh, to allot and divide, would be better than to enclose.

Mr. Ellison, at Sudbrook, remarked to me, that he is clear, if a register of offences at the sessions was kept, it would be found that a very large proportion originated with the inhabitants who lived on commons, and in unenclosed parishes.

Claypool, Beckington, and Doddington, have been enclosed since 1771; were 8*s.* an acre, when open; now 18*s.* 20*s.* and some more.

The country, west of the great north road, to Woolsthorpe, Belvoir-castle, &c. all enclosed: a lordship, which, thirty-two years ago, was 300*l.* a year, is is now 1500*l*. a year. All these have been greatly improved in management, entirely by enclosing; and especially in turnips and seeds, and the breeding of sheep, articles which have taken place only in enclosures.

The open fields about Grimsthorpe, by bad management and constant ploughing, produce very little; Mr. Parker is clear that one-third of the land enclosed would yield more corn and profit. But much has been done in twenty-five years; Corby, Swinstead, Swayfield, Bourn, Norton, Hackenby, South and North Witham, Skillington, and many others have been done; and the rents have been doubled in consequence.

The Duke of Ancaster very justly remarks, that rents are usually raised much too soon upon enclosures taking place; the tenant is put to much inconvenience, and incurs sometimes a very large expense; to raise immediately is unjust; there ought to elapse three years before any increase takes place. His Grace, upon enclosing, has given his tenantry that indulgence; and at Newby, upon asking one of them what would be a fair rise on his farm of 29*l*. a year; the farmer offered 60*l*.; which the Duke thought so honest, that he rewarded him with a lease of twenty-one years.

Recapitulation.

	Old Rent.				New Rent.		
Long Sutton	£.0	5	0		£.2	0	0
Lincoln-heath	0	1	0	....	0	10	0
Do. Lincoln, to beyond Kirton	0	1	9	....	0	10	0
Near Norton	0	2	0	....	0	10	0
Carry forward	£.0	9	9		£.3	10	0

Brought

	Old Rent.				New Rent.		
Brought forward	£.0	9	9		£.3	10	0
Gainsborough	0	8	0	....	1	0	0
Newton	0	3	6	....	1	2	6
Haxey, &c. commons	0	1	0	....	0	10	0
Barton	0	6	6	....	1	1	0
Wintringham	0	7	6	....	1	13	0
Horton	0	10	0	....	1	0	0
Winterton	0	10	0	....	1	0	0
Killingholm	0	4	6	....	0	12	6
Dalby, Driby, Langton, Tetford, Swayby, Belleau, Hagg, Greetham, Ashby, Toynton, Keals, Fulletsby	0	5	0	....	0	15	0
Mr. Parkinson's table	0	4	8	....	0	15	8
Claypool, Beckington, Doddington	0	8	0	....	0	19	0
Woolsthorpe, &c.	0	6	0	....	0	18	0
Several near Grimsthorpe	0	6	0	....	0	12	0
	£.4	10	5		£.15	15	8

The rise is, therefore, on an average, $3\frac{1}{2}$, as appears on this table; but there can be no doubt of the rise being, in fact, more considerable, for reasons already stated; quadruple at least.

The admirable spirit with which enclosures have gone on in this county, is a memorable proof of the enlightened energy which has pervaded it for thirty years past.

Fences.

Fences.

In Holland fen, white thorn fences superior. But few seen in Deeping fen; but enough to shew that they would succeed well.

In the new enclosure on the Heath above Belton, I remarked that the quicks were kept clean, and were very thriving. Expense of a treble rail, on each side, bank and quick, 1*s.* 8*d.* a yard, running measure.

The expense in the new enclosures on the Heath from Norton to Kirton, is 11*s.* a rood of seven yards, and 2*d.* per rood per annum for keeping clean, and re-planting failures for three years.

Mr. Hesselden gives, in the new enclosures of Barton-field, 1½*d.* a rood for three weedings. I observed many of the quicks much neglected.

Mr. Lloyd, of Belesby, is very neat in his fences, keeping them clipped regularly.

Mr. Parkinson, in his business as a commissioner in many enclosures, has necessarily had a great opportunity of seeing the result of various modes of planting and securing quick; and when he enclosed his own estate at Asgarby, he pursued a Leicester method, with one fence of a very small trench, planting the quick upon the surface of the field for the sake of moisture; the other side of the same field he made a double ditch, three feet deep; and the difference in the growth was very great; the former was as good at three years as the other at seven.

CHAP.

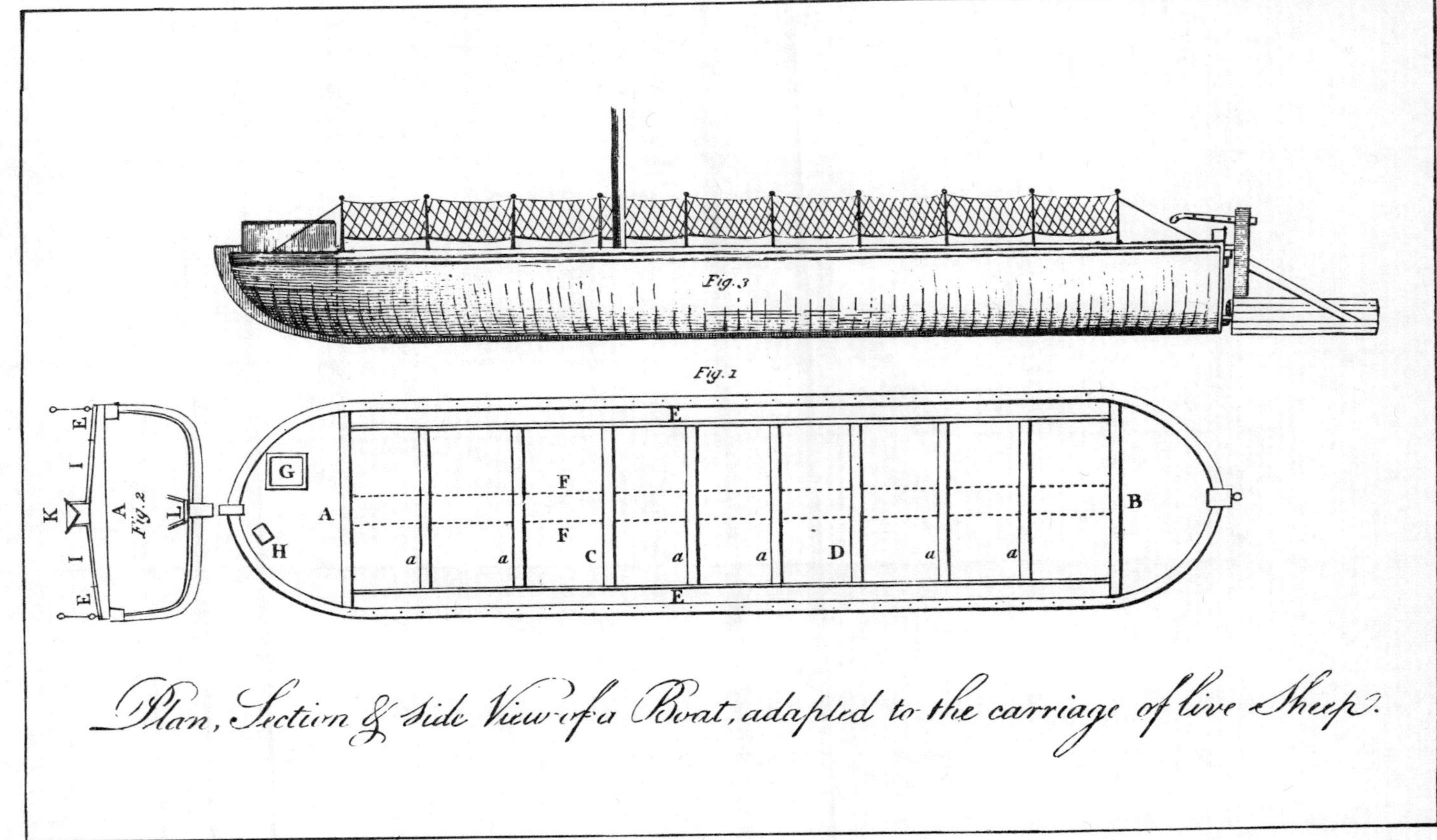

Plan, Section & Side View of a Boat, adapted to the carriage of live Sheep.

Mr. GRABURN's HARROW.

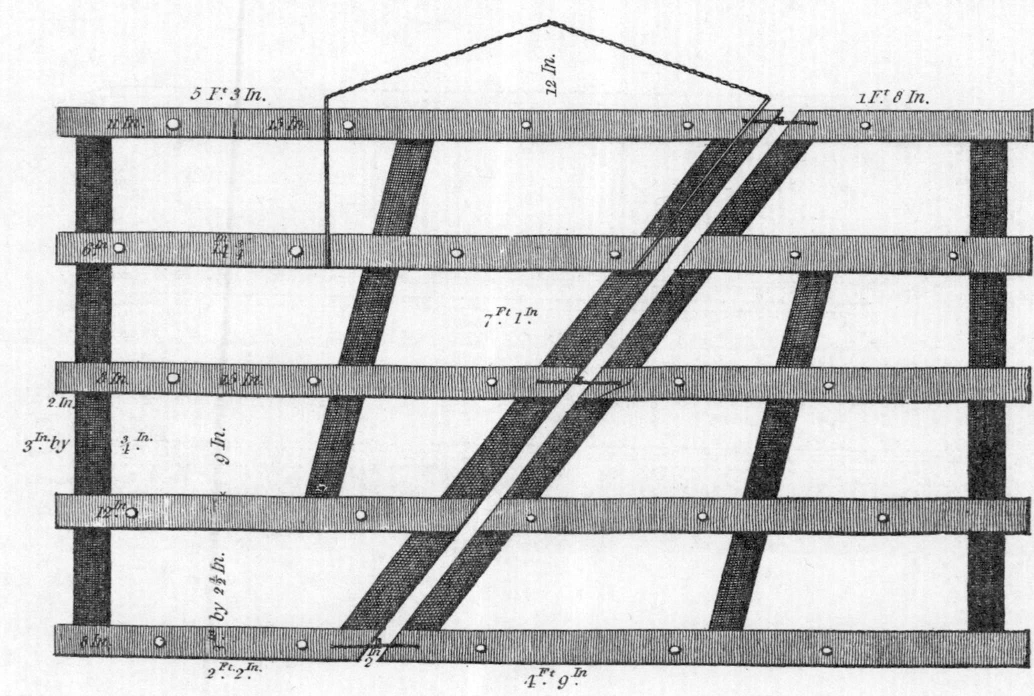

Mr. GRABURN's SCUFFLER.

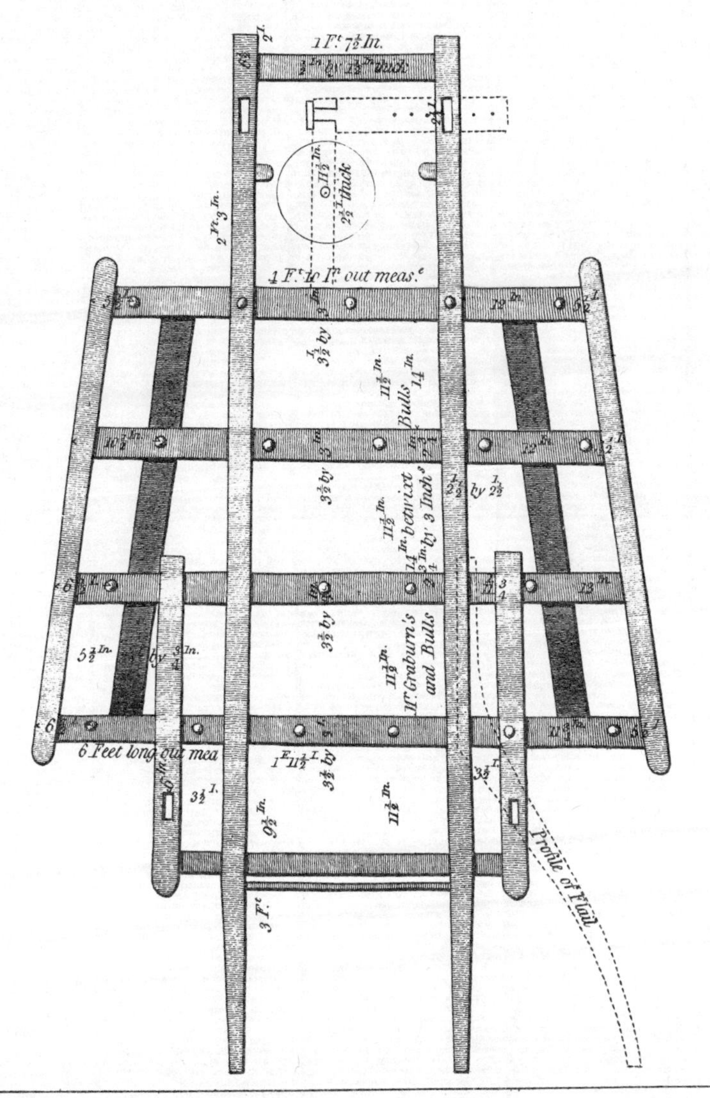

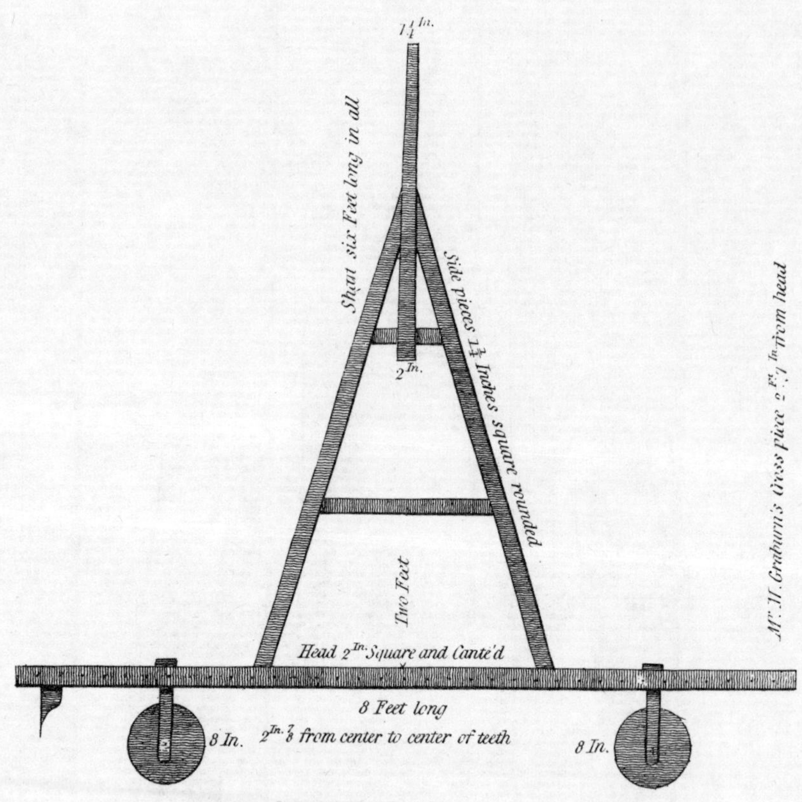

$1\frac{1}{4}$ In.
Shaft six Feet long in all
Side pieces $1\frac{1}{4}$ Inches square rounded
2 In.
Mr. H. Graburn's cross piece 2 Ft. 1 In. from head
Two Feet
Head 2 In. Square and Cante'd
8 Feet long
8 In.
2 In. $\frac{7}{8}$ from center to center of teeth
8 In.
Wheels 1 In. thick in the middle & $\frac{1}{2}$ Inch on the edge

CHAP. VII.

ARABLE LAND.

THE management of arable land in Lincolnshire has never been celebrated; when I was in the county upon a farming tour, above thirty years ago, I saw little but what merited condemnation; and I entered it now expecting to find it in a very backward state. There is certainly much to disapprove in the management of wet clay, but I was very agreeably disappointed in that expectation on most other soils; and I need not observe, that the districts of the kingdom, in which wet arable is well conducted, are extremely few.

SECT. I.—TILLAGE.

In the vicinity of Market Deeping, the arable common fields are ploughed up into broad arched lands, as in the midland counties; but the furrows for three, four, or five yards wide, laid down to grass and mown for hay, while the crowns of the ridges are under corn: this management is excellent, and much superior to having such miserable corn in these furrows, from wetness, as is seen from Chattris towards Whittlesea to Peterborough; the centres of the lands being high, are dry and fit for corn, and the furrows low, and do well for grass.

 Mr.

Mr. Cartwright finds that the best mode of preventing thistles is deep ploughing. The common depth does not exceed three or four inches; but where the soil will admit six, it has a good effect in lessening the number of that pestilent weed. Mr. Cartwright also remarks, that when a thin loam, &c. is found on a clay bottom, the soil may in some cases be clayed advantageously by ploughing deeper; but that then it would be prudent to try the quality of such clay by experiment in some bottomless boxes, by sowing grain in it; and if so ploughed, to begin before winter.

Mr. Trimnell, of Bicker, had a servant who, in a critical season when exertion was necessary, ploughed, with two pair of horses, 45 acres, the seed furrow, in nine days, and in a masterly manner; one man and four horses did therefore five acres a day, which is an extraordinary exertion indeed.

On the heath land at Leadenham they plough their seeds, after resting two years; but once for barley. Mr. Bestal ploughed his, in 1797, three times, but the season proved so wet, that he lost his crop by weeds.

In the new enclosures north of Lincoln, they plough three to four times; for wheat three or four, for barley once, after turnips, fed. Every where with two horses, and no driver.

On the tract of high sand that hangs to the Trent from Gainsborough to Newark, particularly of Knaith, they plough but once after turnips, fed off, for barley; and it is the same often upon Lincoln heath land.

About Normanby, Burton, &c. they plough for barley but once, thinking that by so doing they preserve the manure left by eating off the turnips with sheep; this is general. But at Alkborough, Mr. Sutton ploughs

ploughs on land that is rather strong, twice; on sand only once.

Mr. Graburn, of Barton, has for four years past, tried with success dragging in corn, barley, and oats. After ploughing turnip-fed land once, instead of a second earth, scuffled the seed in with Cook's scufflers; put in 90 acres so, and the crop as good as any. One man and three horses did eight acres a day, a mile from home, which strength would have done but one acre in ploughing and harrowing; but he thinks the drags much better; has dragged in 150 acres with his four-rowed duck-footed drag; sown with seeds, and the land as clean under them as his neighbour's, who put in with ploughing. This year he has tried it with turnips, on 16 acres ploughed twice, and worked with drags, one in winter and one in spring; three of the lands were managed with the plough, and had an earth extra; the turnips dragged are better than where ploughed, and he is determined in future to follow this method. On light Wold land the crop misses much in the common way, and gets too dry.

At Wintringham they plough four, five, or six times for turnips; twice for barley, but some only once. In fallowing for wheat, they stir five times; and the wheat stubble once for beans.

At Alesby, Mr. Skipwith has been ploughing down the old high lands of the country for twenty years past. They were of a bad form, too high for the breadth, which was four, five, to ten yards, crooked, and wider at one end than the other. He ploughs into flat lands three or four yards broad; finds it a great improvement, because he thinks much less manure will do, as it washed off the sharp sides of the old ones. But he narrows his lands on the wettest and strongest soils.

About

About Dalby they plough their turnip land but once for barley. Mr. Wright, of Spilsby, once, and yet gets fine crops. For turnips, three or four.

About Reevesby they plough never less than four times for turnips; then twice for barley, but many only once; all twice, where eaten by January.

At Sudbrook they plough four times turnip land: for barley once: Mr. Ellison's bailiff has ploughed twice, and been the worse for it, if eaten by Candlemas, but if finished early, then he stirs twice. Mr. Ellison has ploughed down all the old high lands as much as possible; but does not approve keeping clay land flat; sand cannot be too level; even this soil here was formerly ploughed up in very high lands, equally with clay.

SECT. II.—FALLOWING.

It would be easy to expatiate under this head, on the propriety of banishing fallows; but as all such observations are equally applicable to every part of the kingdom, and I met with no experiments made expressly on this subject—let me pass on to,

SECT. III.—COURSE OF CROPS.

On breaking up the rich common of Long Sutton,

1. Oats,
2. Oats,
3. Wheat,
4. Cole, fed with sheep,
5. Wheat,
6. Oats,
7. Cole

On

On the black peat land in Deeping fen, Mr. Graves,

1. Pare and burn for coleseed fed,
2. Oats,
3. Cole for seed,
4. Oats,
5. Grasses.

Some farmers in this fen have sown both wheat and barley on fallow, and got large crops.

In Holland fen:

1. Fallow* and cole, fed, eight sheep an acre;
2. Oats,
3. Oats; but best farmers,
3. Clover—others
4. Drilled beans,
4. Wheat, or 3. wheat.

It is, however, necessary to observe, that in the Fens, there is no system generally pursued, except that of *beginning* with paring and burning, in which, most unquestionably, they act wisely, whatever may be thought of repetitions of that practice afterwards: burning a second time is not frequent; but fallowing for cole, to be eaten off with sheep, every third, fourth, or fifth year, is common management. Oats and cole are the only produce till the first luxuriance of the soil is somewhat abated; when the land begins to acquire more consistence, from mixing by tillage, wheat is sown, and forms a very considerable article.

Upon the rich arable at Brothertoft, Mr. Cartwright practises this course, after trying several others.

* Fallowing is not uncommon in the fens; it is called *bobbing*, and performed as follows: plough the land over in the winter, in the spring cross-plough; harrow and plough again in May or June; then with a long-tined wooden harrow, and an instrument called a *bob*, collect the roots of weeds and vegetables together; these shake up and burn: repeat this till the land is perfectly clean; the ashes being spread at each burning, if more than one, and then sown with coleseed.—*MS. of the Board.*

1. Fallow,

1. Fallow, for cole, fed with sheep, and worth 50*s*. an acre;	3. Beans,
	4. Wheat,
2. Oats,	5. Clover mown once, 2 tons hay, and then fed.

To fallow the clover ley is uncommon; but it is sown with wheat, always in a good season; but succeeding three crops, it may, if the year is unfavourable for cleaning beans, not be in such high order as to make a crop of corn advisable: cole on it, following a two years' fallow in succession, must keep the land in great heart. This, 26*s*. or 27*s*. an acre. The clover is sown at the end of March, or beginning of April.

Mr. Stephenson at Swineshead, on the fertile soil of Holland fen:

1. Oats, on layer,	4. Oats,
2. Wheat,	5. White clover and parsley for three years.
3. Cole,	

Mr. Thorold, in Donnington fen, 1. Cole. 2. Oats. This for several years, and the oats regularly the best. No manure.

In Holland fen, and particularly at Swineshead, if wheat is sown on a barley stubble, they get little. Mr. Stephenson has tried this; his predecessor had left a stubble field, of which the greater part had been oats, and a small piece barley. The whole field Mr. Stephenson sowed with wheat, and in the crop at harvest he observed a very great deficiency in the whole of that part which had followed the barley; insomuch that the very shape of the piece, which was remarkable, could be traced with the utmost exactness by the failure of the wheat there, and *no where else*. Not knowing how this spot of land had been previously managed, he would not admit this as a proof, that barley was a worse crop than oats to precede wheat; although he had

had heard that upon ten land it was so. He therefore afterwards made the experiment, by sowing a small piece in a field with barley, of which the rest was oats; all the land being equally good, and prepared alike. The effect as before, in every respect; the barley piece producing only two quarters of wheat per acre, while the oat part yielded four and a half. Nor was the mere deficiency all the difference; for while the wheat after *oats* was *fine and healthy*, that which followed the *barley* was *diseased and blighted*, and required the sickle ten days sooner than the good corn. In 1793 the field adjoining his barn was sown with oats; while a small portion he sowed with barley, to mow for his cart-horses. It was thrice mown, and produced a great burthen of green food. But this application of the barley made no difference in its effect on the crop of wheat which succeeded. After the *oats* it was extremely good; after the barley, the reverse. I am also informed, that in 1792 Mr. Moss of Swineshead experienced the like; and that his wheat after *barley* was *mildewed*, while his wheat after *oats*, in the same field, and with the same management, was very good.

After such facts, may it not even be doubted, whether the intervention of a crop of clover will be sufficient to save the wheat from the ill effects of having preceded it with barley? The great deficiency in my wheats of the present year, 1794, where I had barley in 1792, and clover in 1793, favour, I own, a suspicion of this kind.—*Remark of Mr. Cartwright.*

Mr. Hoyte, upon strong clay:

1. Dibbled beans on old sward.
2. Wheat dibbled.
3. Manured for drilled beans.
4. Wheat, now on land sown with red clover.

Intends

Intends to dress with soot for dibbled wheat. On middling soils:

1. Turnips hoed,
2. Barley,
3. Clover one year, mown once,
4. Dibbled wheat,
5. Pease drilled and hoed,
6. Turnips,
7. Barley,
8. White clover 12 lb.; red, 4 lb.; two years fed with sheep;
9. Dibbled wheat.

Upon still lighter soils:

1. Pease on seeds,
2. Turnips,
3. Barley or oats,
4. White clover; sheep grazed one year;
5. Barley on three ploughings,
6. Turnips,
7. Red clover, mown once, and then pease again.

Some tares, cole, and turnips in same year, after tares.

Mr. Tyndal of Ewerby keeps in the old course of,

1. Fallow and dung,
2. Wheat,
3. Oats.

But upon dry land,

1. Turnips,	3. Clover,
2. Oats,	4. Wheat.

The vast object of a good course of crops is seen strongly in this county in a variety of instances. Mr. Dawson, Berthorp, broke up a field of old grass; on one half of which he sowed oats, and on the other half beans;

beans; he got a good crop of both; the next year the bean half he sowed with wheat, and got a crop, which I saw, of probably four quarters an acre; the oat part he sowed with barley, and it was much damaged with weeds. The difference of profit will not amount to less than 10*l*. an acre. But this is nothing to a neighbour of his, who has now 16 acres of what is called barley after oats, but in reality one entire and most luxuriant crop of sow thistles. Such a sight I never beheld. Had he fed them with sheep, being an excellent plant for them, it would have kept more stock perhaps than any field on his farm. Or he might, at the proper time, have mown the whole for hay, and got ready for turnips; any thing rather than what he has done: as to barley, there is not enough to pay for harvesting. Mr. Dawson in the fen had a field, in which seeds failed, but sow thistles came a full crop; he turned in sheep, which eat them all off, and did exceedingly well on them, and the land afterwards very clean.

Lord Brownlow's rotation upon rich sand:

1. Oats from the ley,
2. Turnips,
3. Oats and grass, ray grass, and white clover.

Upon land kept in tillage,

1. Turnips,
2. Barley,
3. Clover,
4. Wheat.

On Lincoln-heath, above Belton,

1. Turnips,
2. Barley,
3. Oats,
4. Grasses for various terms,
5. Oats.

In the new enclosures that were before field land well managed,

1. Turnips,

1. Turnips,
2. Barley,
3. Seeds; clover if to plough up for wheat, if not, white clover, ray, and trefoil for two, three, or four years; and then,
4. Oats.

At Leadenham, on the Cliff lands,

1. Turnips,
2. Barley,
3. Seeds two years,
4. Barley on one ploughing $3\frac{1}{2}$ quarters.

But so near as Navenby the soil is better; there they are in what is called four fields, retaining the terms of the former open fields:

1. Turnips, fed with sheep,
2. Barley,
3. Clover,
4. Wheat.

At Blackenham the common course is,

1. Turnips,
2. Barley,
3. Barley,
4, 5, 6. Seeds for two years,
7. Oats.

Instead of this Mr. Chaplin prefers,

1. Turnips,
2. Barley,
3. Seeds for two years,
4. Pease.

In one field he practised for eight or nine years the following singular course:

1. Turnips,
2. Barley.

The crops of turnips have never failed, and the barley has

has been constantly productive, yielding at least five quarters, often more; and once eight. Rent of this land 10*s*. subject to tithe; these reddish sandy lands are, however, admirable for barley, and worth more than that rent.

On the Wolds:

1. Turnips,
2. Barley,
3. Turnips,
4. Barley,
5. Seeds for three years,
6. Wheat or oats.

Mr. Cracraft:

1. Turnips,
2. Barley,
3. Seeds, and white red clover, hay-seeds, and trefoil for three years;
4. Oats,

Or,
1. Turnips,
2. Barley,
3. Clover,
4. Wheat.

The common farmers on heath land enclosed:

1. Turnips,
2. Barley,
3. Seeds for three years,
4. Oats or summer fallow for wheat.

On the better land:

1. Turnips,
2. Barley,
3. Clover, mown once or twice,
4. Wheat.

About Norton Place, on the best land:

1. Turnips,
2. Barley,
3. Clover,
4. Wheat.

But on inferior soils varies thus:

1. Turnips,

2. Barley,

2. Barley,
3. Seeds, white clover, and trefoil for two years;
4. Pease,
5. Wheat;

but still with other variations, according to circumstances. Others, in order to be able to secure the right quantity of turnips, when the land will not give them without manure, and that wanted, will, to secure the crop, take

1. Turnips,	5. Barley,
2. Barley,	6. Seeds,
3. Seeds two or three years.	7. Pease,
4. Turnips,	8. Wheat.

The following is not a common course, but has been practised:

1. Rape,
2. Seeds.

Mr. Dalton at Knaith:

1. Turnips,
2. Barley,
3. Clover mown, or trefoil fed,
4. Wheat.

On the rich sands at Martin, the same.

At Haxey,

1. Potatoes,	5. Wheat; if plenty
2. Wheat,	of manure, potatoes
3. Barley,	again; if not,
4. Clover,	6. Barley.

Another,

1. Hemp or potatoes,	5. Barley,
2. Barley,	6. Clover,
3. Beans,	7. Wheat.
4. Wheat,	

On

On clay land:

1. Fallow; and if manured,
2. Barley,
3. Beans,
4. Wheat.

If not manured:

1. Fallow,
2. Wheat,
3. Clover,
4. Wheat.

Mr. William Darrand, on good land, 30*s*. an acre:

1. Potatoes.
2. Wheat,
3. Barley,
4. Clover,
5. Wheat,
6. Flax,
7. Wheat,
8. Flax,
9. Barley,
10. Clover,
11. Wheat,
12. Flax,
13. Barley,
14. Clover,
15. Wheat.

But though fallows in the open fields at Haxey are, in general, banished, they are not totally; for I observed some ploughing, which the farmer told me would sell at 40*l*. an acre.

At Butterwick, in the Isle, they have various courses, which deserve noting:

1. Potatoes,
2. Wheat,
3. Beans,
4. Wheat.

Also,
1. Potatoes or hemp,
2. Flax,
3. Wheat, no clover,
4. Beans,
5. Wheat.

At Garthorpe, in the Marsh, new land broken up:

1. Flax,

1. Flax,
2. Rape,
3. Potatoes,
4. Flax,
5. Rape,
6. Potatoes,
7. Flax,
8. Wheat.

It will certainly bear this for ten years.

About Normanby, Burton &c. on the arable sand of the lightest sorts:

1. Turnips,
2. Barley,
3. Turnips,
4. Barley with grass seeds; with sometimes rye instead of the barley.

Recommended by Mr. Wilson:

1. Turnips,
2. Barley; but, if very light, spring rye.

On the best dry land, one course of

1. Turnips,
2. Barley,
3. Clover,
4. Wheat,
5. Turnips,
6. Barley,
7. White clover, rib, and trefoil; (ray precluded) to be eaten three or four years with sheep; then plough for turnips again. Farmers here wish to break up for corn; and, if a tough sward, permitted.

Upon stronger lands:

1. Oats on ley,
2. Fallow,
3. Wheat,
4. Beans,
5. Fallow.

Open

Open field, strong land:

1. Fallow. 2. Wheat, 3. Oats.

Mr. Goulton's own rotation.

Seeds broken up for:

1. Oats, sometimes beans,
2. Turnips,
3. Barley,
4. Grasses; white clover, trefoil, and rib, and sometimes hay seeds for four years.

In the new enclosure of Barton—before the enclosure it was, 1. fallow; 2. wheat; 3. beans or barley;—but beans seldom a good crop; now the course is,

1. Turnips,
2. Barley,
3. Red clover, or
3. Seeds for 3 or 4 years,
4. Wheat.

On the low land, on Humber.

In Barrow field:

1. Fallow, $5\frac{1}{2}$,
2. Wheat,
3. Beans,
4. Barley.

At Wintringham there are three rotations. On the strong loams, the course prescribed is,

1. Summer fallow,
2. Wheat,
3. Beans.

But on the drier loams it is,

1. Turnips,
2. Barley,
3. Clover,
4. Wheat.

Upon the newly broken up rich marshes, they are allowed to take three crops of white corn; then potatoes; and after that, two crops of white corn to one of potatoes; rape, hemp, flax, excluded.

On

On the Marshes, newly enclosed at Barton:

1. Pare and burn for rape, fed; and the year after; seed four quarters an acre;
2. Oats, 10 quarters,
3. Oats, 10 quarters.

On old pasture:

1. Oats,	1. Oats,
2. Beans,	2. Oats,
3. Beans.	3. Wheat.

On the Wolds at Great Lumber, Mr. Richardson's course is,

1. Pare and burn old layer for turnips,
2. Barley or oats,
3, 4, 5, Seeds; 14 lb. white clover; 4 lb. red; 4 lb. trefoil; left for three years;
6. Turnips, &c.

But the more common one,

1. Pare and burn for turnips,
2. Oats or barley,
3. Oats or barley,
4, 5, 6, 7, Seeds; 14 lb. white clover, and one bushel ray;
8. Pease or oats.

Also, 1. Break up sward for pease or oats,
2. Turnips,
3. Barley,
4, 5, 6, 7, Seeds

At Belesby:

1. Turnips,
2. Barley,
3. Beans. And then Mr. Lloyd adds, if the beans were drilled,
4. Wheat; which is an excellent course on good land.

Other

Other courses here:

1. Fallow,
2. Wheat,
3. Beans.

1. Fallow and dung,
2. Barley,
3. Beans.

Mr. Lloyd is allowed to take two crops of white corn in succession; but never does it.

At Alesby, Mr. Skipwith:

1. Turnips,
2. Barley,
3. Clover,
4. Beans,
5. Wheat, if clean; if not, turnips again.

At Humberston:

1. Fallow,
2. Wheat, or barley,
3. Beans; and this is the general practice.

However, I saw clover; and therefore hope they will get into a better course. I recommended (if they will have fallow), 1. fallow; 2. wheat; 3. clover; 4. beans, dunged for 5. wheat, which Mr. Tomlinson much approved of.—Not however without admitting, and Mr. Bee the same, that the two crops and a fallow was good, and not to be complained of.

For some miles on the Wolds, about Louth, they are very good farmers, indeed, in respect to courses; the following singular one is common:

1. Turnips,
2. Barley.

They assured me that this land, though of 15*s.* an acre, would not do to add clover and wheat; and, upon their poorest soils, another that has merit, if their assertions are correct:

1. Fallow,
2. Oats,
3. Fallow,
4. Oats,
5, 6 Seeds; 14 lb. white clover, 4 lb. trefoil, and a sack or more hay seeds.

 Upon

Upon my objecting to so much fallow on light land, Mr. Cluff, of Gayton, assured me, that upon these distant parts of their farms, they could not get turnips without so much dung as would not answer to carry, nearly so well as to lay it on their better lands; that in this way, they could get six, seven, or eight quarters of oats, which answered much better than any other way of managing.

Mr. Hyde, at Tathwell, practises on a soil of good loam or clay, or rather a flint cledge, and under that, chalk, this singular course:

1. Turnips,
2. Barley or oats; the former four quarters;
3. Clover, first mown, and then eaten.

The turnips manured every second course. The crop of clover extraordinarily great, even three or four loads an acre. The barley, as above noted, inferior to what a course so very favourable to the land ought to produce. Clover recurring so often, the land, I should fear, will soon sicken of it.

1. Fallow,
2. Wheat,
3. Clover,
4. Beans.

This is a wretched arrangement, for want of adding wheat after the beans; only to be effected with propriety, by a much superior culture of beans to any thing known in Lincolnshire.

About Saltfleet, when marsh grass is broken up,

1. Oats,
2. Cole,
3. Oats,
4. Beans,
5. Oats,
6. Wheat.

Some of it inexhaustible by ploughing; and, after a long course of crops, very great products. No hemp or flax.

Mr.

Mr. Bourne, of Dalby, is a great practiser of that singular course above-mentioned: 1. turnips; 2. barley; and, when he finds the land in good heart and order, throws in a crop of oats after the barley; but this will not be oftener than once in six years. And sometimes, on his better lands, 1. turnips; 2. barley; 3. clover; 4. wheat; but this will only answer about once in ten years.

About Spilsby, 1. turnips; 2. barley or oats; 3. oats; 4. turnips; 5. sp. corn; 6. clover, for wheat, or 6. white clover 14 lb. and two or three pecks ray, for two or three years, and then oats. Turnips and barley alternately common.

In the hundred of Skirbeck, in open field:

1. Fallow,
2. Wheat,
3. Beans and pease,
4. Wheat or barley.

But Mr. Linton, in the enclosures, if new broken up,

1. Oats,
2. Oats,
3. Oats,
4. Cole or turnips,
5. Oats,
6. Wheat,
7. Cole or turnips.

If old arable,

1. Cole or turnips,
2. Oats or beans, or barley,
3. Wheat after oats and beans; clover after barley,
4. After clover, wheat.

And many repeat the three first; but Mr. Linton,

1. Cabbages or turnips,
2. Barley,
3. Clover,
4. Wheat,

5. Beans,

5. Beans, manured and drilled,
6. Wheat, which is better than that after clover.

Also, 1. Beans, drilled,
2. Wheat.

Mr. Cracraft, at West Keal, on his new marled sand,

1. Turnips,
2. Barley,
3. Wheat,
4. Clover,
5. Oats.

At Reevesby and Asgarby, &c.

1. Turnips,
2. Barley,
3. Clover,
4. Wheat.

Upon poor land or wolds,

1. Oats on seeds,
2. Turnips,
3. Barley,
4. Turnips,
5. Barley,
6. Turnips,
7. Barley,
8. Seeds for four years.

Mr. Parkinson, on lands at a great distance from the dunghill.

1. Pare and burn for turnips, ten sheep per acre;
2. Barley;
3. White clover for one year, ten sheep an acre;
4. Turnips marled or limed, ten sheep an acre;
5. Oats or barley;
6. Seeds one year, ten sheep an acre;
7. Turnips, and so again.

By this the land receives the manure of twenty sheep in three years; whereas, if it was kept in pasture, it would support only two sheep an acre in summer, and not one in winter, without assistance; and barley straw to make more manure.

Mr. Elmhurst's course on new enclosed dry land, which has been open field arable:

1. Early

1. Early grey pease,
2. Turnips,
3. Turnips, limed, four chaldron per acre;
4. If the land is not quite clean, turnips a third time; but more commonly barley, six quarters;
5. Wheat, often five quarters;
6. Seeds, left for a term of years, according to circumstances.

But this very intelligent cultivator on cold or strong clay land, old pasture, proceeds in the following course:

1. Pare and burn for rape,
2. Rape,
3. Rape,
4. Battledore barley,
5. Wheat,
6. Seed, left for sheep, &c.

At Rankby, on good land,

1. Turnips,
2. Barley,
3. Clover,
4. Wheat.

On poorer light land,

1. Turnips,
2. Barley or oats.

If a difference, it is a crop of pease rarely added; after six years, laid to seeds for two or three years, white clover and hay seed.

Mr. Smith, at South Elkington,

1. Pease or oats on seeds,
2. Turnips,
3. Barley,
4, 5, 6. Seeds.

But on better land he takes,

1. Turnips,
2. Barley,

3. Clover, mown the first growth, fed the second, and adds, sometimes, but not often,
4. Wheat.

On clay soils,

1. Fallow,
2. Wheat,
3. Seeds one year;
4. Beans on one earth.

The Rev. Mr. Allington, at Swinop,

1. Turnips,
2. Barley,
3. Turnips manured,
4. Barley,

5, 6, 7. Seeds.

On the better land, ploughs up the seeds, after two years, for wheat or pease. This course Mr. Allington considers as a very improving one; the only objection which occurs on the soils that are chalky, and where the turnips are manured, and the largest, is that his sheep have died much, when on them, of the red water.

Mr. Holdgate, upon his warren land at Thoresway,

1. Pare and burn for turnips,
2. Turnips,
3. Barley,

4, 5. Seeds two years, and then laid out to the rabbits.

Too much cannot be said in praise of such excellent management; the taking two crops in succession of turnips, is capital husbandry;—the second crop is ploughed for thrice, and it is twice as good as the first.

Mr. Ellison, at Sudbrook, on sand,

1. Oats on seeds,
2. Turnips.
3. Barley,
4. Seeds two to four years.

On

On clay land,

1. Summer fallow,
2. Barley,
3. Seeds two or three years,
4. Wheat or beans, and then fallow.

Has tried wheat after beans broad-cast, but not hand-hoed; it would not do; got four quarters of beans; but the wheat bad.

Mr. Moody at Riseholm,

1. Turnips,
2. Barley,
3. Seeds, two quarters,
4. Wheat.

Also on stiff land,

1. Fallow,
2. Wheat,
3. Seeds, two quarters,
4. Oats.

Again,

1. Turnips,
2. Barley,
3. Seeds, two quarters,
4. Pease or tares,
5. Wheat.

On strong land at Claypool,

1. Summer fallow,
2. Barley,
3. Beans,
4. Wheat.

Excellent husbandry; but they are also disgraced with,

1. Fallow,
2. Wheat,
3. Beans.

Upon the red sand at Marston,

1. Oats on seeds,
2. Turnips,
3. Barley,
4. Seeds three or four years.

Mr. Walker, of Woolsthorpe, on very good red sand,

1. Turnips,
2. Barley,
3. Barley,
4. Oats,
5. Seeds.

West

West of the great north road to Belvoir-castle, chiefly red creech land, sandy loam mixed with stone; and some deeper.

1. Turf broke up oats,
2. Turnips,
3. Barley,
4. Seeds for two or three years, fed with sheep.

1. Oats,
2. Turnips,
3. Clover,
4. Clover,
5. Wheat,
6. Turnips.

This, on good land; as on the lightest they do not sow wheat. These courses, the best managers, for there are many under a much worse husbandry.

About Grimsthorpe many turnips, especially on the creech land.

1. Turnips,
2. Barley,
3. Wheat, on the good creech.

1. Turnips,
2. Barley; this the best mode for poor creech.

On clay:

1. Fallow, 2. Wheat, 3. Beans.

On some white loose sand:

1. Turnips, 2. Oats;

it will bring neither barley nor wheat, but good turnips and good oats.

Upon this greatest of all objects in arable management, I must divide what I have to remark into two considerations: 1. Strong land. 2. Turnip soils.

Upon strong land, the only courses which appear to be very good, are,

Mr. Hoyte—1. beans; 2. wheat; 3. beans; 4. wheat.

At

At Haxey—1. fallow; 2. barley; 3. beans; 4. wheat.

Mr. Linton—1. beans; 2. wheat.

Mr. Ellison—1. fallow; 2. barley; 3. seeds; 4. wheat.

At Claypool—1. fallow; 2. barley; 3. beans; 4. wheat.

The first and the third of these are perfect, when the soil is rich, or manure in plenty: if fallows are esteemed necessary, the others are certainly good courses. But these instances are few in so long a detail. Upon the whole, the article is nearly a blank, and the common system of the country is, 1. fallow; 2. wheat; 3. beans; and, greatly to its disgrace, equally in enclosures and open fields. There is a barbarity in this rotation which admits no excuse. The peculiar quality of beans is to prepare well for wheat; and of all tolerable preparations, fallow and dung is the most unprofitable. To follow beans by fallow, is to secure a slovenly management of the former; for who will treat them in a better manner when his *no lease* ties him to fallow after them? Every link in the chain is equal folly; to be lamented in the thraldom of open fields, but to be severely reprehended in enclosed lands. I have recommended to many persons in Lincolnshire some courses which it may not be improper to note here.

1. Without a fallow:

1. Beans,
2. Oats or barley,
3. Clover,
4. Beans,
5. Wheat.

Upon lands in which clover succeeds with wheat, and which are better adapted to wheat than spring corn:

1. Beans,
2. Wheat,
3. Clover,
4. Beans,
5. Wheat.

2. With

2. With a fallow, where it is apprehended that the culture of beans is not sufficiently understood to be depended on for cleaning the land:

1. Fallow,
2. Oats, or barley or wheat,
3. Clover,
4. Beans,
5. Wheat;

and should a fallow be wanted but once in seven years, to add,

6. Beans,
7. Wheat.

All these courses are proposed on the supposition of beans, when managed to the best advantage, being adequate to keeping the soil clean. The misfortune of fallowing, is, its depending for effect so much on the season; in a wet year it fails so entirely that the year is lost; no crop is had, and the land increases perhaps in foulness. I this year saw hundreds of acres that had not been once ploughed in September, over-run with all manner of trumpery; and other lands, not in better order, that had been once broken.

2. *Turnip Soils*:—Here the spectacle of Lincoln husbandry is seen to vastly greater advantage. I was much surprised to find the immense and rapid progress turnips had made since I was before in the county. A glance of the most careless eye over the preceding minutes, will shew that they enter very generally into the courses on dry land;—that the Norfolk husbandry of, 1. turnips; 2. barley; 3. clover; 4. wheat; is very well established; and that improper deviations do not often occur. But the merit of the farmers of Lincolnshire goes much farther, for in some very singular courses they must be classed among the best cultivators in the kingdom.

Mr.

Mr. Thorold—1. cole fed; 2. oats.

Mr. Chaplin—1. turnips; 2. barley.

Mr. Wilson, at Grimsthorpe; Mr. Bourne, at Asgarby, on the Wolds, and at Normanby—1. turnips; 2. barley; 3. turnips; 4. barley; 5. seeds for three years; 6. wheat or oats.

Norton—1. turnips; 2. barley; 3. seeds two years; 4. pease; 5. wheat.

Ditto—1. cole; 2. grass seeds.

Mr. Lloyd, Mr. Hyde, Mr. Parkinson, and at Rankby—1. turnips; 2. barley; 3. seeds for three years.

Mr. Allington—1. turnips; 2. barley; 3. turnips; 4. barley; 5. seeds three years.

Mr. Holdgate—1. turnips; 2. turnips; 3. barley; 4. seeds for several years.

These are very singular courses, and which, upon various accounts, obvious to a practical reader, prove uncommon merit in the farmers. Men who manage thus, shew that they have no undue eagerness to raise all the corn they might do, but attend with solicitude to keeping their land clean and in heart. There are many districts in this kingdom, where the occasional adoption of these courses would work a considerable improvement.

SECT. IV.—CROPS COMMONLY CULTIVATED.

Corn, Seed, and Produce.

On breakiug up the rich commons of Long Sutton, the corn products have, for seven years, been very great;

great; oats, ten quarters and a half, and wheat five quarters, which continue to be the crops at present.

On the black peat land in Deeping fen, Mr. Graves has had eight, and even ten quarters of oats, after cole, on paring and burning: he sows six bushels. There is now a crop of barley in the fen, estimated at 12 qrs. an acre.

Corn in general upon the rich arable of Holland fen, &c. of an inferior quality and price, which is of course occasioned by the extraordinary fertility giving such a luxuriance of straw.

All corn in Holland fen hand-weeded at a great expense; if the season is such as to oencurage weeds, the expense amounts to 10*s*. or 12*s*. an acre, on an average of the country round. But good farmers have reduced this expense to 2*s*. 6*d*. from 5*s*. Mr. Stephenson, of Swineshead, thinks the time of manuring being changed, has had in this respect a great effect; for instead of manuring for cole, he has spread it on layers, and this has lessened the quantity of weeds.

In Holland fen, oat seed, six bushels of Poland, five of short small; crops seven quarters all through. Wheat seed eight to twelve pecks; crop four quarters through. Flax seed, two bushels; cole, a quarter to half a peck; a little barley and beans, but not much.

Sowing barley, eight bushels an acre, for mowing to soil horses, &c. with in the stable, a singular husbandry in Holland fen; at three mowings an acre will support ten horses.

Mr. Cartwright, after cole, worth 50*s*. an acre, gets eight quarters of oats, then four quarters of beans, and then four quarters and a half of wheat.

The quantity of oat seed in Holland fen is six bushels an

an acre; but Mr. Cartwright tried an experiment in 1797, of comparing six, seven, and eight, in the same field: can only judge by the eye yet; the best crop is where the six and seven bushels were sown, but the eight worst. Of the two former no perceptible difference. In another field five strike were sown, and the crop as fine as possible.

Mr. Hoyte, on middling land, sows three bushels of barley, and gets five quarters; wheat four quarters; pease seed three bushels; crop three quarters and a half.

Around Folkingham, seed and crop,

Wheat three bushels, crop three quarters and a half.

Barley three bushels, crop five quarters.

Oats five bushels, crop six quarters.

Beans four bushels, crop three quarters and a half.

In the new enclosures above Belton, that were field land,

Barley seed four bushels, crop four to five quarters.

Wheat seed three bushels, crop two qrs. and a half.

Oats, black or brown, four bushels white, six to eight; crop five quarters.

In the enclosures from the heath, crop of barley three quarters; oats iour. No wheat.

At Leadenham, barley seed four bushels and a half, crop four quarters.

Wheat seed three ditto.

This on land that will not give red clover to mow, and at 10*s*. rent.

The corn weeded in the newly cultivated fens below Blankney, &c. 12*s*. an acre. Yet I saw there some oats and barley dreadfully over-run with sow-thistles.

At Hackthorne, &c. on the new enclosures north of Lincoln, barley four bushels, crop three quarters and a half.

Wheat

Wheat three bushels, crop three quarters.

Oats five bushels, crop four quarters.

About Norton-place, extending several miles,

Barley seed three bushels, crop two to six quarters; average under four.

Wheat seed three bushels, crop two and a half to three quarters.

Mr. Harrisson has had five quarters of beans clear to market.

Henry Dalton, Esq. at Knaith, and others his neighbours, on the sand district which rises from the Trent,

Barley seed four bushels, crop five quarters.

Wheat ditto ten pecks, crop three quarters.

Rye ditto eight pecks, crop three qrs. and a half.

At Haxey, in Axholm,

Wheat seed nine pecks, crop 24 bushels, 30 great.

Barley seed four bushels, crop four quarters, up to six.

Oats seed four bushels, crop from four quarters to eight; average five.

Beans seed 14 pecks, 36 bushels, very good; average 30. Some drill beans.

At Butterwick in the Isle, their crops are,

Wheat, five quarters, sometimes less.

Beans, four quarters, never rise to seven.

Flax, 50 stone.

Hemp, 50 stone, and more.

Potatoes, 100 sacks, but a very good crop.

About Normanby, Burton, &c.

Wheat seed two bushels and a half, crop three quarters average; but at Winterton four.

Barley seed four bushels, crop four quarters.

Beans seed four bushels, crop three quarters.

Rye

Rye seed two bushels and a half, crop three quarters and a half.

The weaker the land the more the seed; rye very subject to blight, and winter sown most.

In the new enclosure of Barton,

Wheat seed three bushels and a half, crop four quarters, sometimes five.

Barley seed four bushels, crop four or five qrs.

Beans seed three bushels, but few; crop near seven quarters last year; four quarters common.

Mr. Graburn has sown four bushels of wheat on poor Wold land, and not too much; but on the low land on the Humber, rape seed produces to five quarters, oats to thirteen quarters, and all crops very great.

Mr. Graburn sows seven bushels of oats, some only six. Has had beans nine feet high, 75 pods on one stalk, and three or four stalks from one bean on the Marsh-land by Humber. On this crop he sowed two bushels an acre, broad-cast; and dibbled some still less; but in common they sow four bushels. The crop five qrs. an acres, but promised to be seven.

Mr. Buryman at Saxby, had 33 qrs. of barley from four acres of Wold land, after manured turnips; the land in great condition, but not beyond the average in quality.

In Barrow Field, five earths on fallow open field, sow 10 pecks of wheat; crop two quarters and a half per three-rood acre. Plough once for beans.

At Wintringham they sow four bushels of barley, three of wheat on clover, but 10 pecks on fallow; crops are very large. Wheat, on new broken up warp marsh, five or six quarters; on other soils four or five quarters; barley five or six quarters, and sometimes seven. Oats, eight to ten and twelve quarters, on marsh;

marsh; on other soils, five or six quarters. Beans horridly managed, broad-cast five quarters. Their clover land wheat is better in both quantity and quality than the fallow, which gives too much straw; and it is better after two mowings than one or none.

On the new enclosed Barton-marsh, Mr. Scrivenor got rape seed, on paring and burning, four quarters an acre; then oats ten quarters at the least; the Tartarian sort were on the worst land, and much better than Poland on the best; then oats again, ten quarters more. Also oats on another piece twice, first crop eight quarters, second six quarters. Some on old pasture have produced thirteen quarters an acre, Poland.

About Brocklesby on the Wolds, wheat seed used to be two bushels, now three and a half, or four; barley four; oats seven; pease three; beans three; turnips one and a half to three pounds. The quantity of seed wheat high; but they say their winters are so severe, that much is destroyed. Crops; wheat two quarters and a half; barley three quarters and a half; oats five; pease three; but the yellow rouncivals succeed so well, that six are sometimes gained. Beans three.

At Belesby they have a practice, lately introduced, which is to baulk their turnip land on strongish soils, that is, lap a furrow on unstirred land; then harrow down, and cross plough it clean: but on Wold land plough clean, twice for barley; sow four bushels, crop on Wold land four quarters and a half; on strong soils three to six; average five. Down on the Clays four; sow four and a half to five bushels of beans; average crop not three quarters; some six, but uncommon.

An uncommon crop in Lincolnshire is tares; I heard of very few. Mr. Lloyd of Belesby, cultivates them, both

both for soiling in the yard, and also for feeding sheep; five acres last year kept 50 sheep two months.

Mr. Parkinson has sown some every year for five or six years, but they do not answer, and he intends giving them up; the climate not warm enough.

At Humberston they sow eight to twelve pecks of wheat, and the crop two to three quarters; if more, very good. Of barley they sow four, and gain three quarters; for three or four years past this crop has missed much, and I viewed some very inferior to the soil. Of oats they sow seven or eight, and get four quarters. Beans, sow four or five, and get three or four quarters; the latter very good. Such is the farmer's account.

About Saltfleet, when Marsh land is broken up, oats yield ten or twelve quarters; cole seeded five quarters; oats following, nine or ten quarters.

Seed about Louth, beans five bushels; barley five; wheat three; oats six to eight; turnip seed two to four, and even seven pounds.

About Dalby, wheat seed fourteen pecks; barley five bushels; oats eight bushels; turnip seed four pounds. Crops on an average, wheat three quarters; barley nearly four quarters; oats six quarters and a half. All barley, they think, should be in by the 5th of April, and better early in March.

Mr. Wright, of Spilsby, barley four bushels; wheat three and a half; oats, five or six; turnip seed three pounds. Crops; barley five or six quarters; wheat four quarters; oats seven or eight quarters. A last has been gained on the low ground. Some less than these.

The miller at Welton-mill informed me, that he thought the average produce of the Clays, or Middle-marsh, was three quarters and a half of wheat, and of

 that

that part of the Wolds, two quarters and a half. Beans three quarters in the Clay. They are from open fields, and never hoed.

In the hundred of Skirbeck, on the rich clay and Marsh land:

Wheat seed ten pecks; crop three quarters and a half.

Oat seed five bushels; crop seven quarters and a half.

Bean seed four bushels; crop three quarters and a half.

Here they steep wheat seed, by adding to sea-water salt enough to make it bear an egg, and dry with lime; they have scarcely any smut. Mr. Linton, in 1782, had some smutty wheat, for which he was offered *13s.* a quarter, common wheat being *25s.*; he washed it in repeated waters, and dried it in the sun, and in the autumn of the same year, sold it, wheat being advanced, at *39s.*; he washed it in the month of June.

At Reevesby, Asgarby, &c.

Wheat seed three bushels, some four; crop two quarters and a half.

Barley seed four bushels; crop three quarters and a half.

Oat seed five bushels; crop five quarters.

Mr. Parkinson sows:

Of Wheat two bushels; his crop three quarters.

Barley two bushels; crop four quarters and a half.

Oats four bushels; crop eight quarters.

Pease one bushel; crop, in drills three, broad-cast from one to six quarters.

At Ranby, on good land:

Of Wheat seed three bushels; crop three quarters.

Barley seed four bushels; crop three quarters and a half.

Oats

Oat seed six bushels.

Pease seed five bushels.

Ditto, on bad land :

Barley seed five bushels; crop two quarters and a half.

Oat seed five bushels; crop four quarters.

Pease seed five bushels ; crop three quarters.

Mr. Elmhurst sows four bushels of barley, and gets six quarters ; has had eight ; and his best crops have been from seed procured from about Rougham in Norfolk ; four bushels of wheat, crop often five quarters.

Mr. Thomas Tannard, of Frampton, observed to me, in discourse upon the mildew in wheat, that upon a field, on one half of which soil barley was sown, and upon the other half beans ; the year following all was under wheat, which crop was mildewed to an inch after the barley, and not at all after the beans. Upon which I observed, that barley and beans being in the same field, seemed to imply, that one part of the field was a dry soil, and the other probably clay or wet loam, and that it was the soil caused the mildew, and not the preceding crop. He agreed entirely, and stated the fact of soil to be just so. The barberry-bush was mentioned by some gentlemen present, as a cause, and instances given of the fact.

At Swinop, &c.

Barley seed four bushels ; produce four quarters and a half.

Wheat seed three busnels and a half; produce three quarters.

Oat seed six bushels; produce five quarters.

Mr. Ellison, at Sudbrook :

Wheat seed ten pecks ; crop three quarters.

Barley seed four bushels ; crop four quarters.

Oat

Oat seed six bushels; crop five quarters.

Turnip seed three pounds.

I saw some land to the north of Lincoln, very near the town, that had given six quarters an acre of barley, and then seeds that kept 14 hoggets an acre.

On the strong land at Claypool:

Barley seed three and a half to four bushels; crop four and a half or five quarters.

Bean seed two bushels, set by hand, or drilled; crop four and a half or five quarters.

Wheat seed three bushels; crop three and a half to four quarters.

About Woolsthorpe:

Barley seed three bushels; crop four quarters and a half.

Oat seed six bushels; crop six quarters.

Wheat seed two bushels and a half; crop three quarters and a half.

About Grimsthorpe:

Barley seed three bushels; crop three to six, average four quarters and a half.

Wheat seed two bushels and a half and two bushels; crop three quarters to three and a half.

Oat seed eight bushels to four; crop four quarters to six.

Bean seed two bushels and a half or three; crop three to seven, average four quarters.

All, exclusive of fen and open fields; in the latter, the crops are worse, and the fens better.

These

RECAPITULATION.

Places.	Wheat.		Barley.		Oats.		Beans.	
	Seed. bush.	Crop qrs.	Seed. bush.	Crop qrs.	Seed. bush.	Crop qrs.	Seed. bush.	Crop qrs.
Long Sutton -	—	5	—	—	—	10½	—	—
Deeping fen -	—	—	—	—	—	9	—	—
Holla d fen -	2½	4	—	—	6	7	—	—
Mr. Cartwright -	—	4½	—	—	—	8	—	4½
Folkingham -	3	3½	3	5	5	6	4	3½
Belton - -	3	2½	4	4½	7	5	—	—
Ditto Heath -	—	—	—	3	—	4	—	—
Leadenham -	3	—	4½	4	—	—	—	—
Hackthorne -	3	3	4	3½	5	4	—	—
Norton - -	3	2¾	3	4	—	—	—	—
Knaith - -	2½	3	4	5	—	—	—	—
Haxey - -	2¼	3	4	4	4	5	3½	4
Butterwick -	—	5	—	—	—	—	—	4
Normanby -	2½	3	4	4	—	—	4	3
Winterton -	—	4	—	—	—	—	—	—
Barton - -	3½	4	4	4½	—	—	3	4½
Mr. Graburn -	4	—	—	—	7	—	4	5
Mr. Scrivenor -	—	—	—	—	—	10	—	—
Barrow - -	3	3	—	—	—	—	—	—
Wintringham -	3	5	4	6	—	7	—	5
Brocklesby -	3¾	2½	4	4	7	5	3	3
Belesby - -	—	—	4	5	—	—	4½	3
Humberston -	2½	3	4	3	7½	4	4½	3½
Saltfleet - -	—	—	—	—	—	10	—	—
Louth - -	3	—	5	—	7	—	5	—
Dalby - -	3½	3	5	4	8	5½	—	—
Spilsby, Mr. wright	3½	4	4	5½	5½	7½	—	—
Welton - -	—	3½	—	—	—	—	—	3
Ditto - -	—	2½	—	—	—	—	—	—
Skirbeck - -	2½	3¼	—	—	5	7½	4	3½
Reevesby - -	3½	2½	4	3¾	5	5	—	—
Mr. Parkinson -	2	3	2	4½	4	8	—	—
Ranby - -	3	3	4	3½	6	—	—	—
Ditto - -	—	—	—	2½	—	4	—	—
Mr. Elmhurst -	4	5	4	6	—	—	—	—
Swinop - -	3½	3	4	4½	6	5	—	—
Mr. Ellison -	2½	3	4	4	6	5	—	—
Claypool - -	3	3¾	3¾	4¾	—	—	2	4¾
Woolsthorpe -	2½	3½	3	4½	6	6	—	—
Grimsthorpe -	2¼	3¼	3	4½	6	5	2¾	4
Average -	3	3½	3¾	4¼	6	6½	3¾	3¾

These

These averages are, upon the whole, respectable: that of wheat is beyond the medium of the kingdom; and barley being chiefly in light land districts, not of a high rent, is not small; oats are considerable: but soil considered, beans too low; and even $3\frac{1}{4}$ are beyond the fact, were all the open fields included.

Beans.

In Holland fen they are drilled and horse-hoed by some farmers, at two feet.

About Folkingham, most of the farmers either dibble or drill; on sward, one row on a flag dibbled; drilled at 18 inches: most horse-hoe with an expanding horse-hoe, and hand-hoe besides. Hand-hoe the dibbled.

Mr. Hoyte has cultivated beans with success; he has dibbled two bushels an acre on old sward, and got five quarters; and as much by drilling them on manure.

In the strong land open-fields near Belton, they are cultivated broad-cast without any hoeing; and the crops and husbandry as may be supposed.

At Hackthorne there is some dibbling; Mr. Cracroft has planted wheat in this manner, at 9*s*. an acre; also beans and pease, beans on flag sward land has given good crops.

Mr. Webster, at Bankside, drills his beans on ridges, a double row at nine inches, with intervals of 27 inches: he has some equidistant at 12; but prefers the former; he is a great friend to the drill, uses only Mr. Cook's.

About Normanby, &c. they drill beans in a very singular course: they summer-fallow, and then drill beans; hoeing, and sow wheat after. The more common way is to plough the land into narrow ridges, then sow,

sow, broad-cast, and harrow down the ridges; the crop comes up in rows; hand-hoe and weed but few, and little. Mr. Robert Sutton does it well; and he dibbles much upon sward, and with good success. Mr. Goulton, at Alkborough, in 1796, dibbled pease on sward; and got from three acres, seven quarters an acre, wanting one bushel on the three; the grass had been down four years; some ray in it; five or six pecks seed an acre.

At Belesby, they plough once for broad-cast; but twice for drilling; hoe both: get no more one way than they do the other; but the land is cleaner after the drill; by which means Mr. Lloyd, who is an excellent farmer, follows them with wheat. Produce beans up to six quarters, but uncommon. His mode of drilling is cheap and simple. He ploughs for them before winter: in the spring, ploughs clean, but shallow, with one horse in a small light plough; and drills every third furrow with a barrow drill, run by hand. These one-horse ploughs he uses in ploughing for turnips also.

At Alesby, Mr. Skipwith practises a singular course for Lincolnshire: 1. turnips; 2. barley; 3. clover; 4. beans; 5. wheat. The putting in beans upon clover I have recommended to many farmers; but, till now, I have not met with an instance of it in the county: he observes, that beans are always good on clover; he harrows them (five bushels) in on one earth, and feeds with sheep till near blossoming, wanting hands for hoeing; hence he is forced to miss the wheat after, when the land is foul, and take turnips; which, with a better bean culture, would not be the case.

Mr. Linton, of Frieston, has made an experiment, extremely

tremely interesting for Lincolnshire; he has conducted it for five years; it is this course: 1. beans; 2. wheat.

In autumn he ploughs and grips the land for beans, and manures for them ten tons an acre, once in four years. In the spring, ploughs once or twice, according to the state of the land, in order to have a tilth for drilling and hoeing. In March puts in the crop, by drilling, eleven pecks an acre, in rows about two feet asunder; as soon as they appear, harrows; and when weeds come, shims them with the expanding horse-hoe, which is repeated rather deeper than before, as the beans advance; after which they are hand-weeded; immediately before the blossoming, they are earthed up, with the mould-boards added to the hoe. He usually tops them after the pods are sufficiently set, by a man taking two rows with an unsawed sharp reaping hook. The produce, four quarters. After harvest immediately harrow the stubble, and carry off the rubbish; then plough once, sow and harrow in the wheat; which produces from three to five quarters, on land of 21*s*. an acre.

Expenses.

	£.	s.	d.
Manure, 10 loads	£.2	12	6
Ploughing thrice, and harrowing	1	0	0
Seed, 11 pecks, at 32*s*.	0	11	0
Drilling with barrow	0	0	6
Harrowing	0	1	0
Shimming twice	0	3	0
Weeding	0	4	0
Double mould boarding	0	1	6
Carried forward	£.4	13	6

Topping

	£.	s.	d.
Brought forward	£.4	13	6
Topping	0	2	0
Reaping	0	9	6
Leading, &c.	0	6	0
Thrashing	0	5	0
Carrying out	0	3	0
Wheat.—Harrow, stubble, and clearing	0	5	0
Ploughing	0	5	0
Seed, 10 pecks	0	15	0
Sow and harrow	0	2	6
Weeding	0	10	0
Reaping	0	15	0
Leading, &c.	0	5	6
Thrashing four quarters	0	10	0
Carrying out	0	3	0
Beans—as before, except manure	3	6	6
Wheat as before	3	11	0
Four years' rent	4	4	0
Four years' tithe	1	4	0
Four years' town charges	0	14	0
	£.22	9	6

Produce.

	£.	s.	d.
Eight quarters of wheat, at 42*s*.	£.16	16	0
Straw of two crops, as manure is charged	0	16	0
Beans, eight quarters, at 32*s*.	12	16	0
Straw	0	9	0
	£.30	17	0
Expenses	22	9	6
Profit	£.8	7	6
Per acre, per annum	£.2	1	10

But

But Mr. Linton remarks, that in this calculation, though nothing is exaggerated, still expenses will run higher; and articles of tillage, and wear and tear, will amount to some small matter more; and interest of capital, at 5*l.* an acre, will be 20*s.* in the four years. Enough will, however, remain to prove, that this course of crops is vastly important; and I need not add, that it is what I have recommended in various parts of the county.

Mr. Hebb, of Claypool, cultivates beans with great success, upon seeds of six, seven, or eight years, &c.; he dibbles them across the lands, upon one ploughing, the rows two feet asunder. On other lands he sprains in the seed by hand, in every third furrow. In the former way he only hand-hoes, and gets the largest crops, up to six quarters an acre, of a quality remarkably fine. Those that are drilled, as above, he horse-hoes with the expanding shims mentioned before, and earths up; cutting weeds in the rows with hand-hoes. I saw his stubble this year, which, for so wet a season, was clean. Crops up to six quarters.

This article of beans, in Lincolnshire, is so important, that I have been induced to treat the article by itself, to shew how very few instances occurred of good management. As a general fact, it is to be stated, that this crop is broad-cast, never hoed, full of weeds, and wheat consequently not following them. In the wet open fields, fallow usually succeeds. This management is so bad and unprofitable, compared with a better system, that there is scarcely an object in the husbandry of the county which wants more reforming. The preceding accounts were taken as information: I saw very few, if any crops, that merited the least attention; and I am inclined to think, that drilling beans is well understood

derstood by very few persons indeed. It is every where a difficult operation on lands wet and strong; so that I am inclined rather to recommend dibbling them on layers, upon the seed earth. Such soils preclude early tillage in the spring, if they have been previously ploughed; and it is very advantageous to be able to get upon them with the teams at pleasure; a point only to be effected on a ley. One row may be dibbled on every second furrow, in which case they will be equidistant eighteen inches; or, two furrows being dibbled, and one missed, they will rise in double rows at nine inches, with intervals of eighteen; equal to a row at every thirteen inches and a half; in which method I have raised good crops, on land much inferior to the Lincoln soils. Horse and hand-hoeing, and weeding, are absolutely essential: the more money thus bestowed the better for the farmer; those of Kent are dissatisfied, if the expense does not rise from 17*s*. to 20*s*. an acre, as the crop of wheat is sure to suffer, if any neglect takes place in these respects. There is no better preparation, than beans well managed. After harvest, the stubble, in that county, is *broad shared* or, *shimmed*, to cut up all weeds remaining, till, by harrowing, it takes the appearance almost of a well-ordered garden-bed. Farmers, in this enlightened age, travel: a Lincolnshire one, with land proper for this crop, could not do better than view the Kentish management during the growth, and after harvest: he would return home with ideas which he did not before possess. In general, the Kentish bean land is lighter; but he will at once see that their system is applicable on all soils. If a Lincoln strong-land farmer will calculate the expenses and produce of, 1. fallow; 2. wheat; 3. beans;

3. beans; with the vastly better management of, 1. fallow; 2. oats or wheat; 3. clover or seeds; 4. beans; 5. wheat; supposing a fallow periodically necessary (which I do not admit), he will find the superiority of the latter so great, as to induce him to exert himself with vigour, for the introduction of such a culture of beans as shall secure success.

Seeds.

This term is given in Lincolnshire, as well as in many other districts, to the artificial grasses which are sown in common rotations. In most parts of the kingdom there is an idea, that they will not endure, with profit, above one, two, or three years, according to the sorts: when instances to the contrary occur, they should be noted, that the circumstances on which they depend, may at length be ascertained, and disappointments prevented.

Mr. Chaplin, of Blankney, sowed white clover, cow-grass, rib-grass, and hay-seeds, in a course, meaning to leave it while it was good: it remained nine years, answering well to the last; no ray, as he does not, on experience, approve of that grass.

Mr. Dalton, at Knaith, finds that trefoil on his sandy land is remarkably profitable; he has summered from the end of April to the end of August, 30 shearlings, on three acres and a half, the first year.

Ray-grass has been cultivated many years, but is now leaving off very generally; yet upon the very poorest sands they can get nothing else; but it is objected to by all the landlords that are attentive, from long conviction, that land always breaks up poor after it; and this, not from landlords' ideas, but the information

mation given to the gentlemen I conversed with, by very good farmers. Instead of it, prefer white clover 8 lb.; rib 1 lb; trefoil 7 lb.

Mr. Goulton finds that these seeds will last good four years. An acre of seeds, if good, will keep, at Alkborough, ten sheep from May-day to Michaelmas; red clover; but nothing else so much.

Very fine seeds in Barton field new enclosure, will keep seven sheep per acre, besides a two-year old beast; the latter till Midsummer. The seeds sowed are white clover, and hay-seeds; 14 lb. of the clover, and two quarters hay-seeds.

Mr. Goulton, of Onby, sowed seeds alone in June, upon poor Wold land of a cold quality; trefoil and ray-grass, part turnips, part oats the year before; ploughed for them; some part four times, some less. Now, in September, they look very fine, and promise well; intends to pasture them soon with lambs.

Mr. Graburn has sown seeds with rape, and found it answer well, and much better than with corn. Mr. Curtis, of Ashby, near Grimsby, did the same; and when the rape was fed off every one thought the seeds were destroyed; but they were the best on the farm.

Mr. Richardson, at Great Lumber, on the Wolds, with the barley, after paring and burning for turnips, sows white and red clover, and trefoil, leaving it three years; the first it carries six sheep an acre; the second five; and the third three per acre. He for many years disliked ray-grass much; but its value early in the spring is so great *on dry land*, that he is now changing his opinion, and sows it.

Mr. Clough, of Gayton, near Louth, never sows ray; it is good only at one short season; and impoverishes the ground, on comparison with any other sort of of seeds. I asked him if this opinion was general; few, he replied, will now have any thing to do with it; but it has been common.

About Reevesby, Asgarby, &c. they like white clover alone on sandy land, for feeding sheep; because they find it ploughs up cleaner from twitch, than it does when other mixtures are sown; 12 lb. or 14 lb. an acre. Mr. Parkinson finds that his land will not produce red clover in a four years course more than two rounds; he then changes to one bushel ray-grass, 6lb. trefoil, and 6 lb. of red clover for one round; and the next round 8 lb. cow-grass, and 6 lb. of Dutch clover; cow-grass yields a wonderful burthen of hay, nine inches higher than red clover; but the red clover yields the best eddish: it will last two or three years; but better to plough sooner.

Mr. Cracraft, of Keal, summers ten sheep an acre on white clover only, upon sands marled.

The Rev. Mr. Allington, of Swinop, has tried Yorkshire white, and finds that it does not answer: the sheep prefer ray-grass, white clover, and trefoil; which however is no proof that it does not answer.

I saw some land near Lincoln, to the north, that has kept fourteen hoggets per acre, on seeds.

These practices have merit, and shew that the object in general is well understood. That of sowing grasses with rape, is new; and is a thought that deserves attention. I heard it mentioned some years ago in conversation, as having been tried and failed: but not seeing any reason for a want of success, I tried it myself, and it answered well. It is a management that gives full time for cleaning and preparing the land; and for sowing at a season (July or August) probably the best, as new grass seeds are then to be had. Feeding the

rape

rape manures the seeds; and if done with a little attention relative to soil and weather, would very rarely be injurious;—it is a system which should be adopted in other counties*.

Rape.

Much cultivated in Deeping fen on paring and burning; and worth from 40*s*. to 3*l*. an acre, fed with sheep.

In Holland fen it is now generally fed by sheep, and is worth from 40*s*. to 50*s*. an acre; which space will carry ten sheep during twelve weeks; but it is of so feeding a nature, that numbers die on it.

Two acres of land in Holland fen has often produced a last of rape seed, now worth 50 guineas; and seldom worth less than 30 guineas.

In the rape, which several considerable breeders about Folkingham have been accustomed to buy in Holland fen, they have found that an acre will carry ten sheep ten weeks, and worth 6*d*. per head per week.

At Garthorpe in Axholm, rape seed five quarters.

In the north-west angle of the county, Gainsborough to Barton, the farmers say they had rather give 4½*d*. a week to feed sheep with rape, than 3*d*. for turnips.

In the marshes about Saltfleet, this is found a very profitable crop for sheep; but one inconvenience attends it, which occasions great expense or trouble, if not fed off before hard weather comes; their fences being ditches, these freezing, let the sheep of all the country together; they smell cole to a great distance; so that a field of some acres will be eaten up in a night:

* There is nothing more strongly to be recommended to this county, than sowing cocksfoot grass instead of ray: the improvement would be very great indeed.

500 and more have thus been known to get together:— the piece must be netted or hurdled round. When fed, they often seed it; but what is not fed yields much the better crop.

Mr. Lofft, of Marsh Chapel, remarks, that there is a vast difference in cole; that which grows on fresh land, has the stalk as brittle as glass, and will fatten sheep beyond any other food; but what grows on old tillage land, the stalk is tough and wiry, and has little proof in it. An acre of cole will fatten more sheep than an acre of turnips; but turnips will keep more stock sheep than cole.

Turnips.

They are generally hoed in Holland fen; but there are very few: rape only on a large scale.

About Folkingham, all twice hoed. One of the finest crops of turnips I have any where seen, was upon the farm of Mr. Dawson, at Berthorp, near Folkingham. In 1795 the field was ploughed from the old sward; it was sown after tares on a barley stubble, part fed, part mown; the soil red loam. They had been hand-hoed twice, and as well as any in Norfolk; there was not a weed in the field, and the plants of the most beautiful luxuriance. It is a crop that does credit to Lincolnshire.

I was very much pleased with viewing the turnips from Norton to Kirton, by the turnpike, and also by the Cliff road: the quantity great, the crops good and clean, and well hoed, with some few exceptions; it was a change from what I saw here 29 years ago, striking. The best farmers hoe twice; first 5*s*. 6*d*. per acre; second 2*s*. 9*d*. Mr. Thorpe, at Kirton, has some drilled at two feet and a half, in a broad-cast field;

field; and the latter promise to be much the greater crop.

Upon the sand, above the Trent, from Gainsborough to Newark, which extends 25 miles, they plough four or five times for turnips, feed them off with sheep, and are worth 4*l.* an acre.

Excellent turnip hoeing about Alkborough, &c. set out well; 5*s.* to 6*s.* for first hoeing; the second by day; but if lett 2*s.* 6*d.* There is a man at Whitton that has been a turnip hoer 38 years.

At Wintringham they hoe once, and hand-weed. I ought to observe, that upon this admirable soil, I found this crop well managed, and the products very fine. All fed by sheep.

At Barton, hoe once.

About Brocklesby, the chief improvement that has taken place, in cultivation, is the great increase of turnips; and this has depended a good deal on the practice of paring and burning the Wold sheep-walks, and gorse covers. Turnips here are worth 50*s.* to 60*s.* an acre.

At Belesby, plough for them three or four times; hoe all; feed with sheep; value from 40*s.* to 4*l.* They complain much of the distemper called *fingers and toes:* the root, instead of swelling, running into strings of that form, rot, and come to nothing; it is common on all fresh land, and nothing they can do prevents it.

At Alesby also, this distemper does much mischief on all land, but most on fresh broken up. Mr. Skipwith has known it ever since he was a farmer. Tried lime, but had no effect in this respect: ashes he finds the best manure to prevent it; but not wholly. Observes that turnips always do best after wheat, and not

 because

because of manuring for wheat, which is not done, it being spread for the turnips.

About Louth they have been much plagued with fingers and toes; they assured me, that on cutting the roots, they find a worm in them about the eighth of an inch long, and the size of a large pin; worst on the richest land.

At Dalby they reckon that a good acre of turnips will winter ten sheep; and turnips, on an average, seven. They are worth 3*l*. an acre. No fingers and toes; but at some places near they have it.

Mr. Wright, of Spilsby, hoes twice.

About Reevesby, Asgarby, &c. they hoe twice, when the weather will permit; but the men hurry it over too fast. A good acre will winter ten sheep; they are worth from 2*l*. 10*s*. to 4*l*. an acre; cole is worth 35*s*. to 50*s*. Turnips in 25 years wonderfully increased.

Mr. Cracraft, of Keal, reckons that his turnips, on marled land, will winter twelve sheep an acre during twenty weeks.

The late Mr. Cod, of Ranby, often observed, as Mr. Lofft informed me, that turnips, of which he bought many in Yorkshire, would, on fine land, bring on sheep much faster than any at Ranby, though the size of the roots was the same.

Turnips at Ranby will winter eight hogs an acre; very few will carry ten sheep.

Mr. Ellison sows 3 lb. of seed an acre; hand-hoes twice, at 6*s*. or 7*s*. an acre; feeds off all with sheep, giving oil-cake at the same time.

Mr. Walker, of Woolsthorpe, on rich red sand, ploughs his turnip land but once for barley.

Remembering, as I do, this county about forty years ago, no circumstance in it surprised me more than

than the astonishing change effected in respect to this crop. At that time there was scarcely a turnip to be seen, where now thousands of acres flourish; and the few sown in the whole county were unhoed, except by here and there a gentleman. What a change! from such a state of backwardness, in an article so perfectly adapted to the soil, to find them now as plentiful; and in various cases even more so, than in some of our best cultivated counties. This has been a most meritorious progress, closely attending that first of improvements, enclosing heaths and wastes. The crop is not yet perfect in the hands of all farmers, for I cannot say that I saw none unhoed; there are some slovens remaining, who either hoe but little, or doing it by servants, and not being in a regular system, execute it in a very insufficient manner.

But immense tracts are very well managed; and by many persons, in as capital a style as any in Norfolk. This, upon the whole, is a most happy and important change; and has had great effects in improving the size, and increasing the number, of the sheep and cattle of the county.

Drilling.

In this branch of husbandry Mr. Cartwright has practised largely, to three, four, and five score acres; and one year to 150. This year has 50. He drills equi-distant, with Mr. Amos's drill, eight inches; having found that when wheat has been at one foot it ripened much later, and was an inferior crop in every respect, to the eight inches adjoining, which is the distance for all white corn. Beans at twenty-four, and three inches deep; wheat two and a half; and oats two. Quantity of seed; oats four bushels; wheat two; and beans

beans two to two and a half. He is clear that a greater saving of seed than this is pernicious; which amounts to one-fifth, upon comparison with broad-cast. The object is hoeing; twice breast-hoeing the white corn, and hand-hoeing the beans;—the former 2*s*. an acre each time; but if the land is clean, once is enough. Also, if wanted, hand-weeded. The result has been, sometimes the crops have been better than broad-cast, but not always; on the average it has the advantage. Thinks that the superiority is not so great with corn as with woad.

Lord Brownlow's father was at a considerable expense to procure instruments of the best kind for practising the drill husbandry, and spared no expense in conducting it; but was convinced, upon experience, that it was not so profitable as the common method. There has been a good deal of drilling with Mr. Cook's plough, about Grantham; but it does not spread; on the contrary, many have abandoned it. I called at Mr. Scoffin's at Barston, to hear his opinion, but he was absent.

Mr. Harrisson, at Norton, has tried Cook's drill, but laid it aside; not from defects in the tool, but the husbandry *will not do here*. The soil a friable sandy loam.

Mr. Scrivenor, of Barton, drilled turnips in 1796, at eighteen inches, and they were the best in the lordship; some other persons in the neighbourhood have done the same, and with very good success.

Mr. Graburn, of Barton, has drilled barley, and various other crops, and had good ones; yet he finds the system so tedious, that he has given it up, and now sows all broad-cast.

Mr. Linton has been a driller, and an attentive one, of

of wheat, oats, and barley; but finding that it would not answer, gave up the practice.

Mr. Parkinson for some years practised the drill husbandry with Mr. Cook's drill, and by one from Lancashire, and has had good barley; also pease, and wheat; he has this year only seventeen acres of barley drilled, and that is the worst crop on his farm.

Mr. Cod, of Ranby, began drilling in Mr Ducket's method ten years ago: he bought a complete set of his tools; and I saw some large fields of turnips that would do credit to any farmer; also a barley stubble quite clean. Mr. Lofft's opinion of this husbandry is, that it answers perfectly well for turnips, and prefers it as better; the land quite clean, and at a smaller expense than the common way: he approves it also for wheat and barley; but will never use it for oats, which ought to be sown on rich land; and if not plenty of seed, the weeds will prevail. In proof of this, his father sowed four bushels of oats an acre, and the crop was weak and poor: on the same field, after a crop of cole, he himself sowed oats again, eight bushels an acre, and had as fine a crop as could grow; and he has found this to be the case for fourteen years*.

The

* Whether it is from unskilfulness in the use of them, or that the instruments themselves have no intrinsic advantage over the common methods of husbandry, I cannot tell; but I believe it is a fact, that the whole train of drills, scufflers, scarificators, turnip-hoes, &c. &c. which have been imported into this district, have never been found advantageous to their employers.

And though I am now not writing from my own actual observation, I have the testimony of very respectable farmers, that the produce of the lands of Mr. John Cod have never compensated the expenses of his management, in the same proportion with the farms of his neighbours, who

The turnips were ploughed for once, with Ducket's skim-coulter plough, without the skim; harrow, scuffle; once ploughed with common plough, and sometimes the miner, instead of a ploughing; then harrow, and perhaps scuffle again, and drill; the rows nine inches; scarifies the rows nine at a time; then cross the drills with a single rowed scuffler. Sometimes this cross in a diagonal direction; hand work to cut any large weeds, and cut out knots of plants. The horse-hoeing nine rows at a time, will do ten acres a day, a man, a horse, and a boy;—running over with hand-hoes, 1*s*. an acre.

Mr. Walker, of Woolsthorpe, has practised the drill culture largely for wheat, barley, oats, and turnips; but has left it all off:—he has a tolerable opinion of the practice in very fine weather; then the clovers answer well in this way. But he has no drilled crops on his farm except turnips. From drilling nine gallons an acre of wheat, he has had forty-four bushels an acre over eight acres, on the deep sandy loam.

Such are the facts I met with in this inquiry; they confirm the general result through the kingdom. Drilling is a practice which will be found to answer to a certain extent, and with a certain degree of skill and attention.

---

who have simply ploughed well, notwithstanding their management has been termed barbarous in the extreme.

As from what I have here said, it may be supposed that I condemn the drill husbandry in the lump, I think it proper to observe, that I consider drilling as the best method of sowing beans I am acquainted with; for that crop, and for that crop only, have I ever known it to answer any good purpose.—*MS. of the Board.*

Dibbling.

Dibbling.

Mr. Hoyte, of Osbornby, dibbles beans; and gets five quarters from two bushels of seed. Dibbled once six pecks of wheat, and got two quarters; but the frost destroyed much. Others have also dibbled wheat; the expense 10*s*. 6*d*.; and in general the crop has been a sack an acre gain, besides saving six pecks of seed.

Sir Cecil Wray has begun this excellent practice: last year his dibbled wheat beat all his other crops.

Mr. Goulton has dibbled wheat with success; and his tenant, Mr. Richard Langton, of Whitton, has this year thirteen acres. Upon the whole, it has succeeded greatly.

SECT. V.—CROPS NOT COMMONLY CULTIVATED.

Potatoes—Have been largely cultivated about Spalding, but have not answered for bullocks; one man got to 200 acres; but was ruined, though the crops were very great.

Mr. Cartwright, of Brothertoft, has been largely in this crop ever since he has been in this country; has always had from 12 to 15, and once, more than 20 acres. The land has been ploughed before Christmas; in March it is ploughed again, and again the beginning of April, and properly cleaned of twitch, and all rubbish. About the middle of April cart out the dung; 12 three-horse loads per acre; and immediately after three acres of dung being spread, three ploughs should begin; and the length of the furrows being divided into

into sixteen equal parts, one woman being stationed in each division, and a man being fixed to every four women, he rakes the dung on to the potatoes, after the women have laid the sets in the furrows, a little on one side, to be out of the tread of the horses. Ten sacks, or 30 bushels of potatoes, plant an acre, every third furrow; cut large, as being preferable, but the small ones whole; continuing thus, finish four acres and a half a day, each plough doing one acre and a half with two horses. As soon as done, roll down with a light roller. Thus, they are left till they come up; then harrowed lengthways with light harrows. In three or four weeks, according as the season is, skim-hoe them with an expanding horse-hoe (vide Mr. Amos's book); when the weeds are dead, repeat it; then begin to hand-hoe the rows at 3*s*. 6*d*. per acre; in a week or so, earth up with double mould-boards added to the hoe;—and in two or three weeks after repeat this. In August hand-weed them, at 1*s*. an acre. In October pull up the tops, and lay them on the tenth rows; then plough them up, by first turning a furrow from the ridges, as near as can be, without disturbing them; then a large deep furrow without the coulter; 16 women planted at equal distances, as before, to pick into baskets; one man to every four gatherers, unless the weather is very dry, to fork them out. The *pyes* (preserving pits) being ready, six inches deep, and six feet wide, the carts take them home. Pile in form of a roof, well covered with stubble, and earthed a foot thick to near the top, which is left open some time to draw out the steam. Crop 480 bushels, on an average, at 80lb. a bushel.

Expenses.

Expenses.

	£.	s.	d.
Four ploughings, at 5*s.*	£.1	0	0
Three harrowings at 6*d.*	0	1	6
Twelve loads of dung, half price 1*s.* 6*d.*	0	18	0
Carriage of ditto	0	6	0
Dung, filling and spreading	0	2	0
Planting, men and women	0	16	8
Seed, 30 bushels, cut, &c.	2	0	0
Rolling	0	0	6
Skim-hoe twice	0	2	0
Hand-hoe	0	3	6
Earth up twice	0	2	0
Weeding	0	1	6
Gathering tops	0	2	0
Taking up and pying	2	0	0
Rent	1	7	0
Taxes	0	6	0
	£.9	8	8

Produce.

	£.	s.	d.
480 bushels, worth, in feeding bullocks, young cattle, horses, &c. 8*d.* a bushel	16	0	0
Expenses	9	8	8
Profit	£.6	11	4

In regard to their benefit as a preparatory to corn,—wheat is found not to succeed after them,—attributed to making the soil too loose. But get very fine oats after them; as good as after other crops. The culture is much increased in this country.

About Folkingham they have increased very much within

within three or four years; and much among the cottagers. The effect very useful. But the principal place for them is about Tattersal and Coningsby.

At Haxey, in Axholm, plough between November and Christmas; at Candlemas or Lady-day again, and three or four more. Manure 9th or 10th May, 15 loads an acre; short muck for potatoes, but long reckoned good. Some set every other furrow, and some every third, eight sets in a yard; rake in dung upon the sets; eight sacks, or 24 strike, plant an acre. One strong eye, or two weak, to each cutting. When they first appear, harrow along or across the rows. In a week hoe, *3s.* or *3s. 6d.* an acre; when a foot high or less, hill by ploughing with common plough; but they have hilling double ploughs. Weeding is done by children. Take up by pulling up the tops, which they throw aside. Plough out, keeping the plough down under the potatoes; fixing hands in divisions, 20 yards to a gatherer. Harrow the new ridges, and pick again. Plough again in small furrows, when two or three pickers follow the ploughs, turning down the ridges; and harrow; then it is ready for wheat.—Crop: Mr. Durrand has had 80 sacks of ox nobles on two roods and a half, or 330 bushels an acre: but this was an extraordinary crop. A middling one 70 sacks, repeat them on the land every four or five years. Kidneys do not take from the soil so much as ox nobles.

Fifty years ago, on Trent side, Mr. Durrand's father had hemp and flax every year; and as to barley and wheat, could not venture it, so rank and strong; but since potatoes, they have so much reduced the fertility, that corn is common, and often not

not good crops. The expression was, potatoes have quite killed the land.

At Butterwick in the Isle, wheat after potatoes on their inferior soils (but they have no bad land), does not succeed well; but on warp land it does well. They get to 100 sacks an acre.

At Garthorpe, in Axholm, potatoes on new land 80 sacks an acre*.

About Normanby, Burton, &c. &c. they have increased of late very much; but Mr. Wilson thinks, that no crop can be beneficial to an estate, which returns nothing in manure. The land here is not rich enough for them. Nothing in the world exhausts and injures the land so much as potatoes; they are clear of this fact.

At Belesby, Mr. Lloyd, after barley, which yielded five quarters and a half an acre, sowed part of the stubble with tares, and the other part planted with potatoes; manure for neither. He then sowed the whole with wheat, which is now on the ground; the tare part much the greatest crop; too great, being partly down; but the potatoe part, though good indeed the best corn, does not complain of being too rich, for none of it is down.

---

* The Isle of Axholm. The crops there of every kind are almost universally good; I never yet saw any lands so well weeded, so carefully attended to, and kept so generally clean, as those fields; the whole country is quite a garden; the hemp and potatoe crops are *here* acknowledged to be abundant; the other crops I can assert, are generally equally good. It is worthy of remark, that the potatoes produced in this neighbourhood, though apparently equally good, are not in reality so valuable as those grown on the southern banks of the Ouse, in a district called Marshland; those are always preferred for the London market, and generally sell for 2*s.* per sack more than the Trent potatoes.—*MS. of the Board.*

More

More potatoes about Saltfleet than formerly; but still very few, except by the poor people.

Mr. Cod, of Ranby, used to feed his horses of all sorts upon boiled potatoes, on a large scale, and with good success.

Mr. Linton, of Freiston, has cultivated them; but though they are a valuable crop, yet the uncertainty of the sale, and the extraordinary attention they demand, induced him to give up the cultivation. At Leak and Wrangle there are some wastes, which the cottagers sometimes take in, and cultivate potatoes; they have no right, and are rather a lawless set; and the practice is productive, under these circumstances, of some evils.

About Tattersall and Coningsby, they have, for some years, been large cultivators of this crop.

Potatoes at Coningsby.

Dr.

Mr. Faunt's Account.

	£.	s.	d.
Rent for black sandy land*, per acre	£.3	0	0
Tithe	0	6	0
Ploughing	0	6	0
Harrowing	0	2	6
Manure (if land in good order) 10 loads, otherwise 20 loads	1	0	0
Seed, 100 pecks	1	5	0
Cutting	0	2	0
Planting	0	7	6
Hoeing and weeding	0	10	6
Taking up	1	10	0
Pying and carting half a mile	1	10	0
	£.9	19	6

Cr.

	£.	s.	d.
By 1400 pecks of *ox nobles*†, worth upon an average, 2*d*. per peck, or 2*s*. per sack	£.11	13	4
240 pecks of refuse	1	0	0
	£.12	13	4
	9	19	6
Clear gain per acre	£.2	13	10

Best eating potatoes are spotted lemons, old lemons, old rough reds, red nose kidneys, early reds, early manlys, and captain harts, worth upon an average, 3*d*. a peck;—above 1000 pecks per acre, have been had of these, worth 12*l*. 10*s*.

Mr. Chatterton thinks about 900 pecks to an acre.—Average price 3½*d*. per peck; other observations he thinks right.

* Broken land, rye stubble, or wheat stubble. Barley or oats is preferable, if free from twitch.

† Will be good eating upon good sandy land, and no where else.

Woad

Woad.

The culture of this plant has been carried to such perfection, on a very extensive scale, by J. Cartwright, Esq. at Brothertoft farm, near Boston, that it will be sufficient to explain his management. His father had been largely in the old system by moveable colonies, but as the trouble of that method of conducting the business was considerable, his son attempted, and successfully, to fix it to one spot. For this purpose it was necessary, first to secure a tract of land sufficiently large for affording a certain number of acres annually in crop, for keeping the buildings and machinery in work, so that the business might go on with regularity. At Brothertoft he purchased such a tract: it will be proper to consider it under the articles of, 1. Soil; 2. Culture; 3. Manufacture; to render it saleable.

Soil.—Woad being a tap-rooted plant, penetrating eight or nine inches, of a substantial size, it necessarily demands a deep soil; the best is a rich loam; a stiff clay is unfavourable. Here the saline principle of the soil is favourable to this plant, as well as to many others. Deep, fertile, putrid saline, an alluvion of the sea, the richness of which on the dead maritime levels is every where great. Experience has proved, that the plant thrives best on fresh grass land; accordingly it has long been the common practice for the undertakers of this culture to hire grass land, with a permission to break it up and sow woad for a certain number of years; here for four years; in the more upland situations for two; sometimes for three, in the second-rate soils of this country.

Culture.

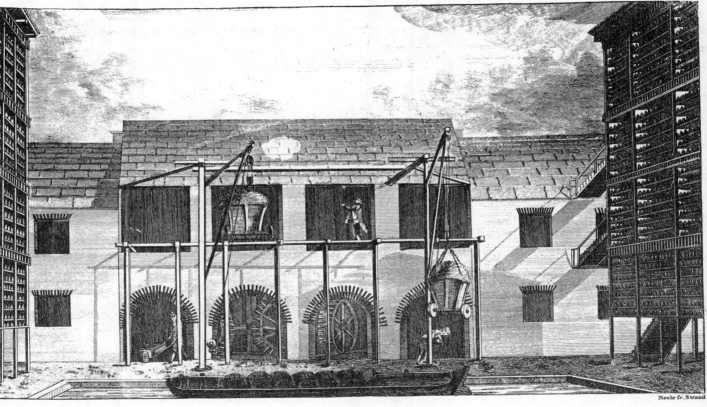

Neele sc. Strand

WOAD APPARATUS.

Neele sc. Strand

WOAD APPARATUS.

Culture.—If the soil is dry enough to permit, the grass should be ploughed early in February; if not later in that month. Great attention should be paid to ploughing it as carefully as possible to the depth of about five inches, with three horses in a plough, followed in the furrow by a man with a spade, so that if the turf is not turned over very flat and well joined, it may be laid completely so by hand. This attention is necessary to prevent the grass rising in the seams; then the land is harrowed often to raise a depth of mould sufficient for the drill to work. The seed is so put in (after a rolling about the middle of March, continuing till the middle of May, in portions, to vary the time of cropping), in equi-distant rows eight or nine inches asunder; if not loose enough, *it is sown broad-cast*, and the seed harrowed in. Quantity of seed per acre, 88 bushels in husk. And the clods raked off into the sides of the furrows, and then rolled again to leave it smooth and neat. In very old grass full of roots, the harrowing is repeated even to twelve or fifteen times; and in cases where the grass is rough and coarse with rushes, sedge, &c. it is necessary to pare and burn it, if the land belongs to the undertaker. And another reason for this practice is, that paring and burning destroys great numbers of the slug which produces the cock-chaffer, as well as the wire-worm, which abounds here in the lighter soils very much; there are also many slugs of a smaller size, of a blueish brown, about an inch long. Being thus far done, the field must be gripped very carefully, for wherever water stands, the woad is entirely destroyed. Upon the first coming up of the plant, attention must be paid to the turnip-fly, and also to frosts, as the plants are sometimes destroyed by both, in which case it must be sown again immediately.

diately. It is not unusual to sow the greatest part of a crop twice or thrice. Begin to weed about old May-day; this is a business that is executed with much attention by men, women, and children, on their knees, using short spuds with one hand, and drawing away the weeds with the other. It is done by contract per acre, for weeding and cropping in one bargain. Weed twice before the first cropping, and once after; which second weeding is given immediately after cropping, which for the first, commonly begins the first week in July here; in the upland countries in the centre of the kingdom, three weeks sooner, owing to the land being warmer and forwarder; the second crop is usually six weeks after the first. Generally every day's cropping is weeded before night. Cropping is performed by the same people: it is gathered by hand, grasping the leaves of the plants, and taking them off with a twist: on a rich soil and favourable season, it will be eight inches high; in bad seasons shorter; 60 or 70 dozen of baskets are spread in the field, ready to receive it, and for this consumption there is a plantation of osiers, for occasionally providing this article. The old method was, to take the crop from the field in very large carts, which were backed to the mill, and shot down for spreading under the grinding wheels. This was a slovenly operation, and rarely kept free from dirt. Mr. Cartwright has improved this part of the apparatus greatly, by substituting one-horse carts, the bodies of which lift from the axis and frame, and are discharged most conveniently, in the manner represented in the annexed plate; being adapted to the contrivance of the mill, which varies considerably from the old ones, and is calculated to do the work of four or five mills on the old construction: it consists of eight wheels for

for grinding, of seven feet diameter on one side, and six on the other, being three feet wide, and formed of iron bars for crushing the woad. The power employed to work it is eight horses, changed twice, sometimes more; always two sets; and when the work is heavy, three; or twenty-four in all.

The body of the cart, when hoisted up by a tackle, rests on a frame-work formed to receive it, upon which it is slid over the mill; and the load discharged by the bottoms of the cart being formed of folding doors, easily opened by a catch, so that the woad drops at once upon the floor under the sliding frames; and around this central receptacle, the floor is pierced in a circle exactly above the grinding wheels, so that the plant is forked down in a few minutes. Much contrivance, and great simplicity is exerted for keeping the woad exactly in the path of the grinding-wheel, which is effected by two sweeps annexed to the wheels, and going the circle with them, one on the outside and one within; and when the work is sufficiently performed, these sweeps vary their motion; and instead of keeping the woad as before, in the track of the wheels, plough it out by obliquely pushing it on the smooth stone floor (that part of which under the wheels is of granite, to resist the iron bruisers) free from the wheels. After this, the fresh woad is delivered to keep the mill going; and the preceding parcel just finished, is thrown with shovels through four windows into two rooms on each side of the mill: in these rooms it is left a short time for the juice to drain from it, till in a proper state to adhere in balls, when men place themselves, by means of proper apparatus, so as to form it into the balls, which are laid upon trays, on which they are conveyed to the drying ranges: there they are placed on grates, so

 contrived

contrived as to form shelves, by sliding upon ledges in the ranges or drying-houses, as represented in the plate. They are on each side of galleries six feet wide, for the conveniency of loading and unloading. Here, in the course of about a week, it is dried sufficiently for preserving in stores over the rooms in which the balls are made, where it remains till all the operations of the field are at an end, and the labourers at liberty to manufacture it. There are eight ranges, each containing 384 grates, below the lowest of which there are spaces for depositing casks, either empty or filled with woad.

Such is the regular daily course of business during the whole cropping season.

The crop is regularly gathered twice, and in favourable seasons a third is either wholly or partially collected: this third makes an inferior woad, the first and second only going into that of the prime quality.

The land is left for winter in that state, well gripped, to keep it dry, ready for ploughing in the spring, which is done as soon as it is in a proper state, which is rarely before the second week in March, when it is prepared, sown, and finished in the same manner as in the preceding year. A portion of every crop is however left, in order to produce seed, the stems of which rise the second year. Some growers gather it once for a crop; but as it is of an inferior quality, Mr. Cartwright has not practised it. One acre of seed will produce enough to sow forty acres. The seed is less than that of the turnip, but the husk is large.

When sowing is very late, and the crop thin, it is a practice to thicken it, by making holes in the vacancies with a triangular hoe, for children to drop seeds in; and this is done so late even as June.

The

The crop is thus sown in succession, as I before remarked, for two, three, or four years. The course of crops in which Mr. Cartwright proposed to introduce it, as a regularly returning crop, is this:

1. Woad.
2. Woad.
3. Woad, and on some of the best land, 4. Woad.
4. Oats.
5. Oats.
6. Cole.
7. Oats.
8. Grasses; white clover, rib, a small portion of trefoil, some of the best hay-seeds that can be procured, parsley, and a proportion of ray-grass.

This grass to be left. Mr. Cartwright not having got round through his old turf yet, can only conjecture that such a layer constantly sheep-fed, with a sprinkling of cattle for keeping the herbage fine, would be fit to plant again in seven or eight years: his buildings and machinery are all calculated for cropping 200 acres every year; thus a tract of 980 acres would (without supposing woad for four years in any part) yield 210 acres annually; consequently, Mr. Cartwright having above 1100 acres, has a power of leaving the grass much longer, if he should think proper. The mill requiring twenty-four horses, but not till the cropping begins in July, of course this strength is free for tillage, &c. all winter, spring, and the beginning of summer, and would be ample for the cultivation of the above tract, with any addition of grazing that might be convenient or profitable. He has now between two and three hundred acres of arable, on land he does not woad, in a course of crops, exclusive of that plant.

To return now to the mill, and winter operations. In

In order to bring the woad into a state ready for the dyer's use, it must go through a fermentative process for seven or eight weeks; this is called *couching*. It is this; the dry balls are taken from the stores, and ground to powder in the same mill, and in the same manner as the green woad. The stores are so situated on the same floor with the central receptacle for the green plant, over the mill, as to be at hand to be turned down, in like manner falling into the track of the wheels; there it is ground to powder, and thrown through the same windows into the adjoining rooms, in which the balling is carried on in the summer. There it is spread about three feet deep, moistened with water, and turned with shovels, which is repeated daily, more or less water being thrown upon it, to keep it in the due state of fermentation which is necessary in this operation, which can only be well conducted under the inspection and attentive care of very experienced woadmen. The bulk of those employed must have acquired skill to regulate the heat (though others work at the more manual parts of it), and cause the fermentation to pervade the whole mass equally. In the act of turning, there is considerable skill in the use of the shovel, so as duly to separate those parts of the woad which are disposed to cling together, and when it has not had the advantage of being well balled, dried, and preserved, it must even be separated by the fingers. In respect to the final state of the commodity, Mr. Cartwright has found very great advantage in being particularly attentive to the drying and storing it completely for preservation, and which he could effect only by means of the apparatus being well calculated for those purposes. Without these attentions the woad will not *beaver* well, a term

term descriptive of the fineness of the capillary filaments into which it draws out when broken between the finger and thumb. The effect of woad in the dyer's blue-vat being not only to give the colour resulting from the woad plant, but also to excite a delicate fermentation, which is the means of making the indigo in the same vat give out its colour in perfection; nor will the woad itself communicate its colour to the material to be dyed, unless this fermentation is properly excited. Hence it is to be observed, that the goodness of woad greatly depends on its being so preserved, and so *couched*, as to answer these ends the most effectually. If the heat in the couching is too great, it becomes what the woadmen term *foxy*; and on the contrary, if the heat has not been sufficient, it becomes what they call *heavy*. Good woad rubbed in the hand will not soil it, but if it is *heavy* it soils the fingers. Towards the latter part of the couching it is cooled gradually, and brought into proper temper to remain in safety, or to be packed into casks, as conveniency may require. It is then ready for use, and is sold to be delivered to the manufacturing towns where used.—Yorkshire and Lancashire the principal demand.

In regard to any idea that may be entertained of a crop which returns nothing to the soil, having an exhausting tendency, Mr. Cartwright observes, that it is probably compensated by the thorough cleaning it receives. On these rich soils he conceives it to be a very beneficial culture, even in this respect. When these grass-lands are broken up for corn, it has not been unusual for the crops to be so luxuriant as to injure themselves greatly. Any crop not fed on the ground will deduct something; and it is beneficial to

put

put one in, which shall do this more moderately than others, and at the same time clean the land. This must be an advantageous mode of breaking up.

It is, however, necessary to add one caution: it should not be imagined that it is an article in which any man with skill, capital, and attention, can enter beneficially. The demand for this commodity is very limited; so that probably besides Mr. Cartwright and three other growers, there are not 50 tons per annum raised in the kingdom. Should a few other persons be added, without these declining business, and the quantity in the market increased considerably, the inevitable consequence would be a fall of price; and the profit, made at present, become loss. Risque, and manufacturing, anxiety considered, nobody without the expectation of a high profit, would enter into such a speculation; and I have doubts, whether on such a soil as will profitably produce woad, there are not other articles of cultivation, more common, less hazardous, and demanding vastly less attention, that would equal, perhaps exceed it in profit.

The annexed plates will give some idea of the erections at Brothertoft for this object. The contrivance of the whole has great merit; and Mr. Cartwright appears to have carried every branch of this cultivation to a degree of perfection, to which no other person has probably attained; the exertions he has made in this pursuit are capital and interesting.

Hemp.

At Swineshead this crop is much cultivated; formerly on the same spots year after year; but now they spread it over a farm accordingly as the soil suits, or the price actuates; and on some lands that are foul, they

they sow it to clean. If the soil is weak they manure for it. Plough at Candlemas, again at Lady-day, and again the middle or the end of May; when they sow three bushels of seed; never weed, as it destroys all. At Old Lammas they pull up, leaving the strongest for seed: they used to take the female from the male, but that is left off. Bind in sheaves, leaving them in shocks of five for a week; then clear the plants from dirt, and turn the sheaves, and set them together again. If they keep the crop till the spring, they bind in larger bundles, and stack and thatch; but reckoned preferable to set it at once; for which purpose they tie it in *gleans* single. Any water will do for retting. If the weather is warm they leave it two weeks; some longer; and when, on examination, they find it retted enough, they load it on slades, and carry it for grassing to an eaten eddish; which it improves much, great grass succeeding it; nor does it taint, so as to make cattle refuse it. After a shower, turn it; leave for three weeks, and turn it again. If the *femble* quits the *bun* easily, it is ready to *lift*; then tied in bundles, and taken to a barn; but must be quite dry. It is next broken and swingled, the price of which operation was 6*d*. a stone, but now 1*s*. Being now ready for the hecklers, it is saleable, and made up in plaited bundles. Sold at 5*s*. to 7*s*. 6*d*. per stone; it has been known at 2*s*. 6*d*. and at 3*s*. 6*d*. within ten years. In 1795 and 1796, from 5*s*. to 7*s*.; 45 stone an average crop, 50 very good.

Account for an Acre.

	£	s.	d.
Three ploughings and harrowing	£.0	15	0
Seed	0	15	0
Sowing	0	0	6
Pulling by the hundred (120) 1100, 1*s*. 6*d*.	0	16	6
Knocking and burning, 6*d*. a hundred	0	5	6
If tied five in one, it is 2*d*. per hundred; or, 6*d*. single tying at the root end, as well as at top	0	1	10
Watering, casting	0	5	6
Spreading, two women	0	2	6
Putting in	0	2	0
Sods and sodding	0	2	0
Taking off sods, and taking out	0	2	6
Carting	0	5	0
Twice turning	0	3	0
Gathering	0	3	0
Carting to barn	0	4	0
Breaking 45 stone	2	5	0
Carrying out, 1*d*. a stone	0	3	9
Rent £.1 10 0			
No tithe; poor-rates 0 5 0			
Drainage tax 0 2 0			
	1	17	0
	£.8	9	7

	£	s.	d.
Produce, 45 stone, at 6*s*.	£.13	10	0
Pullings,—four stone, at 2*s*. 6*d*.	0	10	0
	£.14	0	0
Expenses	8	9	7
Profit	£.5	10	5

This, if no manure.

The

The quality of the hemp is best from old hemp lands, being worth 2*s*. a stone more than from other lands.

At Haxey, sow it after wheat: plough before Christmas; some at Candlemas. Manure after the first ploughing; some turn it in, but not so good; a middling dressing, the shorter the better. Pigeon dung best; (added to dung) a quarter or quarter and half per acre. Like to have it best after wheat that follows clover. Plough again between Candlemas and Lady-day. Plough three or four times; sometimes roll and harrow much more in the spring. Sow about the middle of May, ten pecks a chain acre. Weed out the largest weeds. Pull the femble or male hemp about the 20th of August, leave the female till Michaelmas. Bind the femble into sheaves or *beats*. Cart it to dykes, sod it; water it; lies in two or three weeks, according to weather. Running water very bad for it. Spread it on stubbles for three weeks or a month, till the *bast* clears easy from the bun; turn it once or twice; and when dry bind it in beats; carry home, and stack it, and work it; break and dressing it was 1*s*. a stone, now 1*s*. 4*d*. or 1*s*. 6*d*. then ready for market to sell it to hecklers; 40 stone a good crop, 50 very rare;—30 or 35 an average. Many sell it by the acre: in peace it was 3*l*. or 3*l*. 10*s*. per acre; last year 5*l*. Price per stone from breaker 6*s*. 6*d*. or 7*s*. of late; but was in peace 4*s*. 6*d*. or 5*s*. It is heckled, spun, and woven into cloth, but the farmer has nothing to do with this. As to the hemp left in the field, it is pulled about Michaelmas; bind sheaves, and stooks on the land, and leave it ten days. Thrash it on a cloth in the field; seed twelve to sixteen strike an acre, worth 6*s*. on an average 5*s*. When thrashed,

dyke

dyke it and sod it; when laid five or six weeks, or even ten if frosty weather; has known it the whole winter, and not a bit worse; but must be trodden down once or twice a day, and the femble the same. Do not spread it; but set it up in little stooks to dry, then stack it to be ready to break and dress in the spring. Not so good, but it sells as well as the other. This is yellow hemp; makes sacking and sail cloth; but the other linen. Sow wheat after it generally, but sometimes barley. Get generally too much wheat; but clover land gives a better standing crop, and healthier.

Expense of an Acre.

Five ploughings, 4*s.*				£. 1	0	0
Harrowing, 1*s.* a time				0	5	0
Manuring, 3*s.* a load, 12 loads				1	16	0
Seed $2\frac{1}{2}$ strike				0	15	0
Sowing included in ploughing.						
Weeding				0	1	6
Pulling by women, fembling				0	5	0
Carting, retting, sodding, unsodding, and taking out and treading				0	5	0
Spreading and turning				0	1	6
Gathering, binding, and leading home				0	2	6
Breaking 35 stone, at 1*s.* 6*d.*				2	12	6
Pulling the male hemp				0	5	0
Thrashing and beating				0	6	0
Dyking				0	7	6
Drying and stacking				0	3	0
Rent	£. 1	10	0			
Tithe	0	8	0			
Parish charges	0	5	0			
				2	3	0
				£. 10	8	6

Produce.

Produce.

	£.	s.	d.
35 stone, at 7*s.*	12	15	0
16 strike of seed	4	16	0
	£.17	1	0
	10	8	6
Profit	£.6	12	6

At Butterwick, in the Isle, they generally manure for hemp; and get 50 stone and upwards.

Flax.

Much cultivated at Swineshead; grass land fresh is preferred. Plough for it once, and harrow five times; again with what they call an ox harrow, with a batten set an edge under it, and drawn over to level and pulverize; then sow two bushels an acre, Baltic seed, at 10*s.* 6*d.* a bushel. Harrow two or three times. Pick the broken sods, and lay in furrows. Very little weeding. Mr. Sumpter, of the Griffin, of this place, in twenty-three acres, has weeded only to the amount of eight men for one day. The beginning of August it is pulled by the day, and costs 12*s.* an acre. Tied in sheaves, the size of a man's thigh: next day taken to the dyke to be watered, and the better the flax, the longer it is in the water: from five days to fifteen; ten on an average. Cart it to grass eddish, where it lies till a shower comes, which is necessary; turn it twice. Gather and tie in *bottles*, five or six in one. Cart it to the barn or a stack. If *laid*, it will not do for seed; and the price of the seeded flax is 1*s.* a stone less. Breaking and swingling 2*s.* a stone. When it is ready for market, price 8*s.* a stone. Seldom any pullings, called *snufflings* of flax. This crop is thought

thought to hurt the land. Both it and hemp are damaged by hedges or trees. It is common to sow turnips immediately after it; but Mr. Sumpter, on his own land, ploughs thrice, and sows wheat, getting fine crops.

Account of an Acre.

		£.	s.	d.
One ploughing		£.0	5	0
Harrowing		0	5	0
Ox-harrow and batten		0	2	6
Seed		1	1	0
Sowing		0	0	6
Harrowing		0	5	0
Picking		0	2	0
Weeding (if not sward ground), 10*s*.		0	5	0
Pulling		0	10	0
Dyking and spreading, 5*s*. a bushel		0	10	0
Carting		0	5	0
Twice turning		0	6	0
Gathering		0	6	0
Carting to barn		0	6	0
Breaking 40 stone		4	0	0
Carrying out, and expenses		0	6	8
Rent		4	4	0
		£.12	19	8
Produce, 40 stone, at 8*s*.		£.16	0	0
Turnips after	£.2 0 0			
Deduct tillage, &c.	0 10 0			
		1	10	0
		£.17	10	0
Expenses		12	19	8
Profit		4	10	4

Most

Most profit when seeded; for the crop is from twelve to fifteen bushels, at 10*s*. 6*d*.; but in that case, something is to be deducted from the price of the crop, but not always, as it is the best flax that stands for seed. Getting the seed adds 20*s*. to the expense.

At Haxey, in Axholm, they often sow it upon sward land; but more common on clover ley or wheat stubble. Plough between Christmas and Candlemas; three or four harrowings, and rolling fine; if a fine mould, harrow in the seed on this one earth; if not, skim it with plough very thin to make it fine. Sow two strike an acre; plough it; skim it half in, and half on top, both ways; as opinion leads. Weed it carefully on their knees. Pull it the beginning of August for white line;—sometimes leave it for seed, especially if a slender crop. Bind and dyke it: leave it in about ten days to a fortnight; if very warm, eight days; much treading twice a day in the pit. Grass it on barley stubble, or on eddish, for a month, and to six weeks; turn it once or twice. *Tuffle* it; that is, making it in a loose sheaf, open at bottom. When dry, bind it in bottles, two or three in one. Barn or stack it: after harvest, and in winter, break at 2*s*. a stone. Ready for sale to the hecklers, at 8*s*. 9*s*. and 10*s*. 6*d*. a stone; some 11*s*. last year; average 8*s*. Harrow off the rubbish, and plough twice for wheat.

Account of an Acre.

	£.	s.	d.
One ploughing	0	4	0
Harrowing and rolling	0	4	0
Seed and sowing	0	18	0
Skimming	0	4	0
Carried forward .... £.	1	10	0

Brought

	£.	s.	d.
Brought forward	£.1	10	0
Weeding	0	13	0
Pulling	0	7	6
Leading and retting, &c.	0	10	6
Grassing, &c.	0	5	0
Leading, &c.	0	3	0
Breaking 30 stone, at 2*s*.	3	0	0
Rent, hired for it particularly	3	0	0
Tithe	0	8	0
	£.9	17	0

Produce, 30 stone, at 8*s*.	£.12	0	0
Expenses	9	17	0
Profit	£.2	3	0

If on the sward, the rent will be 40*s*. more; and the crop will be from 40 to 60 stone; about 50 good.

At Butterwick, in the Isle, their best wheat follows flax: the crops of the latter 50 stone.

At Garthorpe, on fresh land, flax produces 50 stone: they sell it as it stands, for 6*l*. or 7*l*. an acre.

Lucern.

This plant has been cultivated on seven acres and a half, by Mr. Cartwright at Brothertoft; his first piece was sown about five years ago, drilled at eighteen inches. The land was not prepared by any particular course of crops, but a deep ploughing. It has yielded large crops for soiling horses; saddle-horses have no corn with it; others, on occasion, have corn; and a large stock of hogs supported on it, without other food. It is cut thrice a year;—cleaned by horse-hoeing; which should be done directly after cutting;

cutting; but Mr. Cartwright has so much other business, that he thinks it will answer better broad-cast, and intends sowing the intervals. In 1796, he drilled clover between the rows, which, with the lucern, gave that year a full crop; the lucern as strong as the clover. This year the first cutting of five acres three roods, fed 36 horses and two bullocks five weeks; but cut late, from the backwardness of the spring. If the horses are reckoned at 2*s*. 6*d*. a week, and the bullocks at 1*s*. 6*d*. this amounts to 4*l*. an acre; and it will be cut twice more; though the last cutting will not be considerable: however, this is a very considerable produce, from an article on which the expense is not high.

I saw some drilled at Mr. Dalton's, at Knaith; the rows two feet, amongst barley: it was very clean, and in good order.

Mr. Webster, at Bankside, has it drilled; and very luxuriant the first year, on a warp bank.

Sainfoin.

The first sainfoin I met with in the county was at Coldharbour, in passing from Folkingham to Grantham; and I found that it had been tried by Lord Brownlow's father at Belton. His Lordship shewed me a field, broken up twenty-eight years ago, on a limestone rock, upon which a singular circumstance occurred: it was a few years ago re-sown with good seed, but it failed: the seed vegetated, but died away as if it were starved. I cannot account for this, as there are well authenticated experiments that prove its success, after a shorter interval.

There is a very moderate quantity of this grass at Leadenham, where it succeeds well, and has been cultivated

tivated these twenty years, and perhaps more. Mr. Betsal gave the hay to his cows; but was forced to leave it off, because of the bad taste it gave the butter.

The reddish sands on the heath at Blankney yield vast crops of this grass, and last well; ten, twelve, or fourteen years; though on the Wolds it endures not more than eight or nine. These red sands are excellent also for turnips and barley.

North of Lincoln, to and about Hackthorn, much of this grass. Mr. Cracraft, from sixteen acres, in 1797, sown among barley in 1795, had thirty-one loads; the abundance enlarged by the rainy season. Prepare for this crop by getting in fine order for turnips; and well dunged, sow it with barley, six bushels to four per acre; lasts ten to fifteen years; but some say less than ten. When they break it up, they fallow for turnips, or wheat, and get as good as after any thing; but turnips they reckon better management. The hay good for every thing; horses, cattle, and sheep.

Mr. Harrisson, in the new enclosed lordship of Kirton, has a beautiful piece of twenty-five acres, on which was mown in 1797, the second year, one load and a half an acre. There is a scattering of it all over that country on the heath enclosures; but much less than there ought to be. He summer-fallowed the land, and sowed it four bushels an acre; no mixture ever with it here, where it has been known, in some measure, to my knowledge, thirty years.

About Normanby, Burton, &c. they sow a good deal on stony lands; it lasts near twenty years, and in a vigorous state; but in common not more than sixteen. Always mow it for hay, but never manure it.

At Alkborough it lasts twelve or fourteen years; and yields vast crops of hay.

At

At Barton, some that has answered very well, has yielded three tons an acre: feed the after-grass with lambs.

Lord Yarborough is clear that there is now much less sainfoin about Brocklesby, than there was thirty-five years ago; now there is none in the immediate neighbourhood; but a little near Louth. Mr. Ancel, at Ormsby, had it to produce hay for his rabbits.

This grass is cultivated to a pretty considerable amount in the neighbourhood of Louth, to the south-west. Mr. Clough, of Gayton, has thirty acres of it; and some farmers have as much as from 100 to 150, particularly Mr. Grant, of Whitgul; also at Hallington, and Stannigate. Upon its giving signs of wearing out, Mr. Clough sowed 30 acres of seed adjoining, to feed the whole with sheep; and 60 acres carried 200 sheep the summer through, near three and a half per acre; but only two to be reckoned to the account of the sainfoin: it had been sown only six years, and they say it generally wears out at six, or seven, or eight years. They are so distressed in the spring, when turnips fail, that I suspect they now and then feed it at that season; if so, no wonder it wears out. When they break it up they sow oats; a very poor crop; 2. oats; 3. turnips; 4. oats; and white clover and hay seeds, left seven or eight years. The land will not be fit for sainfoin again in less than 15 or 16 years. They do not pare and burn sainfoin, though much in the habit of that husbandry for breaking up other seeds, which is singular. The crops amount to two loads an acre of hay, in a good season. All the country is on chalk.

About Spilsby, Dalby, &c. this grass lasts only eight years, yet they never feed it with sheep after Candlemas: sow five bushels; Mr. Bourne, 9lb. of trefoil

 with

with it. Of all other things that can be sowed with it, ray-grass is the worst. Produce one load and a half per acre.

Mr. Parkinson of Asgarby, disapproves of sainfoin, because it makes land poor; but on very barren heath, or Wold land, he thinks it is very useful; as it makes a soil produce a crop of hay, which naturally would only feed rabbits by *shar*-grass.

Twenty acres near Ranby gave 63 loads the second year. The late Mr. Codd had much of this excellent grass. This hay, in the warren at Thoresway, valued only at 25*s*. a load.

Sainfoin is cultivated about Grimsthorpe, on the creech land that is shallow; for this crop will grow where hardly any thing else will, and produce one load and a half an acre, on land that has given miserable barley. It lasts on some lands five or six years, and even to ten. They do not pare or burn it; but plough it for oats or barley. Mr. Parker had ten acres, and never had better crops than after it, in the course of turnips, barley, wheat; and has never, for eight years, had less than five quarters of barley, and about four of wheat: a sure proof that no evil resulted from sainfoin, though there is a notion that it impoverishes, which Mr. Parker thinks idle; not to speak of the manure which arises from great crops of hay.

Onions.

This is an article which I found was not uncommon at Haxey in Axholm. I saw some fields, the crops of which were good. The crop is valuable; and rises even to 50*l*. an acre. They pay 5*l*. an acre for liberty to sow them, the farmer finding one ploughing.

Many were cultivated near Stockworth four or five years ago.

Cow-

Cow-grass.

Mr. Ancel, at Ormsby, got good crops on poor rabbit-land.

Much approved by Mr. Parkinson. See the article *Seeds*. Mr. Ellison approves highly of this grass; he has had crops of it which would have fed ten or twelve hogs an acre for several weeks, and has mown three loads of hay an acre from twenty acres; and will the second year give two loads an acre; whereas if it had been common clover, it would give hardly any thing. Upon the land that yielded three loads, the tenants, for ten years past, could get no crops of common clover worth mowing. It is cultivated for seed at Scorthan, within a mile of Sudbrook.

Swedish Turnip.

Mr. Graburn has tried them, and seen them in several places on the Wolds, but none that ever answered, yet sown early. At Roxby, Mr. Laurence had a very good crop, and stood well when the common turnips were destroyed.

Mr. George Bourne, of Haugh, tried them, and has a few now, because they stand the frost; and Mr. Parkinson the same.

Mr. Walker, of Woolsthorpe, has a very fine crop sown broad-cast in June, after one crop of oats, on a turf about ten years old.

Parsley.

This plant is cultivated as an artificial grass by Mr. Stephenson of Swineshead, mixed with white clover; 14 lb. an acre of the latter, and 2 lb. of the former. It lies three years; and the first supports from six to ten sheep an acre; the second, it is manured, and keeps also from six to ten an acre; the third, it carries from

seven

seven to eleven an acre. The soil is the fertile loam of Holland fen.

About Folkingham, amongst the good farmers, they have sown this plant with clover, 2 lb. an acre, at 8*d*. a pound; and every body that has tried, approves it for sheep, being healthy for them.

Mr. Hesseldon sows 2 lb. of parsley in his seeds; the sheep are so fond of it, that they eat it down so close as to kill the plant

The Rev. Mr. Allington of Swinhop, has sown it four years; and Mr. Whalesby, his tenant on this farm, sowed it eight or ten years before, on the same farm. He has a great opinion of it, and means to have more in future; has not sown more than 2 lb. an acre, but designs more in future, unless the price prevents him; it has increased much in three years.

This plant is uncommon in cultivation in any part of the kingdom; but from these experiments, it seems to merit more attention than it has received, and probably would be found a valuable article upon any sheep-farm.

Cabbages,

Have been largely cultivated by Mr. Cartwright; the management is to plough before Christmas, if the weather permits: in March again, and a third in April; clean it well. The middle of May lay on the dung, twelve loads an acre; not much at once on any crop, as laying it on at twice, better than once; ploughed into four feet ridges, for planting. The seed is sown early in February, upon a very rich spot: never prick out; plant the middle of May, according to weather; but will not cabbage well if run into June. If to be eaten before Christmas, the beginning of May

a better

a better time. When the weeds grow, plough with a common plough from the rows, leaving the plants on a space of eight inches, which hand-hoed well *down*, and clean mould drawn up to cabbages, at 3*s*. 6*d*. or 4*s*. an acre. When weeds dead, return the furrow back. In about a fortnight, with expanding horse-hoe, or double mould-board, scour out the furrows, and drive the earth nearer the plants. If they permit, repeat this. Left thus till harvest, when weeded, and picked of caterpillars; left till used; cut with a sharp tool, and carted home, or to sheep in pastures; and this an excellent use a little before lambing; but not before, for they make the lambs grow too large. Has also fattened oxen with them. Tried for horses, but did not continue long enough to know if they would do well. In the spring of 1796, sheep and beasts were kept on them in April, but refused, and both would have starved; this an exception, and to what owing, not to be ascertained, for it never happened before. Is of opinion, that an acre of cabbages, if good, is equal to four acres of rape, that are worth 50*s*. an acre; 5000 upon an acre. Planting 7*s*.; expense, half the manure reckoned, about 5*l*. an acre. Mr. Cartwright has had up to 46 acres of them in one year.

About Folkingham, upon almost every farm, they have been cultivated on the scale of a few acres, and are very much approved, especially in frosty weather, when turnips are not to be got at. Some beasts have been fattened on them, and have answered exceedingly well.

Mr. Goulton has every year a small piece of the Scotch sort, for his ewes and lambs, and finds them most excellent for that stock.

Mr.

Mr. Linton, of Freiston, cultivates cabbages with great success. He has usually five acres; sows the Scotch drumhead the latter end of February, or beginning of March; raises his own; sows very thin upon land ploughed three times, fine, and well manured, at eighteen tons an acre; does not prick out. Plants land that is autumnal ploughed, and upon that part which is to be planted, first manured in autumn, before ploughing, fifteen tons an acre; the rest after the second ploughing in spring; plough four times; plant two feet eight inches in squares, on flat, for cross horse-hoeing. Horse-hoe thrice each way; the first and second without the mould-board, the rest with it. In regard to the consumption, the winter of 1795 he fed eight bullocks with them, with a small quantity of hay, given in cribs, in a well littered yard; they were, at putting to cabbages, worth 16*l.* each, on the 16th of December; and about the end of February they were sold in Smithfield for 25*l.* each. Their consumption of hay was no more than one-third of their food. Mr. Copeland, a skilful grazier, saw the beasts, and said he never saw any so much improved in an equal time. They ate three acres, which yielded 48*l.* Smithfield charges, about 14*s.* each, leaves 44*l.* 8*s.* or 14*l.* 16*s.* per acre. Mr. Linton remarks, that it must not be expected by those who cultivate cabbage, that such products are to be gained in common, for a good market, and a rise, had their influence in this case. Mr. Linton has turnip for his lambs, and when frosts come, cabbages are of excellent use; for turnips are not to be got; and if got, frozen. In the spring, when turnips fail, folds them off in small pens, as cabbages last three weeks longer than turnips. But the use is incomparable for ewes, rearing lambs with greater suc-

ccss

cess than any other food. From various observations, is of opinion that three acres of cabbages are fully equal to five of turnips.

Mr. Ellison, two years ago, tried an acre of cabbages; got a good crop; gave them to beasts, upon eddish when done; they were foddered twice a day at same time upon hay, and never had beasts do better; as well as upon cake.

Mr. Walker, of Woolsthorpe, cultivated for seven years, and got fine crops; but he thinks turnip as good food, with which crop his soil agrees remarkably; but for stalling beasts has found cabbages preferable.

Cabbages are cultivated about Grimsthorpe, especially by tup-men, who find it necessary, in order to feed their rams; they produce larger crops, and stand the winter better than turnips. It is a great object to keep their rams in high order, and this they find the cheapest and best method; must give corn, if they have not cabbages; and Mr. Parker thinks they do better on them than they would on corn.

Notwithstanding the above-mentioned respectable trials, this appears to be a crop that merits much more attention upon the rich soils of this county, than it has met with. In a district more abounding with sheep than any other in England, such a crop would be peculiarly valuable; and I cannot but recommend it to the attention of the spirited flock-masters, who have made such great exertions in increasing and improving the breed of that animal.

Carrots.

Mr. Hutton, at Burton, near Gainsborough, has sown this crop amongst a new plantation, apparently with good success; the soil, sand. As he fattens beasts

beasts with oil-cake, it is designed for that use, to the saving of cake.

Three years ago Mr. Ellison tried an acre; a very good crop; which he gave to the draught-horses; and the effect was remarkably favourable; they did better without corn than they had done before with it. He also tried beasts with them, and thinks from that trial that no food is better.

Mr. Walker, of Woolsthorpe, has had carrots several years on his rich red sands; his crops have been large, and he has a very high opinion of them for all sorts of stock.

CHAP.

CHAP. VIII.

GRASS.

Rich Grazing Land.

THESE are the glory of Lincolnshire, and demand a singular attention; the soil is a rich loamy clay, some very stiff, but of uncommon fertility, as may be seen by various instances.

Some of the grazing lands in Long Sutton, that were common, will carry five or six sheep an acre, and four bullocks to ten acres. Mr. Scrope there has four acres, which carry 45 sheep in summer, and must be *hobb'd* often to keep it down.

On the grass lands in Deeping fen, improved by paring and burning, Mr. Graves keeps five sheep an acre from Lady-day to Michaelmas, and one and a half in winter; and a bullock of sixty stone to two acres besides in summer.

As a grazier, few men have been in a more extensive business, or practised it with more success, than T. Fydell, Esq. M. P. at Boston. I was therefore particularly solicitous to procure information from a gentleman perfectly competent to give it. Several unfortunate circumstances prevented the interview I hoped for; but by letter afterwards, I received the following account of twenty acres of rich land near Boston, for the year 1796, and a more satisfactory one cannot be wished.

Account

Account for Twenty Acres, 1796.

Dr.						
To 18 beasts, at 12*l.* each				£.216	0	0
To 80 sheep, at 46*s.*				184	0	0
				£.400	0	0
To Expenses, viz.						
Tithe	£.1	10	0			
Dykereeve	3	0	0			
Rates	10	0	0			
Shepherding	3	0	0			
Expenses	5	0	0			
				22	10	0
Loss, supposed one sheep				2	6	0
				£.424	16	0
Interest one year				21	4	0
One year's rent				60	0	0
				£.506	0	0
Hire of a close for the winter for 35 sheep				17	10	0
				£.523	10	0
Profit				87	4	0
				£.610	14	0

Contra Cr.			
By 18 beasts, 19*l.* 5*s.*	£.346	10	0
By 80 sheep, at 55*s.*	220	0	0
By 52 tod of wool, at 17*s.*	44	4	0
	£.610	14	0

The

The difference between the buying and selling price, loss deducted, 208*l.* 8*s.* is the *produce* of the land, or 10*l.* 8*s.* per acre, which is very great indeed, and shews that this land would lett at 5*l.* 4*s.* an acre, *supposing this year to be an average one.* This difference of rent would deduct 44*l.* from the profit of 87*l.* and leave 43*l.*; which with 21*l.* charged, makes 64*l.* interest on the year's advance of 546*l.* or 11½ per cent. As 3*l.* an acre is the highest rent I have heard of in Lincolnshire, and much higher than common, even for the best lands, this account seems to confirm the idea I have entertained, that the rich grazing lands of this county are lower rented than such, or nearly such, lands yield in other parts of the kingdom.

Some further circumstances for which I am indebted to the same gentleman, are,

That the average weight of the beasts is 70 stone, being of the York or Lincoln breed; the sheep all Lincolns. The former are bought in April or May, and all gone by the 11th December; the sheep are bought in May, they are clipped twice, and sold fat in April or May following; that there is little difference in seasons; except that after a bad winter the sheep are not ready for market so soon by a month, as they are after good winters. The loss in weight in driving to Smithfield, very little; the expense, beasts 15*s.* 9*d.*; sheep 1*s.* 9½*d.*

Mr. Fydell held for many years a piece of land in Skirbeck parish, which measured 21 acres, and kept, *com. annis*, from Lady-day to Michaelmas, 19 heavy beasts, and 100 sheep; and wintered 50 sheep.

He now holds a pasture adjoining his garden at Boston, of eight acres, which keeps in summer 10 oxen and 40 sheep; and winters 30 sheep.

The

The finest grazing lands are at Boston, Alderchurch, Fosdyke, Sutterton, Kirton, Frampton, Wyberton, Skirwick; these will carry in summer a bullock to an acre and a half, besides four sheep an acre; and two sheep an acre in winter.

The Rev. Mr. Berridge, of Alderchurch, has near his house 40 acres of the rich grass, upon which the stock is upon an average, 300 sheep, sixteen fatting bullocks, three cows, four horses; and carries through the winter three sheep an acre. This land is valued at 40*s*. an acre. It is a vast stock. He favoured me with these particulars in the presence of a dozen neighbours, and called in his manager to confirm it; it wanted therefore no after corrections.

In the grazing lands at Swineshead, a beast an acre, of 40 to 70 stone, and two or three sheep; also two sheep an acre in winter.

Mr. Tindal, at Ewerby, which is on high land compared with Holland fen, stocks a bullock to two acres and a half, and three sheep per acre in summer; and two sheep an acre in winter.

In the lordships of Horbling, Billingborough, Berthorp, Sempringham, Pointon, Dowsby, Dunsby, and Hackonby, there are extensive tracts of rich grazing land applied to fatting bullocks and sheep, carrying a bullock to two acres, and three sheep per acre, in summer; and two sheep an acre in winter; which lands are generally rented at 30*s*. per acre.

Mr. Elkington, of Howel, keeps one bullock and nine sheep to three acres, and in winter two sheep an acre.

Hanworth, north of Lincoln, is chiefly grass, which is fed by cows, calves, and young cattle.

On the Lawn at Norton-place, which is heath land, two

two couples per acre in summer; but the soil not adapted to permanent grass without great exertion.

There is a tract of pasture land, which is of considerable extent north and south, but very narrow east and west, which lies in the vale between the Heath and the Wolds. I viewed it from Norton-place, in going to Owersby, which is in it; the quality is good, but of the second rate. At Kingerby, a namesake of mine has a farm of it horridly over-run with thistles; were he a tenant, I think the addition of 2*s*. 6*d*. an acre to his rent, would awaken him a little.

The grass land close to Gainsborough letts at 4*l*. and 5*l*. an acre. The marsh grass on the Trent at Knaith, &c. 20*s*. to 30*s*. and produces one and a half or two tons of hay an acre. The marshes on the river are stocked from the 12th April to 12th May; this of late has however been omitted, as they found the grass hurt by it. Clear the hay by Lammas, one to one ton and a half an acre. Then turn in milch cows, and afterwards other stock till November. Rent 20*s*.; but measure short.

At Garthorpe, in marsh land, some rich grazing lands, which will carry a good bullock an acre, but no sheep fed. This land is now lett to break up, at 3*l*. 15*s*. an acre, for fourteen years.

From Normanby to Alkborough all farmers consider grass only as a means of manuring arable, and keep it in bad condition. I met the remark here, and therefore note it; but it is a common observation through half the kingdom.

Mr. Hesselden, at Barton, has four acres near the town; levelled and manured it after the allotment, and this year it feeds four cows, three of them joisted at 3*s*. per week; a produce of twelve guineas.

At

At Immingham and Stallenborough, there are some marsh lands that will carry nine bullocks of 80 stone upon twelve acres, and twelve sheep, and two sheep per acre in winter; some have only one. But the same lordships have clay pastures that will not do any thing like this.

At Thornton-college, Mr. Uppleby has a few closes of extraordinarily fine grazing land, which will carry the largest bullocks, and is worth 50*s*. an acre rent, he thinks.

The marsh on the coast at Grainthorpe, Saltfleetby, and Theddlethorpe, &c. is very good; it will keep three sheep an acre, and an ox to three acres; and one sheep and a half to an acre in winter.

The hilly Wold, good pastures on marl and chalk, at Gayton, near Louth, will carry three ewes and their lambs per acre, and a sprinkling of young cattle, &c. besides. Some only two ewes and lambs, besides cattle: such land as is worth 15*s*. to 20*s*. an acre.

In the marshes that are in the vicinity of Saltfleet and Sutton, there is some distinction, which it will be proper to note by parishes. In Northcots the quality is rather inferior, being chiefly for breeding. Marsh Chapel better; but still weak, and for breeding also. In Grainthorpe, a great deal very good grazing land. Conisholm low, swampy, and but little good. Skidbrook, a great deal very good. South Somercots the same; but 1000 acres of *ings*, or common meadow. The three Saltfleetbys, 5000 acres; and a great deal very strong and good for *feeding* beasts; some of the late Mr. Chaplin's marshes here sold so high as 77*l*. the statute acre. In general, the measure short from Saltfleet to Sutton; there statute. In the Theddlethorpes, much very good; but some low, and not well

well drained. Marblethorpe very good. Sutton remarkably good and strong feeding land. Great Carleton middle marsh, arable, enclosed about twenty years before this Survey was taken, good corn land. Gayton like it; but longer enclosed. Maltby and Strubby, open field arable, in the clays. Hannah and Markby the same. Anderly enclosed lately. Cockerington and Grimoldby arable, enclosed about twenty years before this Survey was taken. Manby open arable. In these marsh parishes the rich grazing ground of the first quality letts at about 40*s*. an acre, and the rest about 30*s*. Such as will not *feed*, but only breed, at 20*s*. to 25*s*. and this distinction of *feeding* and breeding is here also expressed, by saying, that one sort of marsh will *feed* sheep; but the other keep them in *holding* order,—will make them hold the flesh they have got, but not fatten profitably. If the best of these lands are compared with the grazing district of Boston, and its vicinity, it is remarked to me that these are more *naturally* good, and much better watered; they have at all times plenty of fresh water here, which is a great object; but for artificial fertility, locality to fairs and markets, &c. the Boston lands much superior. The measure at Boston, &c. is said to be more than an acre; here less, not more than three roods; and the *ing* land still less. On ten acres at Skidbrook, eight beasts, and sixteen sheep have been summered, and the sheep wintered also. And, in general, the marsh that letts from 30*s*. to 40*s*. will carry a beast to two acres, and two sheep an acre; but perhaps more generally, one sheep and a half.

The

The profit of grazing the best land is thus calculated:

	£	s.	d.
A beast, bought at 20*l.* to two acres, at the profits of 5*l.*	£.2	10	0
Two sheep per acre, bought in at 45*s.* and sold at 55*s.*	1	0	0
Four fleeces, 9½ lb. 38 lb. at 8*d.*	1	5	4
	£.4	15	4

Expenses.

	£	s.	d.	£	s.	d.	£	s.	d.
Rent				£.2	0	0			
Tithe				0	1	0			
Rates				0	3	6			
Dykereeve				0	0	9			
				£.2	5	3			
Shepherding				0	1	0			
Washing and clipping				0	0	6			
Incidents				0	0	6			
Capital employed.—Beast	£.20	0	0						
Sheep	4	10	6						
	£.24	10	6	1	6	6			
A year's rent	2	0	0						
	£.26	10	0						
At 5*l.* per cent.									
							3	13	9
Profit							£.1	1	7

The total interest made is about 9*l.* per cent. on the capital of 26*l.* and this seems to be rather inadequate; for here is nothing for losses, which, in a course of time,

time, must be something considerable. The interest made ought to be, at least 10*l.* per cent. after a proper deduction for losses. Either, therefore, the land carries more stock, or it is too high rented. Grazing is accounted a profitable profession:—but when it is considered, that this 26*l.* capital would stock five acres of good arable land, and that they could not be reckoned to pay a less profit than from 12*s.* to 15*s.* an acre from 3*l.* to 4*l.* 5*s.* it will appear that the plough is much more beneficial than such grazing, *thus calculated.*

Sixty or seventy years ago, Mr. Neve's grandfather rented such marsh as would now lett at 40*s.* for 16*s.* per acre; and rarely went to pay to an old lady his rent, without the salutation, *I hope you are not coming to give up your land?* The advance of times is seen in another circumstance: Mr. Welflet, lately dead, stocked a particular close at Saltfleetby with cows, bought in at 19*s.* 6*d.* a head, and shearling wethers at 20*s.* the sheep costing more than the cows. He was above eighty. A great change has also taken place in the inhabitancy: within forty years, four four-wheeled carriages were kept by graziers in Theddlethorpe, now deserted, few living any where in the marshes, without farms elsewhere: by degrees the Wold farmers have gradually been getting the whole, except some few small occupations. These facts are remarkable, and they tend to contradict materially an idea I have met with, common enough in the county, that this tract of marsh, which extends from the Humber to Long Sutton and Tidd, has not been much improved in rent except by enclosing.—We find, on the contrary, that it has been prodigiously improved; without doubt by the generally operating causes of national prosperity. Wealth regularly increasing has raised

raised the prices of products. A subject that ought to be dwelt on longer here, but it is treated more expressly in another Chapter, the poor have come in for a large, and perhaps an ample share; for the price of labour throughout will surprise those who have been accustomed only to the more southerly counties. Under such a growing system of improvement I must own I feel no regret at the loss of the carriages,—the people have changed place, but they are better employed.

Mr. Bourne's best marsh is at Addlethorpe, worth 40*s*. an acre; it will carry per acre five sheep, and a bullock to one and a half, besides a horse to ten acres; and in winter something more than two fat sheep an acre.

There is marsh land (Mr. Calthorp's at Gosberton), which carries seven sheep an acre, and a bullock also; this must have been large measure; and 300 tod of wool have been clipped from ninety acres In such a case the land could probably have been stocked with nothing but sheep, and must have carried about ten or eleven per acre. It may appear whimsical, that one must go to the Wolds for marsh intelligence; but so it is; the principal Wold farmers have marsh land; and the facts can be got only where the occupiers are to be found.

In the marsh parishes of Burgh, Croft, Wainfleet, Winthorpe, Addlethorpe, much land at 40*s*. an acre which will carry five sheep an acre, and a beast to two acres, and two sheep an acre in winter. Mr. Kershaw, of Driby, and Mr. Bourne, of Haugh, agree in the following Marsh account, for land there at 35*s*.

Produce.

Produce.

Two sheep, at 10*s*. the summer	£.1 0 0
Two ditto in winter	1 0 0
Half the profit of an ox	1 13 4
	£.3 13 4

Expenses.

Rent		£.1 15 0
Tithe		0 3 0
Rates and dykereeve		0 8 0
Shepherding		0 1 0
Cutting thistles and dressing		0 2 0
Ditches, folds, &c.		0 0 6
Interest of capital:		
Bullock, half	£.6 0 0	
Two sheep	3 0 0	0 11 0
Rent	2 0 0	
	£.11 0 0	
Going to look at stock		0 0 6
		£.3 1 0

Produce	3 13 4
Expenses	3 1 0
Profit	£.0 12 4

Gross interest rather better than 10*l*. per cent.

Mr. Parkinson, of Reevesby, observes, that the rich marshes were better managed, and in better order twenty years ago than they are at present; the Wold farmers had not then got such possession of them, and they were in the hands of resident graziers, who attended

tended much more to hobbing, which kept them fine, for nothing hurts marsh land so much as letting it run coarse, from permitting the grass to get a-head.

Mr. Parkinson calculates an acre of rich marsh in Wrangle, &c.

Rent	£.1	16	0
Tithe	0	0	0
Rates	0	6	0
Shepherding	0	1	0
Dykereeve	0	0	8
Ditches, folds, and gates	0	0	6
Interest of capital: Two shearlings £.5 0 0; Bullock to two acres, 20*l*. 10 0 0; Year's rent 2 0 0; £.17 0 0	0	17	0
	£.3	1	2

Produce.

Improvement of two sheep, four fleeces, three to a tod, one tod and a half	£.1	6	8
Difference in price 10*s*.	1	0	0
	2	6	8
Losses 5*l*. per cent.	£.0	2	4
	£.2	4	4
Bullock, profit about 4*l*. £.2 0 0; Losses one-fortieth 0 1 0	1	19	0
	£.4	3	4
Expenses	3	1	2
Profit per acre	£.1	2	2

Or total interest 11*l*. 5*s*. 6*d*. per cent.

John

John Linton, Esq. Freiston.——

The hundred of Skirbeck contains the parishes of Skirbeck, Fishtoft, Freiston, Butterwick, Bennington, Leverton, Leak, and Wrangle. About two-thirds pasture, part mown, and one-third in tillage. The pasture consists of three sorts in point of rent, &c. the highest at about 45*s*. being from 32*s*. to 50*s*. The second from 26*s*. to 32*s*. average 28*s*. The third, average 1*l*. 1*s*. Besides this, a small quantity of open meadow, called *ings*, average about 18*s*. The best kind of pasture is chiefly stocked with shearling wethers, bought at the spring markets at Boston, which, having yielded two fleeces of wool, are sold off easily in the next year; and by beasts in the summer, sold in autumn; some kept on farther in eddish, but all gone in the winter. The second best is chiefly fed by young beasts and hogs, kept on to shearlings: these are well kept, as their value materially depends on it; there are also some few breeding sheep on this division of the pasture. The third class is chiefly mown. But it is to be noted, that all these particulars relate to an acre larger than statute measure, about four roods and three quarters. The first division is stocked at the rate of three sheep per acre, winter and summer, with the overplus of some being bought in the spring, and not cleared from the land 'till some months later than the time at which they are bought. The beasts are in the proportion, on an average, of seven to ten acres, from 54 to 100 stone. The second class winters about five sheep to two acres, with not less than four per acre in summer, with a few cows or young beasts; and on both these there will be some few horses, too uncertain to average. On the best land they are chiefly horses making up for sale; and on the second quality,

quality, horses employed in work, or young ones; it is not usual to keep any horses in summer, except on the pastures. The produce of hay on the third may be about 35*s*. an acre; the eddish eaten by cattle from the other grounds, or by lamb hogs before they go to their winter keeping.

Grazing Account of Ten Acres of the first quality.

	£	s.	d.	£	s.	d.
Rent				£.22	10	0
Tithe, 3*s*.				1	10	0
Town charges:						
Poor and constable, &c.	£.0	2	7			
Church	0	0	3			
Highways	0	0	5			
In the pound	£.0	3	3	3	12	9
				£.27	12	9
Dykereeve 5*d*.				0	4	2
Shepherding, 2*s*. 6*d*. an acre				1	5	0
Fences 1*s*.				0	10	0
				£.29	11	11
Interest of capital, seven oxen, at 14*l*.	£.98	0	0			
Thirty sheep, 45*s*.	67	10	0			
Enters at Lady-day; but a year's charges	27	0	0			
	£.192	10	0			
Surplus necessary because of sheep unsold at time of purchase	18	0	0			
	£.210	10	0			
Carry forward				£.29	11	11

Brought

	£.	s.	d.
Brought forward	£.29	11	11
Interest at 5*l*.	10	10	0
Losses on stock very little indeed, 1*l*. per cent. will probably cover it	2	2	0
Cutting thistles, hobbing equal to it	42	3	11
Stock as above	165	10	0
	£.207	13	11
Incidents	5	0	0
	£.212	13	11
Profit	15	16	1
	£.228	10	0

Produce.

	£.	s.	d.
Seven beasts, at 2*l*. 10*s*.	£.121	10	0
Thirty sheep, at 54*s*.	81	0	0
Sixty fleeces, at 8*s*.	24	0	0
A horse twelve weeks	2	0	0
	£.228	10	0

Per acre 1*l*. 11*s*. 6*d*. profit.
Produce 6*l*. 6*s*. per acre.

It is supposed that the profit upon this first class of land is greater than upon the rest; and that the third sort yields very little profit by grazing, and would pay much better in tillage. There are many graziers here who have no other land than what is upon these flats; and sôme who are supposed to have made by their business, enough to have realized a comfortable subsistence.

In regard to the progress of rent here, it has not advanced nearly in such a proportion as in other districts, having always been naturally in a productive state,

state, and others advanced by artificial means, to be of much more than their former value.

The marshes near the sea, from Wrangle to Sutton, are part divided from the high country by the fens, and part by clay parishes, called middle marshes, which marsh is near the sea, a rich loam, on a silt or clay bottom; the part nearer the villages a very rich soapy clay, best adapted for feeding sheep and beasts; with a smaller share of *ings* for hay; near the middle marshes, cold wet clay.

At Mr. Thomas Tannard's.—The rich grazing lands are in the parishes of Kirton, Frampton, Wiberton, Boston, Skirbeck, Fishtoft, Freiston, Fossdyke, Sutterton, Alderchurch, Wigtoft, Swineshead, Bicker, Donnington, and Quadring. The measure of land in these parishes is larger than the statute, generally five roods; but particularly the copyhold, of which there is much. At Wiberton there is some in the occupation of Mr. Westmoreland, at 57*s.* an acre: it will carry a bullock to two acres, and six sheep an acre; and in winter two sheep and a half an acre. Mr. York of that place has sold land at 60*l.* a chain acre; but this is not high.

The average of Wyberton parish, taken by commissioners, upon oath, by Act of Parliament, for Frampton, and all the other parishes about Boston, viz.

Old enclosures	2045 acres.	Average	27*s.* per acre.
Fen	905 ——	Ditto	23*s.* ditto.
In all	3030 acres.	Rent	3869*l.* per year.

Grazing

Grazing account of certain fields in the occupation of Mr. Loft, of Marsh Chapel.

	£.	s.	d.
Rent	£.1	15	0
Tithe	0	2	0
Rates	0	3	0
Shepherding	0	1	0
Interest of capital	0	12	0
	£.2	13	0

It carries a bullock to two acres, and three sheep per acre.

Produce.

	£.	s.	d.
Half a bullock	£.1	10	0
One sheep and a half	1	10	0
	£.3	0	0
Expenses	2	13	0
Profit	£.0	7	0

Of better land:

	£.	s.	d.
Rent	£.2	5	0
Sundries	0	7	0
Interest of capital	1	4	0
	£.3	16	0

It carries a bullock, and three sheep an acre.

	£.	s.	d.
A bullock	£.3	0	0
Three sheep	3	0	0
	£.6	0	0
Expenses	3	16	0
Profit	£.2	4	0

But

But it is a very few fields will yield any thing like this: he has but one close; and here are some expenses omitted.

From Tealby, on the edge of the Wolds, to Wragby, there is a constant series of grass, with hardly any tillage; it is under sheep, and some breeding cattle, with mowing; and letts about 20*s*.

Mr. Tennison, of Lincoln, has thirteen acres of marsh at Grimsby, that summer-feeds fourteen bullocks; and carries thirty-five sheep the year through.

From Sempringham down to Deeping, a line two or three miles broad of rich grazing land, made in a long course of time, by what has been brought out of the adjoining fens, worth, one with another, 20*s*.; applied to grazing sheep and beasts; though some in tillage.

Observations.

The facts here registered, contain such proofs of fertility as perhaps no other district in the kingdom can equal;—certainly none of equal extent. That the reader may have a clearer idea of these various proportions, I shall draw them into one short table, for the richer pastures.

Places.

Places.	Sheep in Summer per Acre.	Acres per Bullock in Summer with the Sheep.	Sheep in Winter per Acre,	Rent.
Long Sutton - - -	5½	2½	—	—
Mr. Scroop - - -	11	no bullocks	—	—
Boston, &c. - - -	4	1½	2	—
Skirbeck - - - -	5	1¼	2	—
Boston - - - -	5	1	3½	—
Deeping fen, Mr. Graves	5	2	1½	40
Alderchurch, Mr. Berridge	7¾	2	3	—
Swineshead - - -	2½	1	2	—
Ewerby - - - -	3	2½	2	30
Horbling, &c. - - -	3	2	2	—
Howel - - - -	3	3	2	—
Immingham - - -	1	1½	2	—
Grainthorp, &c. - -	3	3	1½	—
Stallenborough - -	2	2	2	—
Skidbrook - - -	1½	1¼	0½	—
Ditto, &c. - - - -	2	2	2	35
Addlethorpe - - -	5	1½	2	40
Gosberton - - -	6	1	—	—
Burgh, &c. - - -	5	2	2	40
Wrangle - - - -	2	2	—	36
Hundred of Skirbeck -	2	1¼	2½	45
Wibberton - - -	5	2	2	—
Marsh Chapel - -	3	2	—	35
Ditto - - - - -	3	1	—	45
Grimsby - - - -	2¾	1	2¾	—
Average - -	3¾	1¾	2	—

Considering the size of these sheep, which cannot be estimated at less than 24 lb. a quarter, on an average; and that the bullocks rise from 50 to 100 stone (14 lb.) this rate of stocking is very great indeed: here are on every acre 360 lb. of mutton, and reckoning the bullocks at 42 stone, dead weight, there is also 336 lb. of beef; in all 696 lb. of meat per acre in summer, besides the winter produce, which is immense. Let us, to simplify the account still more, suppose the whole mutton, and it amounts to seven sheep and a quarter per acre, of 24 lb. a quarter, for summer, besides two in in winter. The wool is another great article; at three sheep and three quarters per acre, and 9 lb. the fleece, each acre gives 43¾ lb. of wool. These products from such a considerable extent of country, are matchless.

Respecting the proportion of rent and produce.

	Rent.			Produce.		
Boston	£. 3	0	0	£. 10	8	0
Saltfleet	2	0	0	4	15	4
Wainfleet	1	15	0	3	13	4
Wrangle	1	16	0	4	16	8
Hundred of Skirbeck	2	5	0	6	6	0
Marsh Chapel	1	15	0	3	0	0
Ditto	2	5	0	6	0	0
	£. 14	16	0	£. 38	19	4

Upon this proportion the landlord, for every 20*s.* produce, takes 7*s.* 7*d.* in rent.

To compare these particulars with the rich marshes of Somerset, we may observe, that Mr. Billingsley, in his able Report for that county, reckons 100 oxen bought in, half at 11*l.* and half at 7*l.* to 200 acres, besides summering 70 sheep, and 100 wintered; the land 40*s.* an acre; this is one beast, and less than half a sheep an acre, the landlord taking in rent 400*l.* out of 830*l.* the proportion is much higher than in Lincolnshire; yet the Lincoln land is much higher stocked, as will appear, if the size of the oxen and of the sheep be considered. And this part of the comparison touches on a point which would probably, could it be estimated, increase our reasons for supposing the Lincoln marshes superior to the others, and that is, the one paying such a produce by a breed of cattle not in general esteem; and the produce of the Somerset land being

being applied to perhaps the most celebrated breed in the island. Is there any land in that county which equals the minutes here noted at Boston, Alderchurch, Long Sutton, and Gosberton ? and which would go much higher than the above produce of 38*l.* on a rental of 14*l.*

Feeding.

In the low land in Barton on the Humber, there was a horse-pasture and a sheep one contiguous, and upon the enclosure it was remarkable to observe the great difference between them; that which had been under sheep was greatly superior.

In the tract of marsh land on the sea-coast they observe, that where most grass is left in autumn, there the herbage is the coarsest and worst next year; the remark was made at Louth, in answer to recommending eddish for spring feeding sheep, which would not do on rich marsh, though it might, they thought, on uplands. It also shews, that the Romney Marsh system of close feeding is right, and would answer as well in Lincolnshire.

In the hundred of Skirbeck they like to have a tolerable head of grass in the spring, before turning in; and afterwards so to stock, as to prevent its getting coarse by *running away*, so as to prevent the necessity of *hobbing*, which, however, must be done in a wet growing season.

Mr. Parkinson observes, that the less sheep are changed the better; this remark, which I take to be very just, demands attention: it bears on the question of folding. Beasts are changed while *hobbing* is done; and the sooner it is hobbed the better; if cut while young, cattle will eat it.

Mowing.

Mowing.

Mowing rich marsh lands cannot be done too tenderly. At Moulton, between Sutton and Spalding, they have greatly damaged their fine lands by overmowing; the same at Woplade.

All land that will feed cattle, Mr. Parkinson observes, should be mown as little as possible; nothing pays worse than the scythe in Lincolnshire; it costs as much labour as a crop of corn, and more than in many counties, and is not of half the value.

Hay.

In making hay, it is observed here, as it has been in many other districts, that clover and sainfoin, and some other grasses, should be left in the swarth for some time, and when stirred, only turned; shaking out is found to be pernicious, not only in loss of leaf, but in exposing to damage. The same observation is found in fresh seeds.

It is observed very generally in Holland fen, that the hay, though upon land of 27*s*. an acre rent, is very bad, and will not fatten a bullock, or contribute to it, as is common in other countries. This must be owing to the bad management in making it: among other instances, it was mentioned to me, and I saw it myself, that they will leave the swarths, as they fall from the scythe, untouched so long, that the grass under them is turned quite yellow.

About Folkingham they mow and leave in swarth, in the manner above described; turn it instead of shaking; the system is therefore the same.

At Ewerby I remarked, that in making haycocks women were employed, who did the work with rakes; the

the consequence is, putting it together in lumps so imperfectly connected, or rather with such great interstices between them, that if rain comes it must do great damage; whereas, when made by men with forks, the bunch over the fork, it laps layer upon layer in a manner to shoot off rain. Every thing in hay-making that I have seen in Lincolnshire, is barbarous. About Grantham and Belton, hay made in the same manner; the grass bleached by the swarths.

From Grantham to Lincoln, Gainsborough, Barton, every where in their hay some time after harvest began; at the latter place, carting hay Sept. 3d! this is too barbarous. About Grimsby, and to Alesby, much hay out, and some not on cock; colour hideous. They defend themselves by saying, that the springs are so cold and backward after turnips are gone, that they are forced to feed all their mowing grounds late. I mentioned to Mr. Skipwith, kept eddish, but it did not make the impression so admirable a provision merits.

From Louth to Saltfleet much hay out, Sept. 15th, and hundreds of loads between Sutton and Alford; indeed very little was cleared. In this tract I saw them drawing hay from all parts of a field to the centre with horses and ropes, in order to form a stack without the trouble of carting; the frame for this work, a plate of which I inserted in my Northern Tour, is much superior.

About Spilsby and Dalby, hay out the 18th of September, arising from want of labourers; not feeding in spring, fit to mow before it was done.

Sept. 26, hay out in the hundred of Skirbeck.

Mr. Parkinson accounts for such lateness by observing, that the county is full of sheep, and they cannot

not spare the land early enough to have a forward crop of hay; not till the pasture land is increased enough to receive the sheep.

Mr. Loft, of Marsh Chapel, defends the practice of being late in the hay; he is not convinced that May-day is not as good a time to save meadows in the Middle Marshes, as Lady-day; and asserts, that the *proof* of such hay in *feeding* cannot be exceeded, though bad for cows: and he remarked, that if marsh hay was *tedded* (strewed out), it would be good for nothing for bullocks; and further, that some rain in making is beneficial; he wonld rather have six hours rain than none at all. Even with what I called execrable management and bad weather, the hay alone, without other food, will make bullocks very fat. Also, that the hay from the *ings*, at 10*s*. an acre rent, is much better for bullocks than that from rich grazing grounds.

The men at Marsh Chapel and Grainthorpe, &c. are famous for cutting hay-stacks *round;* they cut them as true as if turned in a lathe.

Breaking up Grass Lands.

Joshua Scrope, Esq. at Long Sutton, upon the enclosure of that common, lett 60 acres for woad for three years, 4*l*. per acre per annum net rent. After that he took it into his own hands, and ploughed it for oats, getting eleven quarters an acre. Upon the oat stubble he sowed wheat five quarters an acre, at 5*l*. a quarter; clover was sown with it, which was mown and fed, and sowed to wheat again, five quarters an acre, and now would lett at 40*s*. an acre; the land not being the least hurt, either by the woad or the successive tillage.

Some upon breaking up this common, sowed oats at first, but they grew too rank.

Others

Others lett it to flaxmen at 3*l*. or 4*l*. per acre; but they think that flax *draws* the land more than woad. No hemp.

In Holland fen, woad is reckoned of all others the most profitable way of breaking up, for the woad-planter gives 4*l*. or 5*l*. per acre per annum, for three years, for that crop, and then great ones of corn are taken. This is the way Mr. Cartwright has managed. (See *Woad*). Mr. John Tannard had 4*l*. per acre for the woad, and then took two crops of oats, each of an immense produce; and then two crops of wheat, the first six quarters an acre, and the second promises to be as much.

Dr. Johnson, of Spalding, lett 300 acres of Moulton common, on the enclosure, to a woad-grower, at May-day 1797, at 5*l*. per acre per annum, for four years; and four years more for three crops of oats, and a fallow, at 30*s*. an acre, which oat rent, however, is much below the value. He is informed, and believes, that woad does no harm to the land.

No instance of breaking up grass land that I had heard of in Lincolnshire, proves the extraordinary fertility of that county more clearly than that at Wintringham, on the estate of Lord Carrington, who, upon the high price of corn, was willing to indulge his tenants with the leave which they desired, of ploughing 200 acres, and for which they offered a compensation in rent; a great part of which, however, upon the sudden fall in the price of grain, which happened soon afterwards, his Lordship, I was informed, spontaneously remitted. Lord Carrington had requested Thomas Thompson, Esq. of Hull, who has the management of this estate, to meet me at Wintringham, and to give me every information in his power. Mr.

 Thompson

Thompson was so obliging as to do this, in the most liberal manner; and assembling three or four of the most intelligent tenants, I wished to know from themselves, what their expectation of produce was, upon their own calculation, which had induced them to wish for this permission. I held the pen while they gave me, in answer to my inquiries, the following particulars.

The land was warp marsh, on the banks of the Humber; had been under sheep and bullocks, and by the account of one of the tenants, kept heretofore a small bullock and eight sheep an acre; but finding that bullocks did not pay so well as they ought, they were gradually changing them for sheep. The high price of corn was of course their inducement to wish to plough. They have sown two crops of oats. The first crop, nine quarters an acre; and the second promises to be eight quarters.

But one piece of the same fifteen acres was broken up before, and cropped thus:

1792. Oats nine or ten quarters.
1793. Oats.
1794. Oats.
1795. Turnips.
1796. Oats.
1797. Wheat.

Mr. Chapman also has broken up in this course:

1793. 1. Oats, eight quarters.
1794. 2. Rape, five quarters.
1795. 3. Oats, eight quarters.
1796. 4. Rape and potatoes; rape, five quarters; potatoes, 100 sacks.
1797. 5. Wheat, $3\frac{1}{2}$ quarters, being too rank.

Calcu-

Calculation of the Tenant's Course, who supposed the Land worth 5l. 10s. an Acre.

Rent				£.5	10	0
Poor's-rate, &c. 1s. 8d.—Constable 3d per annum; say in all				0	3	0
One ploughing				0	12	0
Harrowing				0	6	0
Seed, one quarter, at				1	10	0
Reaping	£.0	15	0			
Leading three loads	0	4	6			
				0	19	6
Stacking and taking in				0	1	6
Inning in barn				0	1	0
Thrashing ten quarters				0	10	0
Dressing and delivery, 3d. a quarter				0	2	6
				£.9	15	6
Second oats the same, though two ploughings				9	15	6

Potatoes.

Rent, &c.	£.5	13	0
Three ploughings	1	1	0
Seed, seven sacks, 1s. cutting	2	9	0
Planting every third furrow	0	5	0
Hoeing	0	7	6
Ploughing between	0	1	6
Weeding	0	1	0
Ploughing and picking, and pyeing contract	1	11	6
Riddling or hand-picking, and delivery, 80 sacks, 3d.	1	0	0
	£.12	9	6

Price kidney 3s. 9d.—15l.

Refuse ——

Third,

Third, Wheat.

Six quarters expected; let us calculate on five.

	£.	s.	d.
Rent, &c.	£.5	13	0
Ploughing and harrowing	0	7	6
Seed and sowing, at 6*s*. 6*d*.	0	17	6
Gripping	0	1	6
Reaping and harvest	0	17	0
Thrashing five quarters	0	10	0
Dressing and delivering	0	1	6
	£.8	8	0

		£.	s.	d.		£.	s.	d.
Expenses.	Oats	9	15	6	*Produce*, at 30*s*.	15	0	0
	Oats	9	15	6		15	0	0
	Wheat	8	8	0		12	10	0
	Potatoes	12	9	6		15	0	0
		£.40	8	6		£.57	10	0
						40	8	6
						£.4)17	1	6

	£.	s.	d.
Profit per acre, per annum, after reckoning 5*l*. 10*s*. per acre rent	£.4	5	4

Such was the expectation of the Wintringham farmers when they desired liberty to plough; and the vast fall in the price of corn shews that they were not singular in opinion; the plough went merrily to work elsewhere, as well as here. I do not think it a very bad rule, on such occasions, to pursue the reverse of what the world is doing; when every body else is ploughing up, to take that moment to lay land down to grass;

grass; and should such a phenomenon ever be seen, as a rage to lay down, that should be the time for ploughing up. As this case of Wintringham is, however, a remarkable one, it deserves some further attention; for here are documents which not only prove the vast fertility of this estate, but which enables us to calculate the fair rent of such land under different circumstances: and the first object is to suppose an average price of corn, such for instance as 44*s*. for wheat, 24*s*. for barley and beans, and 18*s*. for oats; and we will leave out rent, to be the result, and not the basis of the calculation.

Expenses.

	£.	s.	d.
Of the first oats, rent, and extra price of seed deducted	£.3	10	5
Ditto of the second,	3	10	6
Ditto of the wheat	2	9	0
Ditto of the potatoes	6	16	6
	16	6	6
Interest of the farmer's capital, suppose 7*l*. an acre, at 20*l*. per cent.* 28*s*. for four years	5	12	0
	£.21	18	6

* As the capital is large on these rich soils, and the hazard, from the largeness of the crop, great also; a higher profit than common should be allowed; this hazard will necessarily arise with very heavy crops; in such the produce ought not to be reckoned at as high a price as the seed; they are very liable to be beaten down, and then the quality of the grain suffers considerably.

Produce.

Produce.

	£.	s.	d.
Ten quarters* of oats, at 18*s*.	£.9	0	0
Ten quarters ditto, at 18*s*.	9	0	0
Five quarters of wheat, at 44*s*.	11	0	0
Potatoes	15	0	0
	44	0	0
Expenses	21	18	6
Remains for landlord (tithe free) and poor ..	22	1	6
Per annum	£.5	10	4

But it is further to be observed upon these calculations, that they are applicable to the case no longer than the crops produce, as supposed, ten and five quarters of oats and wheat; if these fall to eight and four, the result will then be as follows:

	£.	s.	d.
Expenses, as before	£.16	6	0

Produce.

	£.	s.	d.
Eight quarters of oats, at 18*s*.	£.7	4	0
Eight ditto, ditto	7	4	0
Four quarters wheat, at 44*s*.	8	16	0
Potatoes	15	0	0
	38	4	0
Expenses	21	18	6
Landlord, church, and poor	16	5	6
Or per annum	£.4	1	4

* This, as a fair produce, I was assured of by other persons.

Without

Without regarding any course of crops which these farmers may now have in contemplation, I shall observe, that as they have taken

1. Oats, 2. Oats;

would it not be beneficial to induce them to go on somewhat in this manner?

3. Potatoes,
4. Wheat,
5. Hemp or flax,
6. Wheat,
7. Beans,
8. Wheat,
9. Rape,
10. Oats,
11. Beans,
12. Wheat.

Here are great objects gained; three crops of white corn in succession are avoided: and no two of such grain follow afterwards. Two crops of beans are had, and only one of potatoes. These circumstances would much more than make amends for the admission of the rape and hemp; nor let it be forgotten, that no crop cleans land like hemp.

From these estimates it is sufficiently clear, that this land cannot be worth, for twelve years, less than 4*l.* per acre, at these prices of the products; and by means of this scale of calculation, it may easily be adapted to any other prices, as well as afford a landlord the means of knowing when, and in what degree, allowances ought to be made for low prices, or a fair increase of rent for high ones. From the known liberality of the noble proprietor, and the integrity of the gentleman who manages for him, I have no doubt of the tenants having every proper inducement for pursuing good courses of crops; and I am very clear (indeed the preceding particulars, taken from their own mouths, prove it) that at average prices of the products, these marsh lands may be kept in tillage, probably for ever, at a

rent

rent of 4*l.* an acre, by proper alternation of grass and corn, &c. to the mutual advantage of both landlord and tenant.

Five acres and a half of horse pasture in the low land on the Humber, at Barton, were broken up and sown with oats, a great crop; and then sown again with oats, which produced 72 quarters.

About Saltfleet there has been some rich marsh land ploughed in this course:

1. Oats, ten or twelve quarters an acre;
2. Cole; when seeded five quarters;
3. Oats, nine or ten quarters;
4. Beans,
5. Oats,
6. Wheat.

Some of it inexhaustible by ploughing; and after a long course of crops yields great products. No hemp or flax; but great tracts have been woaded under the rent of 3*l.* an acre.

At Dalby, when grass land is broken up, Mr. Bourne takes,

1. Oats,
2. Oats,
3. Turnips or cole,
4. Oats or barley,
5. Turnips or cole manured, laid down with grasses.

Mr. Linton, of Freiston,

1. Oats, eight or nine quarters;
2. Beans, four quarters and a half;
3. Wheat, four quarters;
4. Turnips.

In

In common management, they repeat oats twice or thrice, and sometimes a fourth, and after that wheat; a field of thirty acres, wheat after four of oats.

Mr. Parkinson observes, that the less that is broken up the better, except in sandy or convertible, or weak, inferior, dry, open soils, where it is an improvement; on other land, better to leave the grass; but if permitted to plough as they like, they look only to virgin land, and will not pay a proper attention to the landlord's interest. When it is done, it has been under careful landlords, 1. oats; 2. turnips; 3. barley; 4. turnips; 5. barley; and seeds for twenty years. Others have pared and burned for turnips; 2. barley; 3. turnips; 4. barley; and seeds for sheep.

Mr. Lofft, of Marsh Chapel, is of opinion, from considerable experience, that to plough grass which pays well is a bad system; yet much is done so. It is right only on land that is unprofitable, and which will be improved for grass by a course of tillage. Even on the Wolds some lands have been ploughed to great loss; the sheep-walk at Wyham near Louth, was the largest and best in the whole county; and very bad management to plough it. The Rev. Mr. Allington coincides with this idea; and remarks, that the excellence of this walk was possibly owing to the good management long ago, when laid down, as some very large ancient marl pits are on it, which marks attentive husbandry; and as he observes, that for the last three or four years, the appearance seems that it will soon be of no better quality than the rest of the country. I crossed these walks, and may observe, that I found the country, from S. Elkington to Binbrook, in general more like a desart, than what such land should exhibit; extensive fields that had been ploughed up, and

and were over-run with thistles that had seeded, left in such a wild state that it was horrid to see it: warrens join in some places, which account for it partly; they are rarely met with, without seeming to have an ill effect on the minds and conduct of all around.

Laying down to Grass.

A tract of land called the New Marshes, which were ploughed for several years after they were first embanked, and treated much as Sutton commons now are, were immediately upon being laid down, and continue to be, the finest pastures for sheep-feeding of any in the county. So also will those parts of Sutton common be, if properly laid down, where the under-stratum is of a clayey quality:—where it is all silt, as in most of the *old* marshes, all the fallowing, all the manuring, all the new theories on husbandry in the world, will not be able to make such land continue in a feeding capacity. The great disadvantage these marshes are subject to, is the want of fresh water for beasts.—Ponds or pits are obliged to be made here to retain the fresh water; sometimes natural living springs are found, and the water perfectly fresh; but in very dry seasons these reservoirs are either exhausted, or so corrupted by the cattle running into them on hot days, that they cannot thrive; or they take to drinking the salt water, which is taken in at the spring tides to make fences, which scours them, and causes a fever. In wet seasons, from certain saline qualities lurking in the herbage, the effect of which is the same as if they drank the salt water; and if not quickly removed to the old enclosures, or what is better,—some fen land, they speedily die. This inconvenience obliges the grazier to run his sheep thicker, in a wet season especially,

than

than will allow them to fatten, or sometimes even thrive, turning crones, unless removed, and also much affected with the foot-halt.

" Hay-seeds," says Mr. Cartwright, " so called, abound in general with seeds of various plants unfit for either pasture or meadow, with troublesome and pernicious weeds, and even with grasses deserving no better appellation. Hence it seems best wholly to abandon the use of *hay-seeds*, and to lay down land with nothing but such grass-seeds as can be obtained separately and pure; trusting to Nature for a supply of such other grasses as the soil may peculiarly affect.

" We therefore want cultivators of distinct and separate grass, who, in this age of improvement, would probably find their account in such cultivation. For fen land, the *smooth-stalked* and the *rough-stalked meadow grass* deserve to be cultivated largely. In my small experimental meadow, or nursery of grasses, wherein are at present nine sorts, the *rough-stalked meadow grass* is invariably shorn close to the roots by the sheep, whenever they are admitted, and is much preferred to most of the other sorts, particularly the *fescue*, of which I sowed a large plot, in hopes of finding it peculiarly relished by the sheep.

" Of the *smooth-stalked meadow grass*, in the year 1791, I noticed, that in February its growth was vigorous, its verdure deep and bright, and its taste nearly as sweet as liquorice. I thought I had discovered a new species, that for its saccharine juices might rival Fraser's American grass, and accordingly transplanted a large sod into my garden; where in the flowering season its species was ascertained.

" The original maiden pasture of fen land does not wear so good a complexion, nor support so much stock,

stock, as after it has undergone a course of tillage. As this may be attributed in a great degree to bad grasses having possession of the soil, and some of them of an aquatic nature, favoured and established by former inundation and neglect of drainage; so it seems to be of consequence, to keep the land dry in future, that such grasses *may not return*. Both in a state of pasture and of tillage, these lands are very subject to *goose grass (potentilla argentina)*. He who shall teach us how to eradicate this weed, will deserve our thanks. Deep ploughing, and carefully picking out the roots, is the best mode I at present know."

In Holland fen they sow white clover, rib-grass, trefoil, and eight bushels of hay-seeds, and without corn, on which fourteen sheep and fourteen lambs have been summered per acre the whole season through, which is prodigious.

About Folkingham, when they lay down, it is after turnips, and with a crop of spring corn sown thin; the seeds used on heavy soils, trefoil, with red and white clover, and good hay-seeds. On light soils more white clover, less red, and hay-seeds. Mr. Hoyte has laid a boggy meadow drained to grass, by sowing Yorkshire white, one bushel an acre, with white and red clover, and parsley; and it has answered very well, and supported a great stock, which have done exceedingly well.

Mr. Harrisson makes an observation which has a good deal of truth in it; he says, that good old grass should never be broken up, and strong clay arable never laid down; the former is sure to be mishievous to the landlord; and the latter to ruin the tenant; the observation of course goes only to those soils which, after one or two years, refuse to produce grass, wear out,

out, and remain, if kept down for an age, sterile, till time brings a stratum of vegetable mould, to form the matrix of a good turf. The fact is certainly so; and a great desideratum it is to discover plants that would not thus decline. I have no doubt of such existing. On good soils the mere age of grass is of evident consequence in this country; for on the slope of the heath, from Kirton to Glentworth, passing through several lordships, enclosed at very different periods, and laid down to grass at the time, there is a great difference between Hempswell, a new one, and Willoughton, thirty years old; also between Willoughton and Blibo-rough, which may be seventy or eighty years; there is a rich luxuriance in the verdure not easily described, that mark a fertile pasturage, which nothing but age seems to give.

There is no clearer proof of excellent soil than laying down affords; for if the seeds do not after three or four years decline, but keep improving in quality, we may determine safely that the land must be excellent; at Wintringham I saw this proof, amongst a hundred others; I viewed a new ley of Mr. Chapman's in the fourth year, and it was to the eye a rich old pasture, full of white clover, and crested dogstail.

In Barton new enclosed field, I could not but admire Mr. Uppleby's new laid seeds, which were very thick and fine; he sows 16 lb. white clover, 4 lb. trefoil, and eight bushels of hay-seeds, which hay-seeds cost 10*s.*; this expense is enormous, and carried further than necessary, however, the error is on the right side. The second and third years' grass was perfectly fine. The same gentleman has also laid 160 acres in Goxhill fourteen years ago, with 14 lb. white clover, 4 lb. trefoil, and

and one bushel ray-grass; it is now a very fine pasture. On part of it the soil is a strong churlish clay, fit for wheat and beans; yet the grass has taken well, and not declined; much crested dogstail come naturally, which is a good sign.

In all the Wold country near to Broklesby, they have a common custom of laying to grass by sowing the seeds with rape; and they reckon it an excellent custom; indeed the best of all methods. What Lord Yarborough lays down in his park, &c. is done thus.

Mr. Bourne, of Dalby, lays down by sowing white clover, red clover, trefoil, ray-grass, with turnip and cole, and finds it succeeds well.

Best way, Mr. Parkinson says, is 12 lb. white clover, and a bushel of best ray-grass; or better still, three bushels of finest hard hay-seeds from Yorkshire. He does not approve *Yorkshire white*.

The Rev. Mr. Allington has been anxious to lay down with such seeds as will last in the ground; but has not hitherto found any thing better than white clover and trefoil; if with ray-grass, not more than a peck an acre of very clean seeds; he tried Yorkshire white, and does not approve it.

Mr. Holdgate, of Thoresway, in laying down for rabbits, sows 4 lb. or 5 lb. of white clover and trefoil, and two or three pecks of ray-grass, with some hay-seeds; he feeds it with sheep for two years; as he has found if rabbits are admitted sooner, they eat the plants to death in one year. Upon ray-grass he remarked, that there is nothing upon earth so destructive to land as seeding a crop of it; and where land will produce any thing else, the less that is sown of it the better.

Mr. Walker, of Woolsthorpe, 8 lb. red clover, 6 lb. white,

white, half a peck ray-grass to continue, and answers well; and on the red sand a natural herbage of red clover comes.

From these notes it appears, that this very important object is as well understood in Lincolnshire as in any other county of similar climate, and better than in some; but the fact is, that it is well practised commonly in none. Where the soil is so good as to run well to grass, good layers are easily formed; but upon soils which have not this quality, for want of grasses being selected, which are adapted or natural to the land, the new meadow soon wears out, and becomes unprofitable. Mr. Cartwright's observation on the smooth-stalked meadow grass, deserves attention, that it may be propagated and sold. The value of crested dogs-tail is seen in this as in many other counties; and the method of laying down with a crop of rape for sheep feed, is very well worth imitation in many districts. The question of Yorkshire white remains undecided; but opinions are more against than for it. Nor is ray-grass by any means a favourite.

CHAP.

CHAP. IX.

GARDENS AND ORCHARDS.

I cannot let this title pass without observing, that there is nothing in Lincolnshire more mistaken than the idea, that a garden may be considered as an object of luxury, and not of profit. There is no part of a farm that is more beneficially productive, with views of economy, than a well-cultivated garden. It is pleasing to see instances where this observation is realized; and I appeal to Mr. Hoyte, of Osbornby, whether he does not find three roods of land, cultivated as a garden ought to be, without a weed in it as long as a pin, is not a profitable speculation for a family?—His, of that size, produces all the common culinary vegetables, and yields this year 3000 plants, including Swedish turnips, for tups kept in an adjoining close.

CHAP. X.

WOODS AND PLANTATIONS.

THE berry-bearing poplar, brought from Nottinghamshire by Mr. Cartwright into Holland Fen, thrives very greatly, and much exceeds the Lombardy; they are eighteen or twenty feet high in six years.

Mr. Hoyte, of Osbornby, has made some small plantations of the Dishley willow, which have thriven extraordinary well; and yielded him, perhaps, a better produce than any other land on his farm. Neglected, miserable, boggy, and deserted spots, are thus converted to productive gardens; and no attentive farmer should omit a practice so very profitable; his yield twelve guineas an acre*.

Had Sir Cecil Wray been in the country, I should

* The woods in the south part of this county produce *oak*, *ash*, and *poplar*, about one-third of each, and scarce any other sort is to be met with therein, except a tree (the real name of which I could never learn), called by the woodmen *pill-bass*: it seems to be of the poplar class, but a distinct species.—Oak sells at various prices per foot, according to the purpose it is fit for; that sort used for fencing, and other farming purposes, at 1*s.* 6*d.*; but that of larger dimensions for building uses, near double. Ash and poplar have of late years been sold readily at 1*s.* per foot; and the latter is much used in building (since the high price of fir), and proves very durable if kept dry, agreeable to the woodman's adage,

"Cover me well, to keep me dry,
"And *heart* of oak, I do defy."

—*Cragg.*

 have

have had much valuable information from him; but being absent, I took the liberty of troubling him with some inquiries, which he did me the favour of answering.

"My plantations consist of 260 acres; and have been made at such periods (from 1760 to 1794), and in such proportions, that I can give no satisfactory answer on that head: they consist principally of Scotch firs. On my commencement as a planter, I planted oaks, ashes, beeches, elms, silver firs (in small quantities), spruce, larch, and Scotch fir. My purpose was to follow up those species of trees which throve best, as it was essentially necessary for my comfort to clothe, as quick as possible, a situation in which I had not even a thorn or whin growing.

"The larch, oaks, ash, and beech, made no little progress during the first three years; and the Scotch fir got on so well, that I planted for the ensuing ten years scarcely any other sort; a thing I now repent of, as their value is comparatively very small: but in size, I have this year cut up several oaks not six inches round, planted with the Scotch firs, many of which are from four to six feet.

"The silver fir has grown extremely well; but (as it is said) will in all probability be short-lived; they are, however, my finest trees at present.

"The spruce fir also grows well and large; and many of my beeches are as tall, though not so thick, as the firs they grow amongst; but this respects only a few of them, as many do not thrive so well.

"Having some reasons to think better of my larches, I recommenced their propagation about fifteen or sixteen years ago; and now have about fifty-three acres of of them growing completely well; and, from the value of the wood, promise to pay twice as well, at least, as the Scotch.—Last year I sold some larches, which I thinned out of the plantation, at 5*l.* per hundred; Scotch of the same age, at 1*l.* 10*s.* per ditto.

"I cut down every year a quantity of my oldest Scotch firs, to give room to the forest trees, and sell them at 8*d.* per foot, or use them in buildings, for farm-houses, barns, &c. in which they answer very well; also thin about twelve or fifteen acres of the smaller sort, which I sell for rails, &c. to the farmers in the neighbourhood, at 1*l.* 1*s.* 1*l.* 10*s.* 1*l.* 15*s.* per hundred. The whole profits arising annually to me from my plantations, are from 150*l.* to 200*l.* clear of all expenses.

"To state more particularly the profits of thinning a plantation of Scotch firs, I did this year thin twelve acres. The refuse trees (not big enough for a rail), and tops of the others, paid all expenses.

The quantity per acre, 700, at 1*l.* 10*s.*	£.10 10 0

The age of the trees fifteen years; the utmost value of the land 5*s.* per acre. But for several years the cattle and sheep have eaten the grass in the plantation, which is very near as good for the sheep, and better for the cattle, than where not covered with trees. The expense of making and fencing the plantations did not exceed 2*l.* per acre. As to the value of the trees left standing, it is at least equal to those cut down, and in a few years will considerably exceed them.

To

	£.	s.	d.
To state the expense, I should say, to planting	£.2	0	0
To fifteen years' interest on ditto	1	10	0
To ten years' rent of the land	2	10	0
To compound interest on ditto, and other incidents	1	0	0
	£.7	0	0
Total profit	£.3	10	0
Add the wood now growing	10	10	0
I think I do not overstate it at per acre	£. 14	0	0

"Have no doubt that my larches will, at least, be double.

"As to general observations, gentlemen differ so much respecting their modes of planting and management of trees, that I can only give you my opinion. First, that I would always plant each species of trees by itself; at least, I would never plant Scotch firs intermixed with others, on the idea that they are good nurses. Plants require very little shelter in winter; they suffer most in summer; and the Scotch fir soon becomes, from its spreading branches, a bad neighbour. Gentlemen say, they would weed them out; but they never do it in time to prevent the mischief.

"Second, that I would never plant a tree older than two years seedlings.

"Third, that I would never put so many on an acre as the nurserymen pursuade us to do: 2000 the very utmost; 1200 full sufficient.

"Fourth, that I would always trim off the side branches; this should be done when so small as to be cut

cut off with a knife; when delayed till the bough is large, it makes an ugly wound; is long in healing up, and if suffered to die on the tree, makes a hole in the timber: on the contrary, if cut off very soon, it grows over, and the wood has no wound or knot in it. I know this article is much controverted.

"Having rather spoken against Scotch fir, give me leave to say a word in their favour.

"First, they grow fast; and the wood is of sufficient use for farm-houses, &c.

"Second, the poor people supply themselves with very good fuel by gathering the fir-apples, and rotten wood; you will sometimes see twenty children in my plantations, *appleing*, as they call it.

"Third, the green boughs keep deer completely well in winter; and save much hay if given to sheep, particularly in snows: I have sometimes 300 or 400 sheep grazing on them at once.

"Fourth, the boughs are of great use in ovens, fire-wood, fencings, &c. I sell 30*l*. every year."

When it is considered that these observations are the result of such extensive experience, their value will not be doubted.

About Norton-place, Mr. Harrisson has formed a large range of beautiful plantations, which surround and break his lawn, except where it opens to the Wolds; and these in twenty-two years have flourished so rapidly, that he has cut larch of a considerable size; and has enclosed 800 acres from the thinnings.

Of all the planters in the county, Lord Yarborough takes the lead; for ten years past he has planted 100 acres per annum, which he is continuing in the same proportion; but designs soon to lessen it, as the lands he had assigned for that purpose will nearly be covered.

The following is the system of Sir Joseph Banks's woods, which have been very carefully managed since 1727, in a rotation of twenty-three years. The full grown oak timber is weeded out in the proportion of one-fourth, in the woods of the best quality; and one-fifth upon the inferior land. The aquatics, such as willow, sallow, alder, are all cut clean every twenty-three years; the same with hazel, and all other brush. Of ash, elm, &c. the full grown plants are cut, leaving a proportion of the best for the next crop. Of all sorts, such as will pay for a second twenty-three years' growth, are left; and the oak, upon a calculation of four successive growths, being ninety-two years when cut: and in some parts one hundred and fifteen years, or five growths; but of this very little; in general ninety-two. Produce per acre, on an average, 45*l.* consisting of timber, bark, poles, and brush.

Mr. Parkinson notes, that in woods, a forty pole piece of one rood, in some parts, produces oak trees from sixty to eighty feet, value from 8*l.* to 12*l.* and bark 6*l.* 18*s.*; and we have some trees sold for 24*l.*: the common medium average of our wood books are about

Twenty oaks, average 22*s.*	£.22	0	0
Bark about	11	0	0
Poles of ash, sallow, birch, &c.	10	6	8
Brushwood 3*d.*	2	0	4
Total of an acre, cut once in 23 years	£.45	7	0

In four pieces, forty pole each, oak timber 2*s.* and

and 2*s*. 6*d*. per foot, and retailed at 3*s*. and 3*s*. 6*d*. per foot.

If younger oaks are taken, it comes to less.

Annual Sale by Wood and Bark.

Years.		Wood.				Bark.		
1757	....	£.478	2	3	....	£.32	0	0
1758	....	365	14	7	....	18	0	0
1759	....	397	18	4	....	26	0	0
1760	....	437	4	0	....	33	0	0
1761	....	470	15	11	....	33	0	0
1762	....	394	3	5	....	43	0	0
1763	....	433	11	10	....	43	0	0
1764	....	430	9	6	....	41	0	0
1765	....	480	16	6	....	44	0	0
1766	....	454	8	10	....	37	0	0
1767	....	509	16	7	....	37	0	0
1768	....	535	2	6	....	31	0	0
1769	....	488	18	7	....	34	0	0
1770	....	623	4	3	....	50	0	0
1771	....	602	9	6	....	45	0	0
1772	....	667	6	6	....	70	0	0
1773	....	977	13	8	....	100	0	0
1774	....	868	1	0	....	75	0	0
1775	....	856	5	9	....	65	0	0
1776	....	915	14	7	....	80	0	0
1777	....	903	19	10	....	90	0	0
1778	....	1102	15	9	....	90	0	0
1779	....	1067	15	10	....	75	0	0
1780	....	757	8	7	....	73	0	0
1781	....	655	6	2	....	63	0	0
1782	....	642	11	10	....	75	0	0
1783	....	825	4	7	....	95	0	0
1784	....	811	8	7	....	105	0	0

Years.

Years.		Wood.				Bark.		
1785	....	£.879	0	0	....	£.90	0	0
1786	....	787	15	8	....	106	0	0
1787	....	1004	10	1	....	140	0	0
1788	....	1053	10	6	....	112	0	0
1789	....	1258	0	2	....	170	0	0
1790	....	1260	9	1	....	150	0	0
1791	....	1589	8	9	....	166	0	0
1792	....	1752	14	10	....	250	0	0
1795	....	1305	0	0	....	—		
1796	....	1772	0	0	....	—		

The woods covering 805 acres; if 45*l.* 7*s.* be taken as a medium, the produce is 1*l.* 19*s.* 5*d.* per acre per ann. from land, which being amongst the worst in the country, would not produce, in an arable farm, more than 10 or 12*s.* The produce, not only from this fact, but on comparison with woods in general through the kingdom, 20*s.* being a high produce, must evidently be extremely well managed; and to have continued through so long a period to produce that large growth of timber for a regular fall, to be sold as part of the annual produce; and it is upon this circumstance that the great advantage depends.

Timber	£.33
Poles	10
Brush	2
	£.45

Thus the timber is the great object; for 35 acres at 33*l.* are 1150*l.* which, from 805 acres, is 1*l.* 8*s.* 6*d.* per acre per annum. This great produce of near 40*s.* an acre, however, is the result of a vast capital gradu-

ally

ally nursed up in wood always on the land; and it is fair to bring it to some valuation. In conversation with Mr. Parkinson, the steward, I found that the whole produce of an acre at the time of cutting would vary from 150*l.* to 300*l.* in value. It is moderate to call it 200*l.*; hence then the 40*s.* annual produce is the payment from an acre of land united with a capital of 200*l.*; and viewing it in this light, the return of 40*s.* wears a very different aspect. I urged this to Mr. Parkinson, because he seemed to look only at the vast improvement of converting land, which in any other application would not pay more than 10*s.* or 12*s.* to 40*s.* per acre, which is certainly an immense difference. He further urged, that there might be difficulty in selling larger quantities than offered at present. This I cannot admit, for the immense rise in the demand, and consequently of *price*, is evident from the regular rise in value from 1759. But suppose this to have a very great effect, and to reduce the 200*l.* one half, and that only 100*l.* was the produce per acre; here is an addition of 55*l.* which placed at interest, produces 2*l.* 15*s.* for ever; and then the land being clear of all wood, enters on a fresh course as common copse, paying as other woods do in that system. If only 15*s.* per annum, it makes 3*l.* 10*s.* per acre per annum for ever.

I would not be thought to speak with any degree of decision on this subject; but simply to suggest the propriety of re-considering the system. If, as I conceive, the above deduction of half the value would not be found admissible, in fact the loss would appear enormous. But it is an experiment very easily made, and with the greatest probability of at least losing nothing by the trial. Thirty-five acres, at 45*l.* per acre,

acre, produce at present 1575*l.* To receive the same sum at 200*l.* per acre, only eight acres would be cut. At 100*l.* per acre, only sixteen acres. Thus from eight to sixteen acres might be cut; and a new system begun without loading the market more than at present: it would soon appear how much the annual quantity might be increased relative to the market; and whether the additional age (the underwood being such a trifling object) would not render the timber and poles *more* rather than *less* saleable; which has been the assertion to me in various parts of the kingdom where hop-grounds were not the consumption: for all objects of enclosure, the size of a pole for rails, &c. is a benefit, as they rive into any scantlings. The want also of that regularity in the quantity cut, which must be adhered to in the present system, would be a benefit; for it is much better to regulate that quantity by the *demand* than by the *system* of felling. Scantlings of underwood go from Sussex to the Newcastle collieries: surely Lincolnshire is much better situated to supply them? There is not a clearer head in Great Britain than that of the Right Honourable Possessor of these woods; and whenever the immense extent of his respectable pursuits will permit attention to such questions of his private interest, he will doubtless reflect on the vast capital he has thus employed at an interest, to speak in the mildest terms, rather inadequate: 800 acres at 200*l.* are 160,000*l.*; at 100*l.* are 80,000; such sums are worth attending to.

The Duke of Ancaster has woods to the extent of 4 or 500 acres. Cut at eighteen years growth; the whole underwood is cut, and the larger growth taken down in succession. The largest sticks not more than thirty feet;—takes out the wood that will not pay for standing,

standing, being not prosperous in the growth. The value of all cut down would not be more than 40*l*. The value of an acre in eighteen years growth about 14*l*. to 16*l*. The land adjoining letts at 10*s*. 15*s*. and 20*s*. The cold wet land gives the best wood. It is bought for the purposes of fencing new and old enclosures. The eighteen years would not do for this; but that of two to three growths, or fifty-four years, does for these purposes: training up the finest and clearest sticks, in order that they may come to this application. And as His Grace has much wood on a soil, that in other applications would be good for little else, the comparison must not be made with the country in general. An acre of wood is worth, upon an average, from 15*l*. to 20*l*.; or in general 20*s*. an acre. The objection to cutting the whole, is the saleable price; wood is most saleable when it is old; and if the Duke was to say, I will have the wood of eighteen years growth not cut, but leave it to thirty-six, would it be more or less saleable?—The answer was, More, Sir: leaving it to a greater growth would make it of more proportionable value, and more easily saleable. But in this case it would be necessary to cut the underwood, as at present, every eighteen years. The growth chiefly oak and maple; and Mr. Parker makes it a rule to cut them down, because their spreading heads injure the oaks and underwood. Poplar is also very injurious to the oak, from its fast growth; he has observed that it has the effect of injuring the oak, and therefore he always takes it down whenever necessary to make way for the oak. Ash is trained up with care, because it is of as much value as oak; but sallow is not equally valuable, being generally cut down with the underwood. Where land can be lett at 20*s*. an acre, it is much

much more advantageous than what woods will yield in this system. Would you, if the estate were your own, increase or decrease woods?—I would not attend to profit to a certain extent, because the repairs of an estate make it so valuable for buildings and fences, that I would keep a certain portion in wood for those purposes.

The Marquis of Exeter has very extensive woods in Lincolnshire, about Bourn, &c. which pay him by underwood and timber, about 20*s*. per acre per annum. Bark here is sold by a proportion to the value of the timber; for instance, it is 6*s*. in 20*s*. of the gross amount of the tree.

CHAP. XI

WASTES.

I MUST consider commons, however naturally rich in soil, as wastes, and therefore class Spalding, Pinchbeck, and Cabbit commons as such, to the amount of many thousand acres; 15,000 acres from it were enclosed long ago, when in the state of a forest, which the whole has been, as appears from the black oaks dug up every where. If enclosed, it would lett for at least 20*s*. an acre, and probably much more. There is much of it peat, but much also of good mould.

Forty thousand acres in Sir Joseph Banks's fens would, if enclosed, lett for 31*s*. 6*d*. according to the opinion of some; in that of others, for 26*s*. In East Fen are 2000 acres of water; 32 parishes have right of common in these fens. At Brothertoft I crossed the ferry into Wildmore Fen, and the little I saw of it was worth 40*s*.; but whole acres covered with thistles and nettles, four feet high and more. There are men that have vast numbers of geese, even to 1000 and more. Mr. Thacker, of Langrike ferry, has clipped 1200 sheep on Wildmore; and yet he assured me, that he would rather continue at his present rent, and pay the full value for whatever might be allotted to his farm on an enclosure, rather than have the common right

for

for nothing. In 1793 it was estimated that 40,000 sheep, or one per acre, rotted on the three fens. Nor is this the only evil, for the number stole is incredible: they are taken off by whole flocks. So wild a country nurses up a race of people as wild as the fen; and thus the morals and eternal welfare of numbers are hazarded or ruined for want of an enclosure.

There may be five sheep an acre kept in summer on Wildmore and West Fens, besides many horses, young cattle and geese; if there are any persons who profit, it is the people who keep geese. Some keep sheep in winter there, and suffer accordingly.

One of the greatest improvements that has been attempted in England, is now effecting (1808) in East, West, and Wildmore Fens; but I leave the preceding description, that the country, when improved, may be the better compared with its former state.

At Blankney and its vicinity, Mr. Chaplin has 3 or 4000 acres of warrens lett, at the highest at *3s. 6d.* an acre, some at *2s.*; the warreners have permission to plough part, keeping it in tillage for some crops, and then laying it down again for rabbits. In this management they enclose with walls, and pare and burn for turnips: after which they sow barley, then turnips again, and a second crop of barley with seeds, for rabbits; this system may extend to taking in this manner, 50 or 60 acres every year in 1000.

On the common Wold enclosure at Barton, Mr. Graburn stubbed and burnt the gorse cover on a large piece, and ploughed it in the spring for oats; the crop four quarters; then ploughed twice, and then worked it with heavy four-horse drags; rolled and ploughed, and sowed turnips, which were worth *25s.*; winter

ploughed

ploughed and sowed 100 acres of it with barley, and 60 with oats; the former three quarters an acre, the latter five. Now it is under seeds, which he inten is should remain three years for sheep. Surely paring and burning at first for turnips, would have succeeded better at a less expense.

Near Brocklesby, &c. there are large tracts of excellent land under gorse; and at Caburn and Swallow, I passed through the same for miles. It is a beautiful plant to a fox-hunter. Lord Yarborough keeps a pack of hounds; if he has a fall, I hope it will be into a furze-bush; he is too good to be hurt much; but a decent pricking might be beneficial to the country.

In discourse at Louth, upon the characters of the poor, observations were made upon the consequences of great commons, in nursing up a mischievous race of people; and instanced, that on the very day we were talking, a gang of villains were brought to Louth gaol, from Coningsby, who had committed numberless outrages upon cattle and corn; laming, killing, cutting off tails, and wounding a variety of cattle, hogs, and sheep; and that many of them were commoners on the immense fens of East, West, and Wildmore.

Mr. Hyde, at Tathwell, has cleared and cultivated much rough gorse land, covered with ant-hills, without ploughing, and reduced it to profitable pasture. Mr. Pearson, in such cases, mixes lime with the ant-hills; has done to the amount of 2 or 300 loads in a year; the benefit good for barley and seeds, but did none to turnips.

Forty years ago it was all warren for thirty miles from Spilsby to beyond Caistor; and by means of turnips

nips and seeds, there are now at least twenty sheep kept to one there before.

Every circumstance concerning so very large a tract as the undrained fens, deserves attention. For the following particulars, I am indebted to Sir Joseph Banks, who knows more of them, perhaps, than any other person in the county. The East and West Fens were drained by adventurers in the time of Charles I. some account of whose undertakings may be seen in Dugdale's History of Embanking and Draining; they were about that time actually enclosed and cultivated. It is probable that the undertakers and the King, to whom a share was allotted, had taken to themselves a larger portion of the fen than the county thought just and reasonable; for in the time of the great rebellion, a large mob, under pretence of playing at foot-ball, levelled the whole of the enclosures, burnt the corn and houses, destroyed the cattle, and killed many of those who occupied the land. They proceeded to destroy the works of drainage, so that the country was again inundated as it formerly had been. After the Restoration, the adventurers repaired their works, resumed their lots of property, and began again to cultivate them; but the country, who always considered themselves oppressed by trespass upon the grounds, compelled the adventurers to defend their rights by a course of law; in which it was determined, that the original agreement was not valid, and consequently the property of the whole level was vested in its original proprietors. From this time the drainage was carried on under the Court of Sewers, principally by means of the adventurers' drains: but the river Witham being neglected, and nearly silted up, they became so much oppressed, that application was make to Parliament in 1762,

1762, when an Act passed, by which the present works have been made, which are probably sufficient to carry off the whole of the downfall waters; but till a catch-water drain is made to keep separate those that fall upon the hills, from those which fall upon the level, and a proper outfall provided, to carry the hill waters separately to sea, the expense of which will probably be equal, if not exceed that of the Witham drainage, the land can never be considered as safe winter land; neither can it be thought advisable to divide and enclose it. East Fen consists of 12,424 acres one rood one perch. The undertakers' drains left only 2000 acres under water; but I am credibly informed that the outfall of Maudfoster, as that *goat* now lies, is capable of draining dry the deepest pits in that fen.

The West Fen contains 16,924 acres two roods six perches. As the undertakers laid that quite dry, there can be no doubt of the practicability of any undertaking there. The following parishes have a right of commonage on East and West Fens.

Soke of Bolingbroke.—Sibsey, Stickmey, Stickford, West Keal, East Keal, Tointons, Haltons, Steeping, Thorpe, Spilsby, Hundleby, Rathby, Enderby, Lustby, Hareby, Asgarby, Miningsby, East Kirby, Revesby, Hagnaby, Bolingbroke; 21 in number.

Holland Towns.—Boston, Skirbeck, Fishtoft, Freestone, Butterwick, Bennington, Leverton, Leek; eight in number.

On Wildmore Fen.—Haltham, Roughton, Thidesby, Horncastle, Ashby, Low Tointon, High Tointon, Mareham on the Hill, Enderby, Moreby, Wilksby, Mareham le Fen, Coningsby, Scrivelsby cum Dalderby, Tumby, Kirkstead, Fishtoft, Firthbank; 18 in number; in all 47. Would lett at 30*s*.

 Upon

Upon driving West Fen in 1784, there were found, 16th and 17th September, 3936 head of horned cattle. In dry years, it is perfectly white with sheep.

" *An Estimate of the Common Right of a Farm at Revesby, in tenure of Thomas Mackinder.*

" Suppose the farm to contain 195 ewes for tupping, and on an average to raise 180 lambs; the he lambs to be kept in the enclosures, to make wethers for sale, because the common would make them too small and poor to raise much money for rent; but the she hogs may be summered on the common, and by good keeping in the autumn, will be sufficient for ewes to breed;

Consequently, 90 she hogs from the 8th of April to the 1st of October, being 25 weeks, at 2*d*. per head, per week	£. 18	15	0
Suppose the farm to raise eight calves in each year, and to keep the yearlings, cows, and feeding beasts; by that means there remains for the common eight beasts two years old, and eight beasts three years old, being together 16 beasts at 6*s*. per head, for 25 weeks	4	16	0
Brood mares and young horses eight, at 10*s*. per head	4	0	0
Suppose the cart or working horses turned into the common at times when plenty of grass, which may enable the occupier to get more hay from his enclosures, taken at per year	2	2	0
To privilege of getting sods, &c.	1	1	0
Total, ...	30	14	0
Deduct for loss of cattle, taken at one-seventh	4	8	0
Net profit	26	6	0

Brought

	£.	s.	d.
Brought forward	26	6	0
Deduct the tenant's profit in farming the common, with expenses, shepherding, &c.	13	3	0
Clear rent to the landlord £.	13	3	0

"N.B. The same proportion is observed upon all the common rights, in proportion to the lands they possess, to nurture the cattle which go upon the common, with some additions placed to such houses as are situate so near the fen as to enable them to milk their cows upon the common in a fruitful season, and plenty of grass; which are adjusted in proportion to their various situations."

An Estimate of the probable Improvement that may arise by Enclosing the East and West Fens, in the County of Lincoln. By Mr. Parkinson.

The present Value.	Dr.
To the present value of all the common rights in the East and West Fens - -	£.4173 5 0
To the present value of the common rights in the Wildmore Fen - - - -	£.1515 13 1

The improved Value.	A.	R.	P.	Value per Acr.		Rent. Cr.
By the West Fen - -	16,924	2	6	£.20		£.16,924 10 9
By the East Fen - - -	12,424	3	39	15		9318 14 11
Total improved value, Cr. -	29,349	2	5			£.26,343 5 8
Deduct the present value, Dr. - - - -						4173 5 0
Net improvement - - - - - -						£.22,070 0 8
By the Wildmore Fen	10,661	2	25	£.20	£.10,661 13 1½	
Deduct Dr. as opposite - -				-	1515 13 1	
Net improvement -						9146 0 0
The whole improvement of the East, West, and Wildmore Fens - - - - - - -						£.31,216 0 8

The foregoing calculation is taken from the average of the common rights in two different parishes, viz. Lusby and Revesby; the one being detached a great distance from the commons, the other much nearer, which makes a datum for the whole of the towns; and if the common-rights of those two parishes produce a given sum, and their two shares of land-tax amounts to, Lushby 40*l*., Revesby 237*l*.; all the parishes which have right upon the fens, amounting to 3975*l*. 15*s*. produces the above sum of 4173*l*. 5*s*. per year, which gives the present value of the common-rights upon the said East and West Fens, from 29,349 acres, is about 2*s*. 10*d*. per acre; when by the improvement from an enclosure the said 29,349 acres produce 26,243*l*. per year, averages about 17*s*. 11*d*. per acre, which is the moderate average value; although there are certain lands taken in to defray the expense of draining the said West Fen, lett by auction for 34*s*. per acre; in the average about 1000 acres in farms*.

The principal reason why those fens are so unprofitable in their present state, arises from the disorder in stocking; because human nature being in their various capacities anxious of property, some through avarice, or a wish to get rich at once, stock so largely as to injure themselves, and oppress the common; others, in the line of jobbing, put in great quantities of stock to sell again, which are altogether injurious to the fair commoner, who only stocks with what his farm produces. Because, suppose one man stocked a pasture of 29,349 acres, he would consider the different sorts of cattle to be depastured thereon, for each to thrive and yield their proportionable share of profit; but if

* Mr. Parkinson is not very clear in this passage.

3000

3000 men stock, they have different views of supposed interest; some increase their breed of sheep, beasts, horses, geese, &c. There are instances of a cottager renting *5l.* per year, having 1500 or 2000 breeding geese, which must injure his neighbour of *5l.* per year, who has got only a few sheep or a cow.

It appears, that if the said commons were enclosed, they would produce an yearly rent of 26,243*l.* 5*s.* 8*d.* All plough farms here are estimated to produce three years rent, 78,729*l.* 17*s.* which increase of property would employ more poor, maintain more farmers, increase trade, and produce great quantities of grain, which now costs English money to import from foreign nations.

The principal proprietors have long had this improvement in agitation, particularly since so many inferior neighbouring commons have been embanked and enclosed to such great advantage; but this being more extensive, and having large mortmain estates intermixed, and also a difference in the rights between the Soke of Bolingbroke and Holland Town, have hitherto protracted the proceeding.

Along the sea coast of the hundred of Skirbeck, there are about 1000 acres of sea marsh beyond the bank, covered by spring tides, capable of being taken in to very great profit; but not done, waiting for an Act to enclose the fens, in order then to take in the marshes.

Wrangle has a common of 1500 acres belonging to itself; and Leak, besides its right on East and West Fens, has one also of 450. The rest of the parishes in the hundred have a right, as they assert, on both East and West Fens.

Mr. Linton is of opinion, that these fens will never

turn

turn to any personal or public benefit, but by enclosure; for though certain profits are made, yet such losses happen now and then as cut very deep indeed into the benefit.

Mr. Birtwhistle, who lives at Skirbeck, is much spoken of for stocking the East and West Fens, chiefly the latter, with Scotch beasts. It was said here, that the Duke of Buccleugh taking many beasts as rent in kind, this person was a contractor for vast numbers, even to the number of between 7 and 800, and even 1000, which he summered here, and then drove them into Norfolk to sell for turnips; and it is said his father made much money by this practice.

There are about 300 acres of land in East Fen, where cranberries grow in such abundance as to furnish a supply for several adjacent counties. The land is chiefly common, belonging to Wainfleet and Friskney. *Empetrum*, and several other mountain plants, are found upon the cranberry ground, and in no other part of the fens. They are so plentiful, that one man has got nine score pecks in a season.

Sir Joseph Banks had the goodness to order a boat, and accompanied me into the heart of this fen, which in this wet season had the appearance of a chain of lakes, bordered by great crops of reed, *arundo phragmites*. It is in general from three to four feet deep in water, and in one place, a channel between two lakes, five to six feet. The bottom a blue clay, under a loose black mud, two to two feet and a half deep.

Plants

Plants on the Peaty Bogs, &c.

Arundo phragmites.
——— *epigejos.*
Potentilla anserina.
Hydrocotely vulgaris.
Mentha aquatica.
Ophioglossum vulgatum.
Carex cæspitosa.
Carduus palustris.
Salix capræa.
Iris pseudacorus.
Hypnum rutabulum.
Salix repens.
Sonchus palustris.
Sisymbrium amphibium.
Eriophorum polystachium.
Eupatorium cannabinum.
Angelica sylvestris.
Lythrum salicaria.
Caltha palustris.
Lotus corniculata.
Poa aquatica.
Rumex hydrolapathum.
Polygonum amphibium.
Myosotis scorpioides.
Juncus effusus.
Hypericum quadrangulum.
Epilobium hirsutum.
Lychnis flos cuculi.
Selinum palustre.
Lysimachia vulgaris.
Convolvolus sepium.
Comarum palustre.
Acrostichum thelypteris.
Bidens cernua.
Pedicularis palustris.
Senecio Jacobæa.
Alisma plantago aquatica.
Cineraria palustris.
Teucrium scordium.
Schoenus mariscus.
Cicuta virosa.
Menyanthes trifolia.
Myriophyllum verticillatum.
Hydrocharis morsus ranæ.

In both East and Wildmore Fens the poor horses, called Wildmore titts, get on the ice in winter, and are *screeved;* that is, their legs spreading outward, the wretched animals are split.

Upon the enclosure of this great and improvable tract of country, I had much conversation with Sir Joseph Banks, who I was very glad, but not surprised, to find, had the most liberal ideas upon the subject. No man sees clearer the vast advantages which would result

result from the measure to the country in general. No man can be more desirous that it should be effected; but knowing that there will arise difficulties, if the parties concerned do not concur in the design upon an equally liberal footing without previous bargains, by leaving the whole to the decision of commissioners, he has desisted from coming forward himself, at a time when the scarcity of money might render the attempt questionable. He has collected with the utmost assiduity every document necessary for the measure; and is prepared for it in every respect. Nothing is wanting but an application to him from the parties concerned, upon so broad a basis as may shew the measure to be feasible, accompanied with declarations that the money can be procured. He permits me to assert this; and also, that the Dutchy Court of Lancaster will be friendly to the measure, on the assignment of one-sixteenth in lieu of the rights of the Crown. He makes no conditions for himself personally, but will trust all to the commissioners. It is not possible for a man to be more liberal than this: situated and interested as he is, he may most justly expect that the applications should be made to him. The waste and disgraceful state in which so many acres remain, rests not, therefore, at his door. Sincerely do I hope that this public declaration, in the sincerity of which I have not the smallest doubt, will have the proper effect; that meetings will be held for the purpose, with his concurrence; that the Corporation of Boston, so deeply interested for the good of their town, will take the proper measures for being answerable for procuring the money. When such steps are taken, with a general disposition not to meet for making bargains or establishing claims, but to submit them to the

decision

decision of commissioners, the undertaking will be in train, and Sir Joseph Banks, thus properly applied to, will take the lead in a business of such importance, and give that powerful impulse to the measure, which he alone can give.

I am fortunate to say, that the preceding account having been read by many persons in the vicinity, did give occasion to much conversation on the subject, which in a very few years produced the wished-for effect. The necessary Acts of Parliament passed; the drainage is effective, and the land fast cultivating.

In the 41st and 43d years of his present Majesty, Acts passed for draining, dividing, and enclosing them, and the ablest engineers having been employed, the great work of the drainage is completed; the expenses will amount to about 400,000*l.* and the value of the land is pretty well ascertained to be 2,000,000*l.* thus leaving a profit to the proprietors of 1,600,000*l.* All the land that was sold in order to pay the expenses, has been pared and burnt, and sown with oats; some has yielded one crop, some two, and some three crops of that grain, and none has yielded less than a last, or ten quarters per acre; and the high price of oats has been so great an encouragement to the cultivation, that it has proceeded with an extraordinary rapidity. The following table will shew many of the prices at which much of the land was sold.

Sale

Sales of Lands in the East, West, and Wildmore Fens, to 17th October, 1807, for Drainage.

Sales.	West Fen.			Price.		Wildmore Fen.			Price.		East Fen.			Price.
	A.	R.	P.	£.	s.	A.	R.	P.	£.	s.	A.	R.	P.	£.
1802. Feb. 17	358	0	25	14,820	0	—			—		—			—
18	—			—		1000	0	0	37,970	0	—			—
Mar. 31	968	2	15	38,160	0	—			—		—			—
Oct. 13	638	0	39	17,175	0	230	3	7	7245	0	—			—
14	751	0	31	27,060	0	—			—		—			—
1804. Sept. 28	424	3	34	19,536	10	29	0	7	1979	10	—			—
1805. Oct. 17	249	0	2	12,640	0	322	0	24	17,945	0	—			—
18	919	2	0	45,120	0	—			—		—			—
1806. Oct. 16	622	3	0	31,430	0	—			—		—			—
17	874	3	0	45,505	0	—			—		—			—
1807. Oct. 16	—			—		—			—		1564	3	16	52,410
17	—			—		73	2	2	5240	0	240	0	0	10,270
	5807	0	26	251,446	10	1655	2	0	70,379	10	1804	3	16	62,680

For Division of the East and West Fens.

		West Fen.				Price.
		A.	R.	P.		
1804. September 28	-	537	3	29	-	£.21,400

For Division of Wildmore Fen.

			Wildmore Fen.			Price.
			A.	R.	P.	£.
1802.	October	18	356	0	1	9370
1804.	May	12	46	0	0	1410
	September	27	203	0	24	8640
1805.	October	21	90	0	33	5875
1807.	October	13	47	2	16	2610
			742	3	34	27,914

Collection.

	Drainage.			Price.		Division.			Price.	Totals. Sold in each Fen.			Price.	
	A.	R.	P.	£.	s.	A.	R.	P.	£.	A.	R.	P.	£.	s.
West Fen	5807	0	26	251,446	10	537	3	29	21,400	6345	0	15	272,846	10
Wildmore Fen	1655	2	0	70,379	10	742	3	34	27,914	2398	1	34	98,293	10
East Fen	1804	3	16	62,680	0	—			—	1804	3	16	62,680	0
	9267	2	2	384,506	0	1280	3	23	49,314	10,548	1	25	433,820	0

This table suggested to me many inquiries, which I did not fail to make of the proper persons: it is a fresh proof of what I have often experienced, that satisfactory information is only to be had by travelling to the spot, on publishing new editions of the Reports. Sending the Surveyors a second time to the former field of their researches, is essentially necessary for rendering such editions valuable. With such limited funds as those entrusted to the Board, this is impossible. For the little I have gained, I am obliged to Sir Joseph Banks, the great patron of the undertaking.

Between Lincoln and Newark I passed very extensive waste commons, which produce nothing but gorse and rushes; and a little further, enclo ures that wore no better face. In Stapleford also are many moors.

CHAP. XII.

IMPROVEMENTS.

SECT. I.—DRAINAGE.

DEEPING Fen, which extends most of the eleven miles from that town to Spalding, is a very capital improvement by draining. Twenty years ago the lands sold for about 3*l.* an acre; some was then lett at 7*s.* or 8*s.* an acre; and a great deal was in such a state that nobody would rent it: now it is in general worth 20*s.* an acre, and sells at 20*l.* an acre: 10,000 acres of it are taxable under commissioners, pay up to 20*s.* an acre; but so low as 2*s.*; average 4*s.* including poor-rates, and all tithe-free. There are 5000 acres free land, but subject to poor-rates. The free land also sells from 15*l.* to 20*l.* an acre; and more three or four years ago.

Through all the fens of Lincolnshire we hear much of the *soak;* by which expression is meant the subterranean water which is found at various depths, usually but a very few feet below the surface: this rises and sinks according to seasons, and is supposed, from its saline quality, to be the sea water filtered through a stratum of silt. Major Cartwright in Holland Fen observes upon it:

"The substratum of *silt* seems to be very general in this neighbourhood, and not often, as I should suppose, at any very considerable depth. It seems to be a con-

A MAP of the SOUTH DRAINAGES of LINCOLNSHIRE.

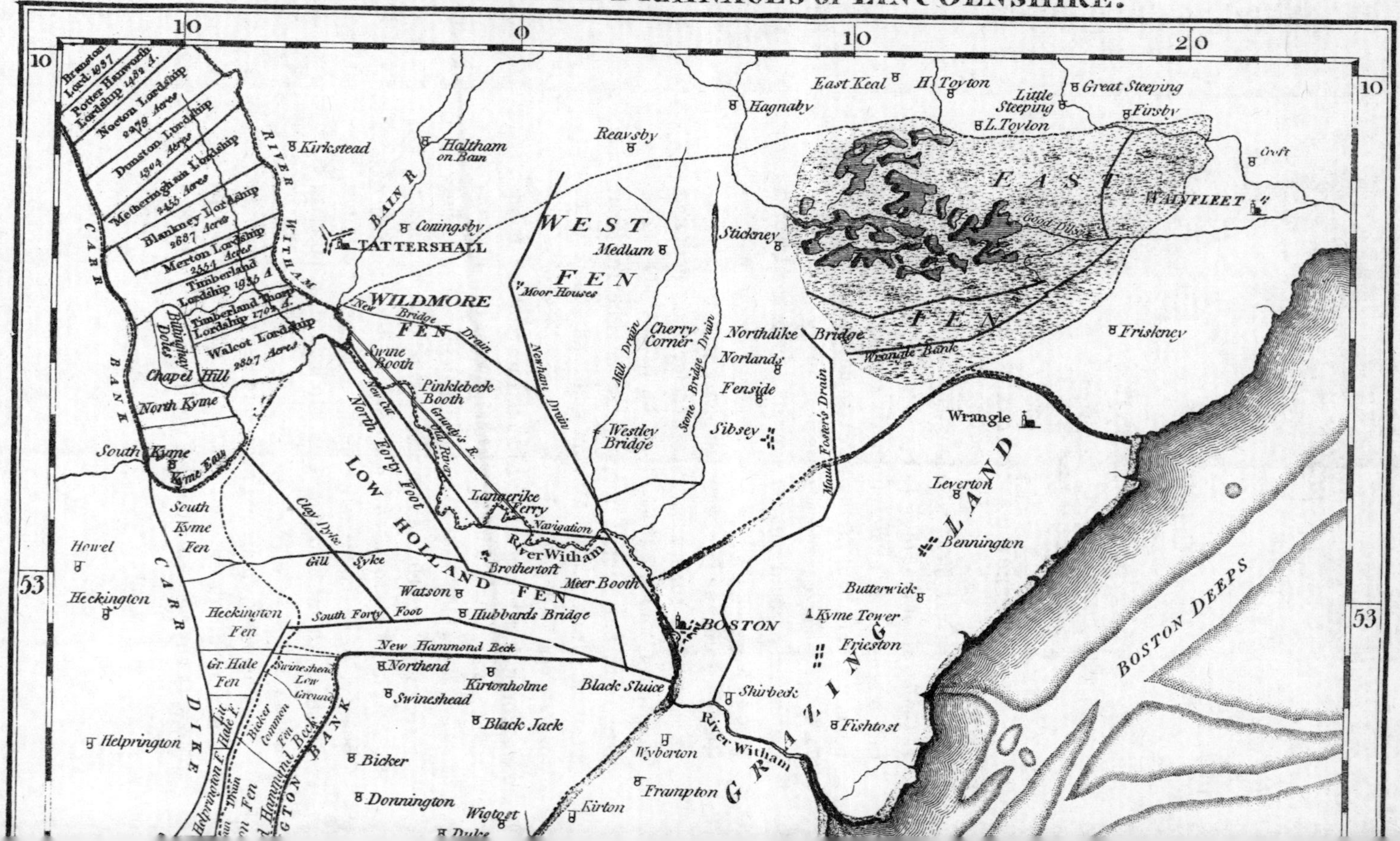

10
0
10
20
10
10
53
53

Branston Lord. 1937
Potter Hanworth Lordship 1483 A.
Nocton Lordship 2279 Acres
Dunston Lordship 1904 Acres
Metheringham Lordship 2455 Acres
Blankney Lordship 2687 Acres
Merton Lordship 2554 Acres
Timberland Lordship 1935 A.
Timberland Thorp Lordship 1705 A.
Walcot Lordship 2867 Acres
Billinghay Doles
Chapel Hill
North Kyme
South Kyme
Kyme Eau
CARR BANK
CARR DIKE
RIVER WITHAM
Kirkstead
Haltham on Bain
BAIN R.
Coningsby
TATTERSHALL
WILDMORE FEN
New Bridge
Drain
Moor Houses
WEST FEN
Medlam
Reavsby
Hagnaby
East Keal
H. Toyton
Little Steeping
L. Toyton
Great Steeping
Firsby
Croft
EAST FEN
WAINFLEET
Good Dike
Wrangle Bank
Friskney
Stickney
Cherry Corner
Mill Drain
Stone Bridge Drain
Northdike Bridge
Norland
Fenside
Sibsey
Westley Bridge
Maud Foster's Drain
Newham Drain
Kyme Booth
Pinklebeck Booth
New Cut
Grundy's R.
Old River
North Forty Foot
Langrike Ferry
Navigation
River Witham
Brothertoft
LOW HOLLAND FEN
Clay Dyke
Gill Syke
Watson
Meer Booth
Hubbards Bridge
South Forty Foot
South Kyme Fen
Howel
Heckington
Heckington Fen
Gr. Hale Fen
Lit. Hale F.
Swineshead Low Ground
Bicker Common Fen
Hammond Beck
Helprington F.
Drain
Fen
Helprington
New Hammond Beck
Northend
Kirtonholme
Swineshead
Black Sluice
Black Jack
Bicker
Donnington
Wigtoft
Duke
BANK
BOSTON
Shirbeck
River Witham
Wyberton
Frampton
Kirton
Fishtost
Frieston
Kyme Tower
Butterwick
Bennington
Leverton
Wrangle
GRAZING LAND
BOSTON DEEPS

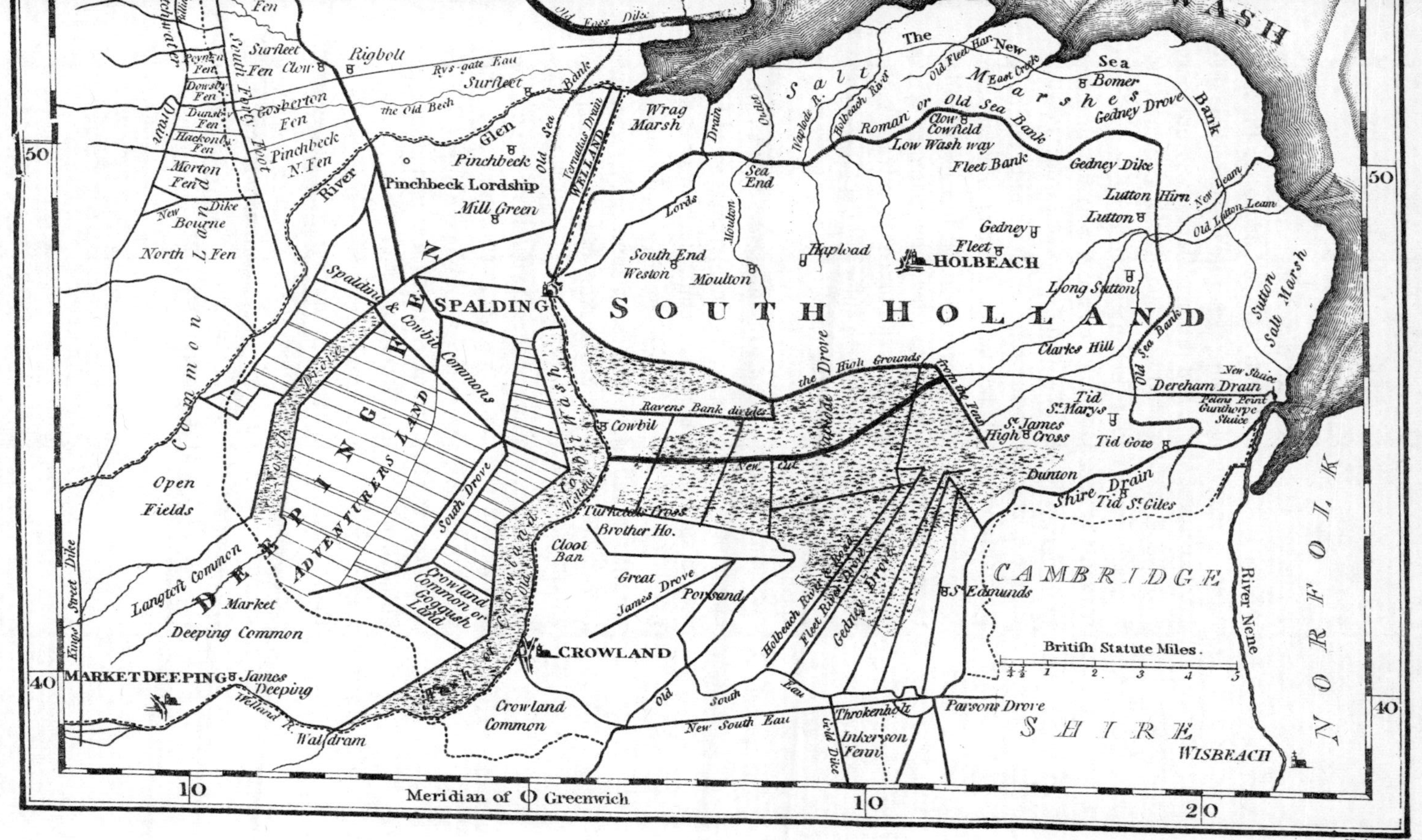
WASH
SOUTH HOLLAND
DEEPING FEN
ADVENTURERS LAND
CAMBRIDGE SHIRE
NORFOLK
SPALDING
HOLBEACH
CROWLAND
MARKET DEEPING
WISBEACH
Pinchbeck Lordship
Pinchbeck
Mill Green
Glen
Surfleet
Rigbolt
Gosberton Fen
Pinchbeck N. Fen
Morton Fen
North Fen
Bourne
Wrag Marsh
Salt Marshes
Roman or Old Sea Bank
Low Wash way
Fleet Bank
Gedney Dike
Gedney Drove
Lutton Hirn
Lutton
Gedney
Fleet
Long Sutton
Sutton Salt Marsh
Clarks Hill
Dereham Drain
Tid St. Marys
St. James High Cross
Tid Gote
Dunton
Shire Drain
Tid St. Giles
St. Edmunds
River Nene
Parsons Drove
Throkenholt
Inkerson Fenn
New South Eau
Old South Eau
Crowland Common
Cloot Ban
Brother Ho.
Great James Drove
Porsand
Cowbil
Ravens Bank divides
Spalding & Cowbil Commons
South Drove
Crowland Common or Goggush Land
Open Fields
Langtoft Common
Deeping Common
James Deeping
Welland R.
Waldram
Kings Street Dike
Common
Weston
South End
Moulton
Hapload
Sea End
British Statute Miles.
Meridian of Greenwich
Neele sc.

conductor of water in all directions; so that when the main drains of the country are full of water, the *soak* must lie high in the land, even through the whole distances between drain and drain. Hence it is obvious, that the lower the land is situated, the later must be its seed time; and I presume that many parts of the fen must be incapable of so complete a natural drainage in winter, as to bear the plough at that season. Possibly the use of engines in the form of windmills might be profitably extended beyond the limits hitherto contemplated. I have not heard of their being intended to do more than relieve the surface from water; whereas they might perhaps be employed to advantage in keeping down the soak to a sufficient depth below the surface, to prevent the *chill*, and to forward the spring seed time.

"But the inconvenience of this under-ground circulation of water in winter, is much compensated by its uses in spring and summer; and I have reason to believe that the *salt* with which, as already observed, the *silt*, as well as the top-soil is impregnated, contributes much to the activity of the water's summer circulation; and particularly operates in the most advantageous manner in dry seasons; when it raises moisture in this soil to a much higher level than on any other soil, not of a saline quality, would be the case. It was in the course of last summer that I first noticed the peculiar attraction of moisture from the ditches, to a much higher level above the surface of the water in the same, than I had been accustomed to observe in other soils. Just at the time the cause of the phenomenon struck me, a circumstance presented itself which confirmed the opinion. In the face of a new cut ditch, where the moisture had in general been attracted to *a considerable*

derable height, I perceived that in one particular spot, the attraction had raised it *much* nearer to the surface. Immediately prior to the cutting of this ditch, I had, in an experiment, dug in this spot to the depth of two feet or more, and having thrown back the earth into its place again, it now formed a loose porous mould, much less compact than the soil adjoining. Soon after, in a field sown with barley, and in a spot more inclining to sand than the rest, there was a low pan, into which water had flowed by a small grip or gutter from an adjacent ditch, where I had a farther opportunity of observing how very powerfully the soil attracted moisture, and to what an uncommon height from the level of the adjacent water it was thereby raised. It was only a very small spot in the centre of the pan, where the fluid was seen in the form of *water;* but the surface of the land for many yards around was perfectly and visibly *wet;* at a level not less than twenty inches, as I should imagine, above the surface of that water. In some of the furrows, I remarked a white powder-like appearance, which upon examination proved to be salt, and was easily distinguished as such by the tongue.

"It has been remarked of this district, although retaining its ancient name of *fen*, that upon the whole it is liable to suffer more in summer from *want of water*, than in winter from a superabundance; for any thing in the nature of a *flood,* to which the valleys in other parts of the kingdom are so much exposed, has been unknown in this neighbourhood, ever since the grand system of drainage took place. But I incline to think that the foregoing remark has been founded only in the *visible* want of water for the *cattle*, when, upon a drought, the great drains become very shallow,

and

and the *soak*, or water retained in the earth, passes in a great measure, off through the filtering stratum of silt; at which time we must dig deep to find the fluid in the form of *water*. But even in such seasons of drought, I conceive the earth, by means of its *saline* quality, to attract and retain so much of the fluid, in the form of *moisture*, as to be of the greatest use in refreshing and feeding the roots of corn. Hence the weighty crops of grain we get in very dry seasons, when other soils through drought become comparatively barren. Hence also the importance of correcting every top-soil of a stiff and too tenacious clay, with silt enough to render it pervious to the moisture from below. A crop of barley in the late droughty season, on the land above-mentioned, which I estimate at seven quarters an acre, seems to confirm this reasoning.

" My potatoes also, and my cabbages, contrasted with my rape, may possibly throw farther light on the question. In 1793, and again in 1794, both potatoes and cabbages grew and flourished remarkably, notwithstanding *severe drought:* while my rape, in both seasons, failed very much. In 1793, it was sown *thrice*, and in the first week of September the field was like a mere fallow; except where the potatoes were, then in full luxuriance; never from the first setting having shewn the smallest check in their growth, or the least symptom of wanting moisture. The potatoes, deposited *under furrow*, and the cabbage plants, by means of their *long roots*, reached levels to which the moisture was powerfully attracted by the salt in the soil; the rape-seed, sown on the surface of the fallowed land, could not be harrowed in deep enough to receive the same benefit; and possibly its oily quality may be a *repellent* of moisture, and so add to the grievance of

a very

a very dry season. Hence I am cautioned against *late* sowing of rape-seed, and against working my fallows with defective implements, so as to promote the evaporation of their moisture for want of dispatch in this necessary operation. I know not how cabbages and potatoes have succeeded this year, and the last, in other parts of the country where there was *equal drought*, but *not a saline soil:* if they had equal drought, but did not flourish as mine did, the fact will corroborate my argument in respect to *attraction:* if they did stand as great droughts as mine did, and flourished equally well, it will be a striking proof of the immense value of those plants in husbandry."

Matthew Allen, of Brothertoft, before the enclosure and draining of Holland Fen, paid 20*s*. rent for a cottage and croft. His stock on the fen was 400 sheep, 500 geese, seven milch cows, ten or twelve young horses, and ten young beasts. Such a person, if ever one was heard of, must have been injured by an enclosure; for never could be known a more perfect contrast between the rent and stock of a holding. He now rents about 50 acres of the enclosure at 25*s*. an acre; has a wife, five children, and two servants, and greatly prefers his present situation, not only for comfort, but profit also.

Mr. Hoyte, of Osbornby, has made some drains that have laid several of his fields dry, at a onsiderable expense; he has changed the course of the water in some instances; and by means of irrigation, has converted his worst enemy into his best friend; where necessary, he has made also hollow drains, with sides of stone and capped, and the cavity filled with small ones: by such means he has converted some boggy spots into sound meadow.

 In

In that long reach of fen, which extends from Tattersal to Lincoln, a vast improvement by embanking and draining, has been ten years effecting. The first Act passed in 1787 or 1788; and through a senseless opposition, an extent of a mile in breadth was left out, lest the waters should in floods be too much confined, and the other side of the river overflowed: better ideas, however, having taken place, a new Act to take in the land to the river, has passed. This is a vast work, which in the whole has drained, enclosed, and built and cultivated, between 20 and 30 square miles of country (including the works now undertaking). Its produce before little, letting for not more than 1*s*. 6*d*. an acre, now from 11*s*. to 17*s*. an acre.

Mr. Chaplin had 300 acres of this, which were never lett for more than 10*l*. a year; now he could lett it at 11*s*. or 12*s*. per acre; probably more. What an improvement over a country twelve or fourteen miles long, and from two to three broad!

It is subject to the tax of 1*s*. an acre to the Witham drainage; and not exceeding 1*s*. 6*d*. to its own; but this is not more than 1*s*. Land here now sells at 25*l*. an acre. This vast work is effected by a moderate embankment, and the erection of windmills for throwing out the superfluous water. The best of these, which cost 1000*l*. erecting, Mr. Chaplin, of Blankney, who is a large proprietor here, and keeps 300 acres of fen in his own hands, as well as 400 of upland, had the goodness to shew me, and ordered to be set to work. The sails go 70 rounds, and it raises 60 tons of water every minute, when in full work. The bucket wheel in the mills of Cambridgeshire are perpendicular without the mill; this, which is called *dritch*, has it in a sloping direction, in an angle of about 40 degrees, and

and within the mill. It raises water four feet. Two men are necessary in winter, working night and day, at 10*s*. 6*d*. each a week, with coals for a fire; add the expense of repairs, grease, and all together will amount to 2*l*. per cent. on the 1000*l*. first cost. Mr. Eckard of Chelsea and Dover-street, was the engineer. It drains 1900 acres. Two years ago the floods overtopped the banks, and it cleared the water out so quickly, that not a single year was lost. The management in cultivating this fen has been,

1. Pare and burn for cole, which has been worth from 40*s*. to 60*s*. an acre. A few have seeded three quarters an acre.
2. Oats.
3. Oats; from eight to nine quarters an acre each.
4. Seeds for three years.
5. Pare and burn for cole; but as thin as possible: others after the seeds fallow for cole; and wheat has been taken by others; by some with good success.

Mr. Hill, tenant to Mr. King, has had five quarters of wheat an acre, having dibbled it; and when I was there had a crop; but though the ears are very long and full, yet it is not a great produce, being too thin. This gentleman informed me, that nothing would do here but paring and burning; he has fallowed instead of it, but cannot get nearly so good layers without that operation. The soil in this fen is a light peat moor, three to six and more feet deep, upon a whitish silty clay, as described to me.

In the north part of the county, the drainage of the Ankholm is another great work, extending from Bishop Bridge to the Humber, in a curved line; but by an

Act

Act passed about 33 years ago, was carried in a straight line through the level, for the purposes of draining and navigation. Before the draining, it was worth but from 1*s.* to 3*s.* 6*d* per acre; now it is from 10*s.* to 30*s.* Much of it arable, and much in grass.

The low lands that are taxed to the drainage amount to 17,197 acres; the tax amounts to 2149*l.* per annum, or 2*s.* 6*d.* an acre. It is now chiefly pasture and meadow; but the *cars*, which were rough and rushy, have been pared and burned, and sowed with rape for sheep; and then with oats for a crop or two; and on the better parts some wheat, then laid to grass: there is not a great deal kept under the plough.

Mr. Thorpe, at Kirton, has made some hollow-drains filled with stone, to cut off some springs, done in a very effective manner; but apparently more of them than necessary for the purpose. I saw the same thing on the fine farm of Mr. Moody at Riseholm.

About Normanby, Burton, &c. there are many lands that would be much improved by draining the springs; but nothing yet done in it.

Revesby.—Sir Joseph Banks has made an experiment here, founded upon Mr. Elkington's reasoning; and which he undertook as a trial, to convince him whether or not he had made himself master of Elkington's mode of drainage, when he attended him as one of the Committee of the Board of Agriculture.

Sir Joseph's house stands in a park situate on the root of these hills, which as they rise higher, become the Wolds of Lincolnshire.

The great West Fen is south of him about a mile distant; and the high-water mark there is about sixty feet lower than the site of his house.

Behind the house the slope of the hill rises gradually, and

and the highest part of the park is about eighty feet above the house.

About forty feet above the house a small spring had been long known to issuse into the side of a pond; but its produce was trifling, not being more than a pint in a minute; so that although some unsuccessful attempts had been made to increase it, by digging in order to get a supply of water for the house, it had been totally abandoned by his father.

On this hill-side, about the level of the spring, Sir Joseph commenced his operations in 1795; and concluding the whole hill-side must contain water, he began to bore in various parts in order to examine.

He found the hill to consist of coarse Norfolk marl, from eleven to thirteen feet thick; and under that, every where of solid blue clay.

He deduced from thence, that all the rain which sinks into the hill, must descend down its slope upon the surface of the blue clay, working its way gradually through the permeable stratum above it, and standing in that permeable stratum at a higher or a lower level, according to the wetness or dryness of the season.

He found this reasoning justified by the state of the water in his bore-holes, all of which were carefully plugged, and frequently examined. The season was very dry; and it rose in them to different heights, the surfaces of which made a curve somewhat conformable to the slope of the hill, though not so much so as he expected.

He fixed upon a point about thirty-seven feet above the level of his house, where the water stood within less than four feet of the surface; and from thence he carried a line of bore-holes along the side of the hill, gradually, but gently ascending.

Having

Having examined the height at which the water stood in these bore-holes, he began a trench, sinking it, in the first instance, eight feet below the surface of the earth, which is four below the height to which the water then rose; and he contrived the bottom of his trench in such a manner as generally to be about six feet below the surface of the earth, and never less than two and a half or three below that of the water in the bore-holes, which were about two chains asunder.

At the bottom of this drain, which was covered as it was made, he put a brick channel, one brick across, and one or two on each side, as the ground was more or less firm, and he dug it in the whole about twenty-six chains long.

From the lowest end of this trench a channel is brought down the hill till it comes to the surface: here the water is collected in a wooden spout, and falling into a little pit dug for the purpose, from the bottom of which it is also conducted away lower down, it is easy at any time to measure the produce of this artificial spring.

When I saw it, the season had been remarkably wet, which no doubt increased very materially the quantity of water yielded by it; and it had been so lately finished, that no opportunity of measuring the quantity produced in a dry season had occurred.

It yielded twelve gallons in a minute, and formed a very respectable rill, which emptied itself into a fish-pond about fourteen chains below. A little above the place where it first issues from the earth, the channel made to contain it had bent, owing to the additional quantity of water procured by lengthening the trench in the course of the last winter, and had formed a complete quaking-bog, in the midst of firm dry land; the

rushes

rushes which had already appeared, were matted with the grass, and capable of bearing a small animal; and the water, which issued from little holes, brought with it that ferruginous matter which is often deposited by bog springs.

This Sir Joseph calls a synthetical bog; and says, he flatters himself he shall become master of Mr. Elkington's mode of drainage soon, as he had succeeded in a synthetical, as well as in an analytical experiment.

The slope of this hill for about three miles is in his possession, and he supposes, that if he was to make a trench for that length upon the surface of the blue clay, puddle the lower side of it, where any inequality in the surface of the blue clay rendered it necessary, and put a three-feet brick arch in the bottom of his drain, he could, by taking the whole soakage of the hill, produce a river capable of turning a considerable mill, or of supplying many miles of navigable canal with sufficiency of water in the driest seasons.

Sir Joseph declared to me, that he never should have thought of this experiment, had it not been for the conversations he had with Elkington; and he insisted that the whole merit of it should be placed to Elkington's account: he is confident, he says, that his father, who resided in the country, and who spent some money in search of water at a high level near the spring mentioned before, would willingly have given a thousand pounds for the run of water he has now obtained. Indeed it is very unlikely that any gentleman of opulence, who has not a spring near him at a higher level than the site of his house, would bid less money at market for such a spring, 37 feet above his level, and 37 chains only from his house, could it be obtained by purchase.

About

About Mavis, Enderby, Bolingbroke, &c. the wetness of the sides of the hills is lamentable: bogs are so numerous, that he is a desperate fox-hunter, who ventures to ride here without being well acquainted with the ground. I have rarely seen a country that wants exertions in draining more than this. Many similar springy sides of hills are to be met with all the way to Ranby, and thence by Oxcomb to Louth.

Mr. Parkinson's Table of the Improvements in Drainage, by Acts in which he was a Commissioner.

	Acres.	Improved Value.	Old Value.	Improvement.
	£.	£.	£.	£.
Tattersal embankment	892	838	387	450
Alnwick Fen	1097	703	54	648
The nine embanked fens to Lincoln	19,418	15,534	1941	13,592
Holland Fen, eleven towns	22,000	25,300	3600	21,700
	43,407	42,375	5982	36,390

Upon the subsidence of drained fens Mr. Elmhurst remarks, that by draining, ploughing, and consolidating the particles, the lands are (eighteen *inches)* lower than they *appeared* to be, before they ever were ploughed; and that by paring, &c. they have been made *firmer*, and of a *more solid* texture, than they were before, and of course lower. So it will be very difficult for any one to *prove*, that *any of those lands* have been *really* reduced and lowered (eighteen inches) *entirely* by the *fatal* practice, and reprobated mode of burn-bating.

By the annexed Map of the drainages in the south-east district of the county, united with the improvements

on

on the Ancholm, and in Axholm, it will appear that there is not probably a county in the kingdom that has made equal exertions in this very important work of draining. The quantity of land thus added to the kingdom has been great; fens of water, mud, wild fowl, frogs, and agues, have been converted to rich pasture and arable, worth from 20*s*. to 40*s*. an acre: health improved, morals corrected, and the community enriched. These, when carried to such an extent, are great works, and reflect the highest credit on the good sense and energy of the proprietors. Without going back to very remote periods, there cannot have been less than 150,000 acres drained and improved, on an average, from 5*s*. an acre to 25*s*.; or a rental created of 150,000*l*. a year. But suppose it only 100,000*l*. and that the profit has on an average been received during the period of thirty years; the rental has in that time amounted to three millions, and the produce to near ten; and when, with the views of a political arithmetician, we reflect on the circulation that has attended this creation of wealth through industry; the number of people supported; the consumption of manufactures; the shipping employed; the taxes levied by the State; and all the classes of the community benefited; the magnitude and importance of such works will be seen; and the propriety well understood of giving all imaginable encouragement and facility to their execution. These are the results of that Government, which so many living and fattening under its protection, wish to exchange or hazard, for speculative legislation of a more popular cast. Early in the days of republican France, decrees issued for draining marshes: I do not ask, what progress has been made? but I would demand, if any drainages equal to this

have

have been executed in that kingdom during a century? From Bourdeaux to Bayonne, in one of the finest climates of Europe, nearly all is marsh. What Frenchman has been so actuated by the blessings of republican security, as to lay out one Louis on that or any other marsh or bog? These undertakings prove the reliance of the people on the secure possession of what their industry creates; and had it not been for common-rights, all England would long ago have been cultivated and improved; no cause preserves our wastes in their present state, but the tenderness of Government in touching private property. A farming traveller must examine this country with a cold heart, who does not pray for the continuance of a system of legislation which has tended so powerfully to adorn, improve, and cultivate the country, and to diffuse prosperity and happiness through the whole society.

SECT. II.—PARING AND BURNING.

Practised with great success in Deeping Fen. Mr. Graves, of Spalding, sows coleseed on this operation, which he performs with a plough. He finds horses and ploughs, and puts out the labour, including a ploughing to turn in the ashes, at 7*s*. an acre; the cole is fed with sheep, and is worth 3*l*. an acre, but selling price 40*s*. to 50*s*. Then oats 8 qrs. an acre, and has had 10 qrs.; then cole and oats again; and being laid down with 14 lb. white clover, and one peck of ray, the grass would lett at 20*s*.; this is found a great and permanent improvement. And that this is a low estimate, appears from its keeping five

five sheep an acre from Lady-day till Michaelmas, and one acre and a half in winter. Where then is the supposed mischief of paring and burning*?

But little pared and burned in Holland Fen.

A great field for this improvement in Lincolnshire, has been Lincoln Heath; in that long range of high country which extends from Stamford to the Humber, a vast number of lordships have been enclosed in the

* Many objections have been made to this practice in the fens, particularly that it reduces the soil greatly, visible in the sinking of drained lands that have been pared; but it is remarked, that a series of ploughing and cropping stiffens, concentrates, and diminishes, the lighter kinds of fen soils, and that the stratum of black peat earth, which, on their first breaking up, was considerably deeper than the plough ran, has been, within the memory of the present occupiers, without any fresh paring and burning, so far reduced, that without taking more mould, or ploughing deeper than they formerly had been accustomed to do, they have not only passed the whole of the black peat stratum, but have ploughed up two or three inches of the clay beneath it: and if it be granted, which I think will scarcely be denied, that the surface of the adjacent depastured fen lands, from the decay of vegetables, dung of animals, and the soil brought thither by the waters from the neighbouring high lands, has been continually, though slowly increasing, there will then appear other reasons for their present different level, than mere paring and burning. It is well known that earth is not to be dissipated by combustion; it is more likely that this appearance proceeds in the first place from the light peaty earth of a fen soil being gradually consolidated by alternate cultivation and pasturage, so as to sink below the level it formerly preserved in its uncultivated state; and in the next place, may it not proceed from the commons gradually rising higher by the accumulation of mud and soil deposited by the upland waters?

A material objection to paring and burning is, that in very dry seasons, when the moisture of the earth is very low, the fire catches the soil below, and causes what is called *pitting*, making great unsightly holes in the bottom of the moor, which with great difficulty are extinguished. About thirteen years ago, a large common at Chatteris in the Isle of Ely, was thus burnt up, sixteen or eighteen inches deep, to the very gravel.—*MS. of the Board.*

last

last thirty years, by Act of Parliament. In the tract above Grantham and Belton, I viewed some lands in the parishes of Londonthorp, Spittlegate, Welby, Harrowby, &c. and found that the mode of first breaking up by paring and burning had been very general: landlords have usually restricted their tenants to do it but once; but there have been some few exceptions, in which it has been executed twice. I found a prejudice against it, but the farmers were so strongly convinced that their profit depended on it, that it was not easy to find tenants who would hire at any fair rent, if they were debarred from a mode they thought so essential; hence it has been complied with. They would not give, on a lease, more than 10*s*. for land that would otherwise lett for 14*s*. if prevented paring; and as long leases are very much sought for, a security that a landlord's estate should not be exhausted in a few years, and then thrown into his hands, there seemed to be no reason adequate to the refusal. Lord Brownlow ties them up to pare and burn but once; to have one-fifth of the arable every year in turnips, and not to take more than two crops in succession of white corn, without a fallow for turnips, or of clover, &c.; but they may pare for any crop, and take two in succession. Those who apprehend that this husbandry is dangerous, should secure themselves by the clauses of their leases; the clause now recited does not seem sufficient to restrain a bad farmer, for by it he might burn for wheat, then ake a crop of oats with clover; plough up that for wheat, and follow it again with oats; after which (to go no further) the land would be in a state not much for the credit of burning. The lands which were shewn to me as proofs of the bad effects of burning, conveyed no such conclusion; they were stated by Mr.

Mr. Abbot, Lord Brownlow's bailiff, as producing on an average 3qrs. of barley and four of oats, if turnips were gained; and this upon the rent of 9*s*. an acre, tithe-free; crops fairly equal to the rent in any part of England, where burning was never heard of. Another circumstance against it was, that in some farms at Welby, rents which seventeen years ago were at 9*s*. were sunk, in 1795, to 7*s*. on this account, in the report of the country, for there was no certainty of the fact. This is marvellous, that land should be burned mischievously so long ago; that *bad times* should follow, when the effect must be well known, if ever it was; and that rents should be lowered, when prices were of a complexion that would not admit of any such effect rationally. Such are the facts I met with against the practice, in a ride taken professedly to convince me of its injurious tendency; not by Lord Brownlow himself, who admits the practice; but by his bailiff, an able and practical farmer.

At Leadenham, paring and burning the heath land at first breaking up was general, there being no other way of killing the sedge and other rubbish; all for turnips, some few have done it twice, the second time after seeds that rested seven or eight years, but this is rare; no objection here is urged against the practice, either by landlord or tenant, and no appearance of it having injured the land.

Charles Chaplin, Esq. at Blankney, has improved a black hungry gravel, between the high lands and the fen, effectively. He grubbed the gorse, then pared and burned, and sowed turnips; then took a crop of oats; after this turnips again, and oats a second time; then turnips again and rye with seeds, which laid two years; broken up again for oats; then turnips; then oats

oats and seeds again, which I viewed, worth 9*s*. or 10*s*. an acre. Here is a very great improvement made without any cultivation, that would not pay as it advanced. Upon the heath land it has also been much practised here, and has not been attended, in Mr. Chaplin's ideas, with any ill effect; though improperly cropping and running the land after it, has occasioned some pieces, intended to be kept in tillage, to be thrown back again to warren; but not resulting from the burning, as is evident from others better managed, remaining good. Price per acre for paring, burning, and spreading the ashes, 1*l*. 1*s*.

North of Lincoln, on the new enclosed heath, all broken up by paring and burning, but now debarred by landlords from being repeated.

In the cold rough clay land behind Gainsborough, when they break up grass, it is by paring and burning; and Mr. Dalton, at Knaith, has observed the husbandry, and thinks it right *on this soil*.

Paring and burning is very common on the Wolds, about Brocklesby, in taking up any old sheep-walk, or gorse cover; and some farmers will do it upon newer layers of ten or twelve years; and the best farmers approve of it when the natural bad grasses come after the sown ones wear out, and the surface is become hide-bound, mossy, and unproductive: price of the operation 25*s*. an acre. I inquired particularly for some fields, if any such there were, that had been ruined by this practice, but though many had been very ill managed, none could be found that were materially hurt. Many of the farms are extensive, and the home-steads very ill situated, so that without this practice they would not know how to manure the distant parts at all.

Mr.

Mr. Lloyd, at Belesby, much against the practice; thinks it unnecessary, and that there are better ways of managing.

On the Wolds near Louth, much practised, and will do it on land that has not been down above five or six years. A good way of performing the operation has been to make the heaps in exact rows in the middle of the lands, to plough close to them when burnt, and then to spread the ashes on the surface of the ploughed land, in order to keep the ashes above, and not below the furrow.

Mr. Kershaw, of Driby, breaks up sainfoin by paring and burning. Upon 30 acres of worn out and old sainfoin, run to rough grass, he did it at a considerable expense, for he was forced to burn it in large heaps; he sowed oats, and got as fine a crop as ever seen; then cole and turnips, which were not great, succeeded by wheat, which was a very fine crop; laid down with this wheat, to white clover, trefoil, and ray-grass, which turned out as fine as possible; before it was not worth more than 2*s*. to 5*s*. an acre; now very fine: a capital and vast improvement, which it was impossible to have effected without paring and burning. In all this account I use his own expressions; but I must add a word to the visionary enemies on mere theory to this admirable practice, to consider well the force of this instance, and indeed of hundreds I have given to the same purpose, before they determine to continue blindly to condemn a practice, because some bad farmers will abuse it. Asking a party of farmers at Mr. Bourne's at Dalby, what was the greatest of improvements for poor land in this country? *Oh! that is easily answered: paring and burning, and sainfoin.*

Mr.

Mr. Elmhurst, near Horncastle, gave me the following account of his practice:

"Upon old and common land, which has never been ploughed, of a strong or cold clayey sort, and full of large ant-hills, the which I have always managed in quite a different manner; and the which I beg leave to mention and recommend. As I ever treat and manage the lands I *rent*, and my *own estate*, equally alike, I shall endeavour to be as concise as I possibly can, and therefore shall not particularize any, or describe any particular lordships, as the same sorts of lands, *i. e.* soil, I ever have used and managed in the very same manner, and by the same mode of husbandry.

"So soon as I have got the plots, or parcels staked out, and perhaps fenced, I lett the piece I intend to break up first to men to pare, the which I *see* to have as well done as may be; and generally about Lady-day that I begin; then so soon as the sods are dry enough, I set in my burners, women, boys, and girls, with my ground-keeper to see that the work is well and *properly* done (going myself at times to see that it is so), though at the distance of from eight to twelve or fourteen miles (the which I *used* to do with *pleasure*; for it is *oft* the *master's eye* that makes the sow fat!); then so soon as a side or screed is well burned, I set men on with digs (or large hoes) made on purpose to dig down, and chop in pieces, all and every ant-hill, great and small, before *any* of the ashes are spread; the which is easily and expeditiously done, if ever so hard; and much more expeditiously and easier for the men, than by *any other* means; when that is done, and levelled properly (as it always is by the diggers as they proceed), I then have the ashes spread, as level

as

as may be, over all the surface; when that is done, and the whole work completed, or that the weather suits by coming a seasonable rain, I set on a large, heavy, close-shod harrow, with two horses only; and have the ground run over once, twice, or three times, as it may require, which breaks the hill clods, already calcined by the sun, and mixes them and the ashes pretty well together; and when the time comes, and the season seems to suit, I set in my ploughs, and lightly *scratch* it over, as it were; for *no* pared and burned land should ever be ploughed *deep* (nor should any kind of manure, whether common or artificial, be *buried* deep); and when the land is so ploughed, and as it is ploughed I sow my rape-seed, and harrow it in; and *then* the whole is done, except *proper* gripping; for there scarcely *ever* comes *any* weeds; but I often hoe, or harrow over *my* rape, where I think it *too thick;* and if the season be not over contrary and unfavourable, I scarcely ever fail of getting a *very* good crop. And I will maintain it, even in the faces of any who seem to be such violent enemies to paring and burning, and who talk in such a glossed-up and theoretical style against it, that there is *no mode whatever* of treating and managing *such* land equal to this, either for quantity of *such proper* manure, cheapness to the occupier, so profitable, or so *good* for the land, as this noble quantity of calcined manure. What these gentlemen theorists may either say or think of *this, my declaration,* I neither know nor care; for it is all a true and *practical* narrative, and a real fact; and facts are stubborn things!

" Then for *further* encouragement, I will proceed and shew in what manner I ever have managed (a *great* number of acres, and for many, very many years) *this* sort of land, the following years (the which I choose to do, in order, if possible, to confute some of their *settled* notions and prejudices against the whole practice of *paring* and *burning*, so strongly and repeatedly urged, and so much exploded). So soon as the land is *dry enough*, I set to ploughing it over a *little* deeper (and *clear)* than before, so as to keep the ashes near the surface (for if *any* manure is ploughed in deep, it is nearly lost); and then when dry enough, I harrow it, so as to mix altogether as well as I can, or is reasonable; that perhaps is in May; then when the *season seems* to suit (from the middle of June to the first or second week in July) I set on to plough it very nicely (for Lincolnshire), laying all the lands equal in breadth (four yards, if not *very wet*, or less if *so*, or *too flat)*, but I ever make it a rule *never* to ridge up, or plough *any* land (so laid out) more than *one* turn, or cast upwards; for it *never* can be drained *so well* if it is laid high, neither is there any occasion for it, when the lands are all narrow and ploughed straight; for then there wants nothing more than reasonable and nice gripping, after the furrows are drawn clean, with a proper plough (one horse) quite through the field; so that by this method, I get a *very* excellent crop of rape the second year; upon which (and *always* the same) I keep a great quantity of sheep hogs, chiefly *folded*, the same as upon turnips, to prevent them from death, by *too luxurious* feeding; and I have, by this mode, been so very fortunate (under Providence), as not to lose a hog in several years together (chance only excepted, such as overthrown or giddy); even by such very rich food! Sometimes I feed wethers and drape ewes upon my *great* crops, and I give *them* larger pieces.

"Now

" Now for the third year:

" I always sow this sort of land, so managed, the third year also with rape; as I then can have the soils and ashes all thoroughly mixed and incorporated together; and the land laid proper for draining, &c. and to my liking (before I grow *any* corn upon it) and in nice order for laying down; then the next spring, so soon as the land is dry enough I plough it, and sow pat, or battle-dore barley; and *never* fail having a very great and yielding crop of excellent and *clean* corn; when that is got in, and the stubbles *well* ate off, I plough the land *well*, and sow wheat in the same way as before spoke to, and harrow well in, drawing all the furrows as clean as may be, and grip neatly and properly (as us Lincolnshire farmers know how!); then in the spring, and so *soon* as the land and wheat are in proper order, I sow a sufficient quantity of good sheep-grass seeds, such as white clover (from 7 lb. to 10 lb. per acre), 3 lb. or 4 lb. of red ditto, 5 lb. or 6 lb. of rib-grass, and from two to four *pecks* of *good* ray-grass seed per acre; and when I *think* the land *requires it*, I run a *muzzled* harrow over the land, once in a place, before I sow the seeds, which make then the seeds fall and lay evener upon the surface; then as the men proceed in sowing, I have it covered with the same harrows, or a bush-harrow (which may suit best), once in a place; and I never have failed having a *very good* crop of pasturage; and *sometimes* I have it mown the next year, if the land should be like to be *too tender* to bear stock. And I ever proceed in the management of all and every piece of land I have; and so in rotation over again, except that I *never* pare and burn a *second* time; nor is there *ever* an occasion, as the lands are both light wold land, or heavy, cold, and strong clays."

Mr.

Mr. Loft, of Marsh Chapel, broke up a walk of *shar* grass, which he cultivated thus:

1. Pared and burned for cole,
2. Oats,
3. Cole,
4. Oats,
5. Seeds.

And he had a neighbour did the same, nearly contiguous, and on the same soil, but without burning; and such was the difference of their success, that if his neighbour had no rent to pay but poor-rates, and Mr. Loft 20*s*. an acre, he would have had treble the advantage.

The Rev. Mr. Allington, of Swinop, has made various observations on the effect of paring and burning; and he is decidedly of opinion, that it is the most expeditious way of bringing any land that has long been under rabbits, or any spontaneous growth, into cultivation, by means of turnips. This operation secures that crop; and when mischief ensues, he conceives it to be owing to a bad and exhausting course of crops. He admits that there are fields in a wretched state, which have been burned; but at the same time, not in a worse state than other fields not burned, but managed in relation to cropping equally ill. The first crop of turnips sometimes is not regular; but well ploughed, this is not the case; when it is a second crop, after one of corn, is usually better; and he esteems a good crop of turnips so much the basis of every thing on these hills, that if a man fails of success afterwards, it is his own fault, generally by over-cropping. On the whole, he considers it, with proper management, as an unexceptionable practice here, and would permit any tenant to do it, with no other regulation than forbidding two successive crops of corn.

At

At Turgundby, I viewed a crop of turnips, which succeeded oats, upon a warren broken up without paring and burning. The tenant I was told came from Yorkshire, and is an enemy to that method; but these turnips shewed manifest want of the influence of fire: they failed for many acres together. Had it been pared, this crop would have been capital; and all succeeding would have repaid the expense amply. The oats, I understand, were a middling crop.

At Stainton, rode through the beginning of some improvements by Mr. Otter (I regretted his absence), on the estate of Mr. Angerstein. It was with great pleasure I saw the effect of paring and burning gorse land, adjoining the warren of Thoresway, which had produced even in this very wet season, so unfavourable to the operation, a fine crop of turnips. I was with my horse's hind legs in gorse, and his fore ones in turnips worth 3*l*. an acre; formed like enchantment in the short space of four months; and yet visionaries remain, who will plead against so admirable a mode of converting a desart to cultivation! By no other means upon earth could this have been effected.

Mr. Ellison, at Sudbrook, has practised this husbandry largely; and one instance I saw of its effect well deserves noting:—he has a crop of rape all pared and burned for; but from one part the ashes taken off, on account of an intended water which was to have been cut through the land; where the ashes were spread as burned, the crop is most luxuriant indeed; worth in this dear year from 4*l*. to 5*l*. an acre; where the ashes were taken away, it is very mean, not worth more than 10*s*. an acre; except in a part near the hedge, where it is much better, probably owing to cattle and sheep having laid there for shelter; but this shews, that

that paring (this was done an inch deep) and burning does not exhaust the fertility lodged in a soil, from various circumstances, for this part of the crop, though by no means equal to the best, is trebly better than the worst part. Whenever such circumstances occur they should be noted, whether for or against a practice; as it is only from a great variety of facts that the merit or deficiency of any husbandry can be ascertained.

Mr. Ellison never breaks up any sort of grass land but in this method, and has every reason imaginable to be well satisfied with it; but it must be old enough to admit burning, which will not be less than ten or twelve years.

1. Turnips, very good, winter eight hogs an acre.
2. Barley, 4 qrs.
3. Turnips, as before.
4. Barley, 4 qrs. or four and a half.
5, 6, 7, or 8, or as it may be, seeds, white clover 21 lb.; 4 lb. cow-grass; 3 lb. rib-grass; and four bushels hay-seeds, clean.

This on sandy land; but on clay land, add another sack of hay-seeds. They will summer four ewes and lambs the first year, from Lady-day to near Michaelmas.

Much heath land broken up by paring and burning at Skellington, Gunby, North Witham, Stainby, &c. and it has succeeded very well; but they have done it only once.

General Result.

1. It appears from these facts, that upon the various soils mentioned, this practice has succeeded to such a degree, as to justify the warmest approbation of the husbandry in the county of Lincoln.

2. That

2. That it has in several cases been attended with a general good effect, even with an incorrect course of crops.

3. That no instance has occurred in this examination, where land has been materially injured.

4. That where it has been attended with an ill effect, it has evidently arisen from injudicious management.

5. That by no other method can waste lands be so speedily, effectually, and profitably improved.

6. That the benefit results from the ashes; as if they are removed, the crops suffer greatly.

7. That the fire has not the effect of dissipating or destroying the fertility resulting from previous manuring; as the crop, after the operation, is proportioned to such previous fertility from manures.

SECT. III.—MANURING.

Fish

STICKLEBACKS in the East and West Fens are so numerous, that a man has made 4*s*. a day by selling them at a halfpenny a bushel. They come from the sea into Boston haven also, and the use of them, whenever to be had, is immensely beneficial: they are the most powerful of all manures. Mr. Cartwright has found them to exceed whale-refuse. It is a whimsical fact, that the farmers of Holland Fen, and also to the east of Boston, reject the use of pigeon-dung, having tried it; and they now sell it to the heath farmers beyond Sleaford. This is singular. Boston haven muddy silt has been tried; Mr. Cartwright has had 1000 loads; upon the first application for rape, it being

being laid on raw, it did not appear to have any effect, or rather a bad one, upon that crop; nor was there any difference in the succeeding oats and clover, and other crops.

It is a circumstance that ought to be noted, as a warning in case of future drainages, that manure brought from Boston on the Witham navigation, pays 1*s*. 6*d*. a ton, from a mere omission in the Act of Parliament; and it is the same whether carried one mile or thirty-six.

Lime.

Lime has been used in small quantities about Folkingham; they burn at the expense of 14*s*. to 15*s*. a chaldron; lay on two and a half per acre for turnips, and the effect does not shew itself in the turnips or barley; but the seeds are better for it. About Belton this manure has been used, limestone being plentiful; they lay two chaldrons an acre, and with good effect, on sand; not on clay. But it will not bring turnips on the heath land.

Mr. Goulton tried lime, limestone, and marl, on pieces contiguous; but there was no difference at all.

Mr. Graburn covered limestone land with limestone, but saw no effect from it: the soil hungry sandy land.

Mr. Bourne, of Dalby, has limed, but does not find it beneficial enough to induce him to do much of it. Mr. Kershaw, of Driby, has laid three chaldrons an acre for turnips, but has not found it beneficial to that crop, unless mixed with earth; but for corn and seeds it does good, though the soil is on chalk. Considering the improbability that lime should be beneficial on a thin soil on chalk, I made particular inquiries into this practice; several farmers confirmed the account.

account. Perhaps the loam is deep: perhaps there might be on the surface of some fields an accidental, rather than an inherent quality, that gave the effect; the expense 30*s*. an acre. It is but feebly prosecuted; not one acre in a thousand. Mr. Bourne, of Haugh, has observed, that when both dung and lime are laid on the same spot, the effect is considerable; the dung has then a greater effect than when laid alone. This should seem to intimate that the operation was by assisting putrefaction, as all the dung on every part of the Wolds is carried long from the yard.

At Claypool, &c. they manure with lime from Newark, eight or ten quarters an acre, at 2*s*. 6*d*. to 3*s*. a quarter. It does more good for the seeds on arable land than for the corn. And upon the red sands at Marston it has had the effect of improving them for barley much.

Mr. Walker, of Woolsthorpe, limes on a large scale; he has used 800 quarters in one year; lays generally twelve quarters an acre, at 4*s*. a quarter, and twenty quarters an acre over twenty acres. It is of little or no benefit to his turnips, but of much to both corn and seeds; the soil flat red sand, much improved by draining.

Mr. Clough, of Gayton, near Louth, limes here, and at Tathwell, on loamy lands, that are the farthest from the chalk, which is under all the country.

At Tathwell, Mr. Hyde spreads three and a half to four chaldrons per acre of 32 bushels, at 13*s*. a chaldron; lasts four years, and does much good for seeds and clover, and sometimes for corn; but none to turnips. Mr. Pearson tried marl, but did no good.

Rape

Rape Cake.

Mr. Bunby, of Temple Brewer, on Lincoln Heath, manures largely with rape cake in powder, which he brings from Gainsborough—the success great.

Marl.

Mr. Dalton, at Knaith, has manured his sand there with blue marl; sixty four-horse loads an acre, which is attended with a very great improvement.

Mr. Clough, of Gayton, near Louth, has a small marl pit on his farm, from which he made an experiment, by marling a part of a field for turnips, and dunging the rest; he carried about twenty loads of it, does not know exactly how many per acre; the effect was equal to that of the dung. At Kelton they have laid it on seeds, and left it some time before ploughing, and it has answered well for twelve years; but it may easily be supposed upon what scale, with men who none of them have leases. Mr. Clough's is a white clay marl.

In the vicinity of Revesby there is a very commendable use made of white blue, and red marl. Mr. Cracraft, at West Keal, has done most of the sandy fields of his farm. He lays forty large loads an acre; and is forced to pay 1*s.* a load for permission to dig it in a neighbour's ground. He spreads it on a sand, which is said to have been infertile before, but highly improved by this manure; before, the turnips ran to *fingers and toes*, and were rarely worth more than 10*s.* or 12*s.* an acre; but now, that distemper disappears as soon as the marl gets mixed with the soil, and the crops are worth 3*l.* or 4*l.* an acre; barley used to produce about two quarters an acre; now five or six. He finds

finds the blue marl the best, and next the white, which however is better than the blue for the red loamy sands. The red is much the worst. Much of his land was a fox cover of gorse: the rent 4*s*. or 5*s*.; now it would lett from 14*s*. to 20*s*. Before he marled, dung was of little worth on the sand; but since, the effect is very great. He has tried lime on land that had been marled, and with effect.

Mr. Parkinson, of Asgarby, steward to Sir Joseph Banks, has also marled a sandy farm largely, and with very great effect; he spreads forty loads an acre. He shewed me a field of 36 acres under turnips, a small part of which, by a mistake of his men, was not marled; and the difference in the turnips is prodigious: where the manure was spread, a very fine crop; but in the spot not marled, they had almost entirely failed, and the land was covered with weeds. I have rarely seen a difference in crop more striking. He has six or seven quarters an acre of barley, which succeed turnips on marled land.

Mr. Elmhurst has practised marling for 35 years with great success.

At Kelston, adjoining South Elkington, the farmers have marled more than in any other part of the country; and no where has the effect been greater: their turnips before were all fingers and toes; but since have been very fine, and free from that distemper.

Bones.

Mr. Sutton, at Alkborough, manured with bones from Sheffield at 5*l*. an acre, sixty bushels; the first year six bushels of wheat more for them; the next it was sown with beans; got a quarter of crop more; this year fallow, and the ketlocks there vastly more luxu-

luxuriant; now manures next part of it with dung, and expects the boned land will equal it.

Mr. Graburn, at Barton, collects bones at 6*d.* a bushel, unbroken; breaks them with two cylinders of cast-iron, with teeth that lock into each other; lays on twenty-five strikes an acre, and has done fifty acres this year; yet the turnips this year not good; but on all other occasions the success remarkable, so that he can see to an inch where laid five years ago. No manure equal to them. Has tried whale-blubber, and the effect great, but did not answer the expense. Has mixed two strikes of ashes with one of pigeon manure, and spreads fifty strikes an acre; the effect is great; it is sure to secure a good crop of turnips, as good as eight loads of yard-dung, a ton each. Soot upon sainfoin, Mr. Graburn has tried thirty bushels, at 9*d.* a bushel, with good success; and finds that yard-manure answers well on it. Also upon seeds, and did perfectly.

Five years ago he manured with thirty strikes an acre of bones, and a part contiguous with eight loads yard-manure, sown with turnips; which after the bones, were much better than any of the rest. On the second year of the seeds, covered the dunged part with yard-manure a second time; and two years after, a third time with yard-manure; then ploughed, and sowed a sack of wheat an acre; and the boned land was rather better than thrice dunging, which was weaker even in straw. It is now turnips, and covered all over with bones, and you may see to a yard where the former bones were laid. Also in a sixteen acre piece he manured part of a field for turnips with bones; and four years after sown with wheat, having been three years under seeds: the superiority of the boned piece is a quarter an acre more than any part of the field.

Silt.

Silt.

Upon the use of silt Mr. Cartwright remarks, "the mode of mixing soils I last winter carried into execution, in a large experiment. I had a field of 24 acres, the top-soil of which was, for the most part, a hungry stubborn clay, of no considerable depth, and very poor. Observing that on these parts of the field I was likely, through the drought of last summer, to have a very bad crop of barley, while, on the borders of the field, furnished with much silt* in making the original ditches, the crop was very heavy: it determined me how to act. Early in the winter I ploughed the field, and as soon as the frost enabled me to lead upon it, I commenced the operation by enlarging the ditches round the whole field both in breadth and depth, and cutting an additional ditch longitudinally through the middle of the field (leaving the head land at each end untouched); I obtained as much silt as I wanted. With a strong gang of teams and men I made the most of my time, for fear of a change of weather; and, with a few interruptions from open weather, accomplished my purpose in the course of three weeks, or less. Although the digging and spreading was done by measure, and the material so conveniently come at, the operation cost about five guineas an acre; for I laid it on abundantly. The crop of beans this year, and the new appearance of the land, satisfied me it was money well laid out. The land, prior to this operation, was not worth more than 12*s*. per acre; whereas now I consider it as cheap at 20*s*. as a permanent rent. It ought,

* It is a fine sand, so called from the upper part of the stratum having in it a portion of loam, which makes it rather slimy when wet. The deeper we dig, the cleaner and sharper the silt.

however.

however, to be noticed, that the stratum of *silt* in this neighbourhood is every where impregnated with *salt*, and consequently superior to mere sand."

Buck-Wheat.

At Wolloughby on the Wolds, for several years they sowed buck-wheat to plough in for manure; and repeated it till conviction was gained that it would do no good. It was tried completely, and given up.

Time of Manuring.

Mr. Graburn, in a field of eighteen acres of wold land, manured seeds in the spring after the barley was off, with yard-manure, eight tons an acre; another part no manure, but in the same manner, in the following spring. The year of the second manuring, stocked early in the spring with sheep; and the bit first manured ate remarkably close and fine, so that the natural grass did not rise; the other was so long with natural grass, that cattle would not eat it; but it was mown to be able to sow wheat, which is now much finer on the first manuring; arising, doubtless, from the manure left by the sheep, and by the preventing the natural grass rising; this was of more consequence therefore than the wheat coming sooner after the dung.

Mr. Skipwith, at Alesby, varies the common practice of manuring for turnips; which is to spread it towards the end of the year, and plough it in, which he thinks bad, as the wash of the winter carries it down below the plough, where much is lost. He ploughs first, and then spreads the dung, which he thinks answers better. Upon land not very dry, I should suppose this could only be done in a frost.

He observes invariably, that where dung is carted for turnips to the land long before sowing, so as to give

give time for mixing with the soil by the plough, the crop much exceeds that which is spread before the last ploughing only.

Long and Short Dung.

Upon poor, thin, gorse, wold land, Mr. Goulton has remarked, that upon a piece of turnips, where manured with long dung fresh from the yard, the crop is not nearly so good as where manured with short dung, made the year before: the difference striking; nor is the corn so good sown after those turnips.

The best farmers at Wintringham are of opinion, that laying yard-dung on heaps is very bad; much better to cart it once to the land. And Mr. Crust remarked, that he has observed, that those who make heaps, and consequently rot it much, never have such a return from their dung as they would by a different management.

Mr. Lloyd is much against hilling of manure, always carrying it *long* from the yard; has made repeated observations on the comparison, and is decided in the result. He remarked also to me, on shewing his farm-yard, that in his opinion, a yard should always be on a descent, for if the straw lies wet, it will not rot; on a descent, it rots as well again: not that the urine should be lost, there may be a reservoir to catch it; his runs to a small pond, which is emptied often on that account. Soap-suds he finds an excellent manure for fruit trees, making them shoot in a manner they never did before. His ashes he is careful to save dry, and finds them to be, by that means, a much better manure: this is well known elsewhere; but it is not common in Lincolnshire.

Mr. Clough leads the dung directly from the yard; never

never hills it, which is utterly disapproved of. No standing sheep-folds to make dung.

Composts.

Mr. Graburn has mixed earth and dung; and some others have done the same; but from whatever he has observed, could never see that it answered at all.

Burnt Straw.

The most singular practice which I ever met with in manuring, subsists on the Wolds; it is that of spreading dry straw on the land and burning it. At Lord Yarborough's I first heard of this custom. His Lordship's tenant, Mr. Richardson, a very good and intelligent farmer, gave me the account, having long practised it with success. The quantity is about five tons an acre. At Great Lumber he straw-burnt a piece in the middle of a field preparing for turnips, and on each side of it manured with ten loads an acre of yard-dung, and the burned part was visibly superior in the crop. In another piece the same comparative trial was made in 1796, for turnips, which crop was much the best on the burnt part; and the next year the barley was equally superior. On another farm he had at Wold Newton he did it for turnips, then barley, and laid with sainfoin; and the burnt straw was better in all those crops than yard-dung. Burning gorse in this manner returns great crops, but the expense is too high. He is clearly of opinion, that it is the warmth from the fire that has the effect, and not the ashes; for the quantity is nothing, and would blow away at one blast. It is proper to observe, that they do not value straw used in feeding cattle, at more than 4*s*. or 5*s*. a ton.

Mr.

Mr. Mallis, of Lumber, is of the same opinion, and thinks four ton is enough; never knew that quantity fail for turnips.

This straw-burning husbandry I found again at Belesby: Mr. Lloyd, who I should observe, is an excellent farmer, thinks that it takes six ton per acre, which will last longer in its effect, and beat the dung which that straw would make; and in general lasts longer than common dunging. Keeping much cattle, he cannot practise, but highly approves it.

In discourse at Horncastle ordinary, on burning straw, the practice was much reprobated, yet an instance was produced, that seemed to make in favour of it. Mr. Elmhurst, of Hazlethorpe, burnt twelve acres of *coleseed* straw on eight acres of the twelve, and the effect was very great, and seen even for twenty years; he sowed wheat on it, four bushels an acre, and had five quarters; the four acres upon which nothing was burnt much the better land, yet the crops on the burnt part were by that made equal to the rest. But in another similar experiment for turnips, Mr. Rancliff observed the result, and the effect, though good, lasted only for one crop. Mr. Kirkham, who was in company, gave it as his opinion, that as cattle would not eat stubble, it might be beneficial to collect and stack that, and before turnip-sowing burn it,

The Rev. Mr. Allington, of Swinop, has cut and carried gorse, and spread it on other land, and burnt it in May for a manuring for turnips: he has done it twice, and it answered very well; but of course it is to be noted, that this is done only when it cannot be sold for faggots, which sell at 8*s*. a hundred, so that the expense would be 4*l*. an acre, as 1000 are produced per acre, and he burnt the produce of one acre upon

 another:

another: the effect was great in the turnips; the barley was better for it; but he has not attended to it in the seeds, because hard stocked with sheep. He has burnt on the land for turnips, the long straw dung from the surface of the farm-yard, and has had better turnips there than where the dung was laid. This has been the case in two experiments he has made.

About Tathwell there is no burning straw upon land; Mr. Clough, Mr. Hyde, and Mr. Pearson, scouted the idea of such a thing being common. It has, however, been here tried; for Mr. Oldham, of Elkington, did it after ploughing for turnips, with long straw *from the yard*, and he succeeded well for the most part.

Oil-Cake Feeding.

Mr. Ellison, at Sudbrook, fattens many beasts every year on oil-cake, and finds the dung they make so rich, that by mixing it with straw-dung, the whole is made good manure. His bailiff carts it out at Christmas; and in April, on to a hill, where it remain still the following autumn; if dry, to spread it on seeds; and if the autumn is wet, to cart it in frosts. While in the hill, turns once. He has tried carting it from the stalls directly to the field, but finds it a bad way, except for strong clay land, upon which it does very well; even for clay he would hill it, if for seeds. Hilling loses much in quantity, but adds greatly, the bailiff thinks, in quality; he puts fifteen or sixteen loads (three horses) per acre.

Remarks.—One considerable benefit of examining the agriculture of any district on the sp t, is the opportunity it affords of gleaning carefully in conversation.

tion. Many able farmers make experiments without minuting them on paper. If they were not drawn forth sometimes, by conversing on very different subjects, the result would die with the men who make them. But such circumstances are too valuable to be lost. What an immense mass of information would be the result, if all such trials and remarks were collected from one end of the kingdom to the other. Experimental certainty would be the result, the cause of all apparent contradictions would be cleared up, and one harmonious system extracted from what at present seems confusion. An effect that never can flow from dissertations; it can arise from nothing but multiplied facts

SECT. IV.—EMBANKING.

SINCE 1630, 10,000 acres have been saved from the sea in the parish of Long Sutton, and 7000 acres more might now be taken in, by altering the channel of the river.

Holland Fen is a country that absolutely exists but by the security of its banks; they are under Commissioners, and very well attended to.

Upon taking in new tracts from the sea by embankment, it is always an object of consequence to know what should be done with the land. There is a new tract taken in by Act of Parliament at Wintringham, and some failures of crops makes it an interesting object. The second year after excluding the sea, they ploughed and sowed beans: but the crop so bad (being in some places for acres together absolutely destroyed), that

that the management is plainly bad. The farmers, Mr. Peacock and Mr. Johnson, attributed it to the salt being too fresh and strong, and probably they are right; however, the spots in the field which were a little dry from inequality of surface, had beans though bad, but the flat spaces none. From observations made in other places, I am inclined to think that the land should be pastured for three years after excluding the sea, after which, ploughing will succeed without hazard.

At Humberstone there is a large piece taken in from the sea by a low bank, which is well sloped to the sea, but too steep to the land, so that if the sea topped it, the bank must break. In these works it is always necessary to provide against high tides, that in case of such rising above the bank, and consequently flowing over it, the bank itself may remain undamaged; which if steep to the land, cannot be the case; it must give way. The marsh taken in is not yet ploughed; indeed it should always remain some years, to prepare it for ploughing.

Great tracts of valuable land remain yet to be taken in from the sea about North Somercots, and other places on that coast; but I do not find that any experiments have been made in Sir Hyde Page's method, of making hedges of gorse fascines, and leaving the sand to accumulate of itself into a bank. Mentioning this to Mr. Neve, he informed me, that he had observed at least a hundred times, that if a gorse bush, or any other impediment, was by accident met with by the sea, it was sure to form a hillock of sand. The extent of sand, dry at low water, on this coast is very great; the difference between high and low water mark extending even to two miles.

In

In the reparation of the banks which secure the marsh land from the sea, the frontage towns are at the expense; but in case of such a breach as renders a new bank necessary, the expense is assessed according to the highest tides ever known, by level over all the country below such level of high water, under the direction of the Commissioners of Sewers; the distance from the sea subject to drainage, will therefore vary according to the level of the country.

An Act of Parliament passed in 1792, for embanking and draining certain salt marshes and low lands in Spalding, Moulton, Whaplode, Holbeach, and Gedney, containing in all about 5339 acres.

South Holland, grossly estimated at 100,000 acres within the Old Sea-dyke bank, has long been an object of embankment. Ravenbank, the origin of which is quite unknown, appears to have been the third which had been formed for securing a small part of this tract from the sea, leading from Cowbit to Tidd St. Mary's. About six miles nearer to the sea is another bank, called the Old Sea-dyke bank, which is unquestionably a Roman work. A very curious circumstance is, that a fifth bank, called the New Sea-dyke bank, two miles nearer than the Roman, remains, but it is utterly unknown when or by whom it was made. The new bank mentioned above, takes in about two miles more in breadth. In taking the levels for making the new drain, it was found that the surface of the country, on coming to the Roman bank, suddenly rose six feet, being six feet higher on the sea side than on the land side, and then continues on that higher level, being the depth of warp, or silt, deposited by the sea since that bank was made. The estimated expense of the drain, 17,985*l*. 8*s*. 6*d*. Sir Joseph Banks (from whom

I receive

I receive this intelligence) has made this note on the back of Dugdale's map, in which no trace of the New Sea-dyke bank appears: "Dugdale's History of Embankment and Draining was published in 1662; hence we may conclude, that the Old Sea-dyke bank was then the outermost boundary of the enclosed marshes. It appears by Hayward's map, published by Badeslade, that it was also so in 1605; notwithstanding the New Sea-dyke is said by Mr. Maxwell to have been made about 1640." The embankment in consequence of the Act of 1792, is nearly completed, and will prove an excellent work to the public, as well as to the proprietors. The drainage of South Holland, 100,000 acres, is in its progress, and will also prove a work of immense consequence; and it deserves noting, that this business goes forward at present, because it is not effected by borrowing money on the credit of a tax, but the capital levied on the proprietors, who have now paid two instalments of 10*s*. an acre each.

An Act passed in 1794, for improving the outfall of the river Welland, and better draining the low grounds, and discharging their waters into the sea. The plan of this undertaking is to cut an immense canal from the reservoir below Spalding, capable of carrying the whole waters of the river Welland, and issuing them into the Witham below Boston. It is expected that the consequence of this will be, not only the drainage of Deeping Fen, and all the adjoining lands, as well as those in Kirton wapentake, through the middle of which the canal is intended to pass, but also that the present bed of the river Welland, and of the Fossdike Wash, will shortly be converted into marsh land of the richest quality, there being a great disposition to warp up in that river; and so fully have the undertakers

takers been convinced that this would be the case, that they have provided in the Act, for making a turnpike road across Fossdike Wash, which they conclude will become perfectly dry. But in consequence of the scarcity of money, arising from the war, they have not been able to raise the money · but it is hoped that the return of peace will remove this obstacle, and set this great work in full action.

The first navigable canal that was made in England, is in all probability that which was made from Lincoln to Torksey; it is evidently a part of the Cardike, an immense Roman work, which served to prevent the living waters from running down upon the fens, and, skirting the whole of them from Peterborough to Lincoln, afforded a navigation of the utmost consequence to this fertile country. That the Fossdike was a Roman work, is fully proved by the discovery of a figure of Mercury, of Roman workmanship, with a Latin inscription on its base, a figure of which is given in Mr. Gough's edition of Camden's Britannia; it was dug out of the mud below its present bottom. It is more than probable that that half of the present Sleaford navigation, reaching to the river Witham, was the second; the stream of Kyme-eau, the water which feeds the navigation, in all probability had its issue at Bickerhaven, near Donnington, an estuary, the banks of which are still remaining. The Earl of Angos, of whose navigable canal Dugdale gives an account in his work on Embanking and Draining, in all likelihood changed its course from its ancient one to its present issue, into the Witham near Dogdike.

The embankments which have been carried on are, upon the whole, very considerable; no country from its relative situation wanted them more, nor does any other

other possess them of equal extent; they are so connected with the great object of parliamentary drainages, that wherever one is found, the other is implied; an idea may be therefore formed of embankments, by inspecting the drainage map.

SECT. V.—WATERING.

THE first irrigation I heard of in the county, was at Osbornby, by Mr. Hoyte; the lordship being enclosed by Act of Parliament in 1796, that very spirited improver took advantage of the capability of some of the lands to be irrigated, and advised the Commissioners to award a power of taking water from a catch-water drain that was necessarily made, and offered to take from his own allotment, some lands reckoned of an inferior quality, because he perceived they would admit of this improvement. He immediately set to work, and built sluices, formed carrier trenches and drains; and thus watered fifty acres, which was performed at an expense of about 50*l*. He has had time to mow only once; the effect such as to prove the magnitude of the advantage, which would have been greater had he been able to have effected a private exchange with a neighbour. And thus this first of all improvements is introduced. The regular stream at the bottom affords water all the year, except in very dry seasons; and the catch-water drain runs all winter, taking the shoot from an extensive range of hills, and bringing in floods much of the finer and richer particles, the washings of those hills, the soil of which is very good. In working the meadows, Mr. Hoyte observed, and effected by the

the cuts, that the water should always be active, never resting; watered three or four days, and then shifted alternately. He watered some sedgy pieces, whenever he could, in frosts, as a means of destroying that weed; it did much that way the first season, and he expected in another to destroy more. On this worst land white clover was brought up, which never appeared there before; the soil a loamy clay, with gravel at three or three feet and a half deep; watered till the latter end of March; turned in ewes and lambs the first week in April, and kept till the middle of May; fed thus 35 acres; five ewes and their lambs per acre, a feeding worth 6*d*. a head at least, the advantage of which was great. Turnips were destroyed, seeds backward, so that this resource was great, and amounted at this first spring to 15*s*. an acre. After feeding, watered directly for a week; and then, in eight weeks, being delayed by bad weather, mowed two tons an acre, on land which never produced much more than a ton on an average: here was, therefore, near a ton of hay, and 15*s*. spring-feed, gained by water; the after-grass much the same. Mr. Hoyte observes, that by thus keeping such a stock of ewes, the grasses of his farm are so favoured as to be a great reservation; and the additional produce of hay is so much addition to the manure made on the farm, which implies a constantly accumulating improvement of the other lands. The increasing quantity of live stock thus secured, must increase the heart and vigour of the whole farm. I viewed these works with pleasure; they are well planned; and great attention paid to catching every drop of water that can possibly be got: no winter runs are neglected; and upon slopes that were laid down in ridge and furrow, the carriers are well levelled, backing the

the angles, to lead from the crown of one ridge to the crown of the next. Such exertions can scarcely fail to find imitators in a country abounding with streams that are perennial.

The river which rises at Binbrook, Stainton, &c. flows through those parishes, and Irford, Swinop, Thurgunby, Hackliff, Barnaby, Le Beck, Brigsley, and Wayth, to Tetney and the sea, has on its banks a range of low ground highly capable of watering at a very small expense; but not one acre done; a neglect that merits the severest condemnation, in a country so full of sheep, and often so distressed for spring food.

SECT. VI.—WARPING.

The husbandry which I am about to describe under this title, is one of the most singular improvements I have any where met with; and far exceeding any other that has been heard of.

The water of the tides that come up the Trent, Ouse, Dun, and other rivers, which empty themselves into the great estuary of the Humber, is muddy to an excess; insomuch that in summer, if a cylindrical glass twelve or fifteen inches long be filled with it, it will presently deposit an inch, and sometimes more, of what is called warp. Where it comes from, is a dispute: the Humber, at its mouth, is clear water; and no floods in the countries washed by the warp rivers bring it; but on the contrary, do much mischief by spoiling the warp. In the very driest seasons, and longest droughts, it is best and most plentiful. The improvement is perfectly simple, and consists in nothing

thing more than letting in the tide at high water to deposit the warp, and permitting it to run off again as the tide falls: this is the aim and effect. But to render it efficacious, the water must be at command, to keep it out and let it in at pleasure, so that there must not only be a cut or canal made to join the river, but a sluice at the mouth to open or shut, as wanted; and that the water may be of a proper depth on the land to be warped, and also prevented flowing over contiguous lands, whether cultivated or not, banks are raised around the fields to be warped, from three or four to six or seven feet high, according to circumstances. Thus, if the tract is large, the canal which takes the water, and which, as in irrigation, might be called the grand *carrier*, may be made several miles long; it has been tried as far as four, so as to warp the lands on each side the whole way; and lateral cuts made in any direction for the same purpose; observing, however, that the effect lessens as you recede from the river; that is, it demands longer time to deposit warp enough.

But the effect is very different from that of irrigation; for it is not the water that works the effect, but the mud, so that in floods the business ceases, as also in winter; and it is not to manure the soil, but to create it. What the land is, intended to be warped, is not of the smallest consequence; a bog, clay, sand, peat, or a barn floor; all one; as the warp raises it in one summer from six to sixteeen inches thick, and in hollows, or low places, two, three, or four feet, so as to leave the whole piece level. Thus a soil of any depth you please is formed, which consists of mud of a vast fertility, though containing not *much* besides sand; but a sand unique. Mr. Dalton, of Knaith, sent some

to

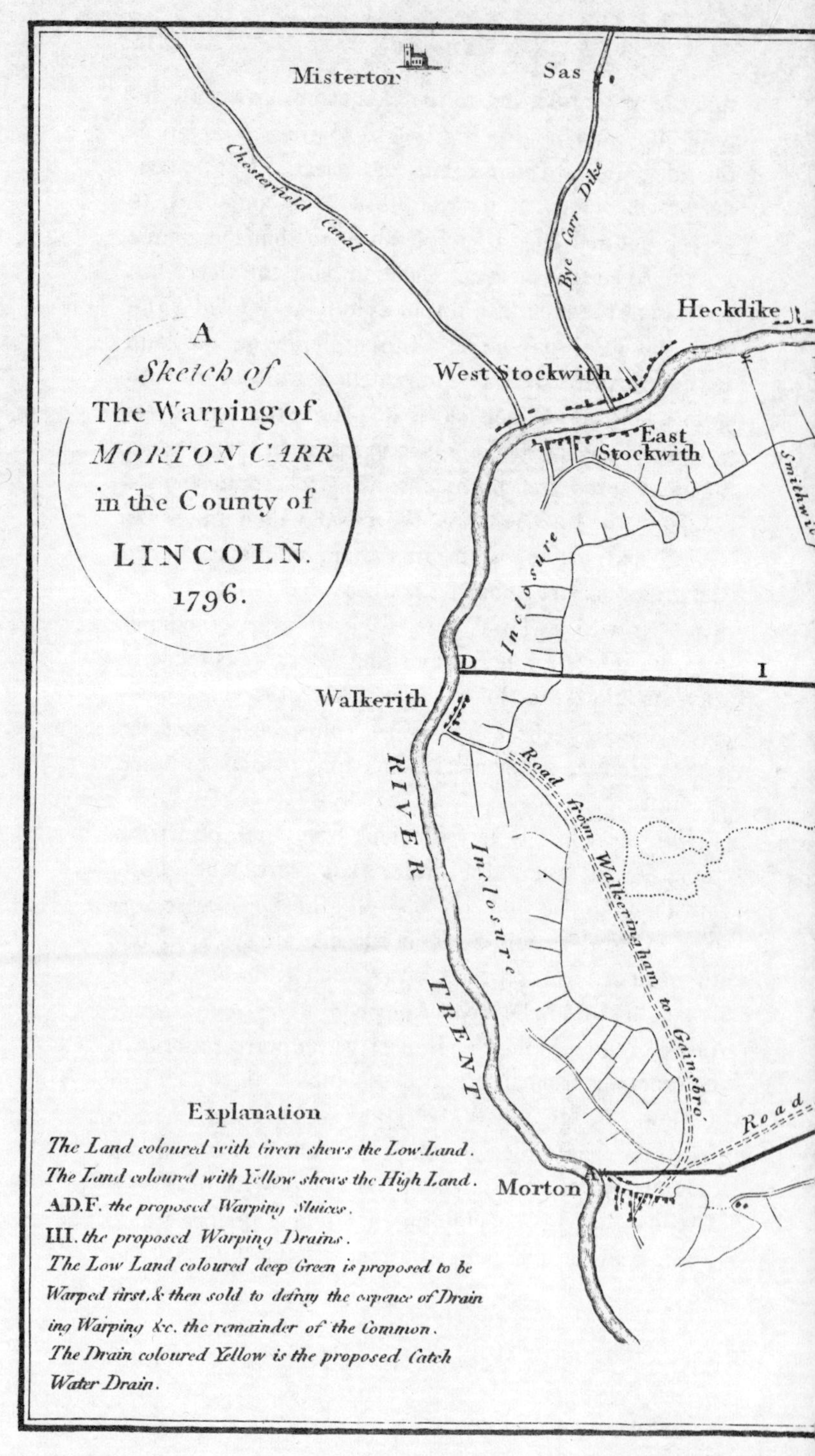
A
Sketch of
The Warping of
MORTON CARR
in the County of
LINCOLN.
1796.
Misterton
Sas
Chesterfield Canal
Bye Carr Dike
Heckdike
West Stockwith
East
Stockwith
Smithwic
Inclosure
D
I
Walkerith
RIVER
TRENT
Road from Walkeringham to Gainsbro.
Inclosure
Road
Morton
A
Explanation
The Land coloured with Green shews the Low Land.
The Land coloured with Yellow shews the High Land.
A.D.F. the proposed Warping Sluices.
I.I.I. the proposed Warping Drains.
The Low Land coloured deep Green is proposed to be
Warped first, & then sold to defray the expence of Drain
ing Warping &c. the remainder of the Common.
The Drain coloured Yellow is the proposed Catch
Water Drain.

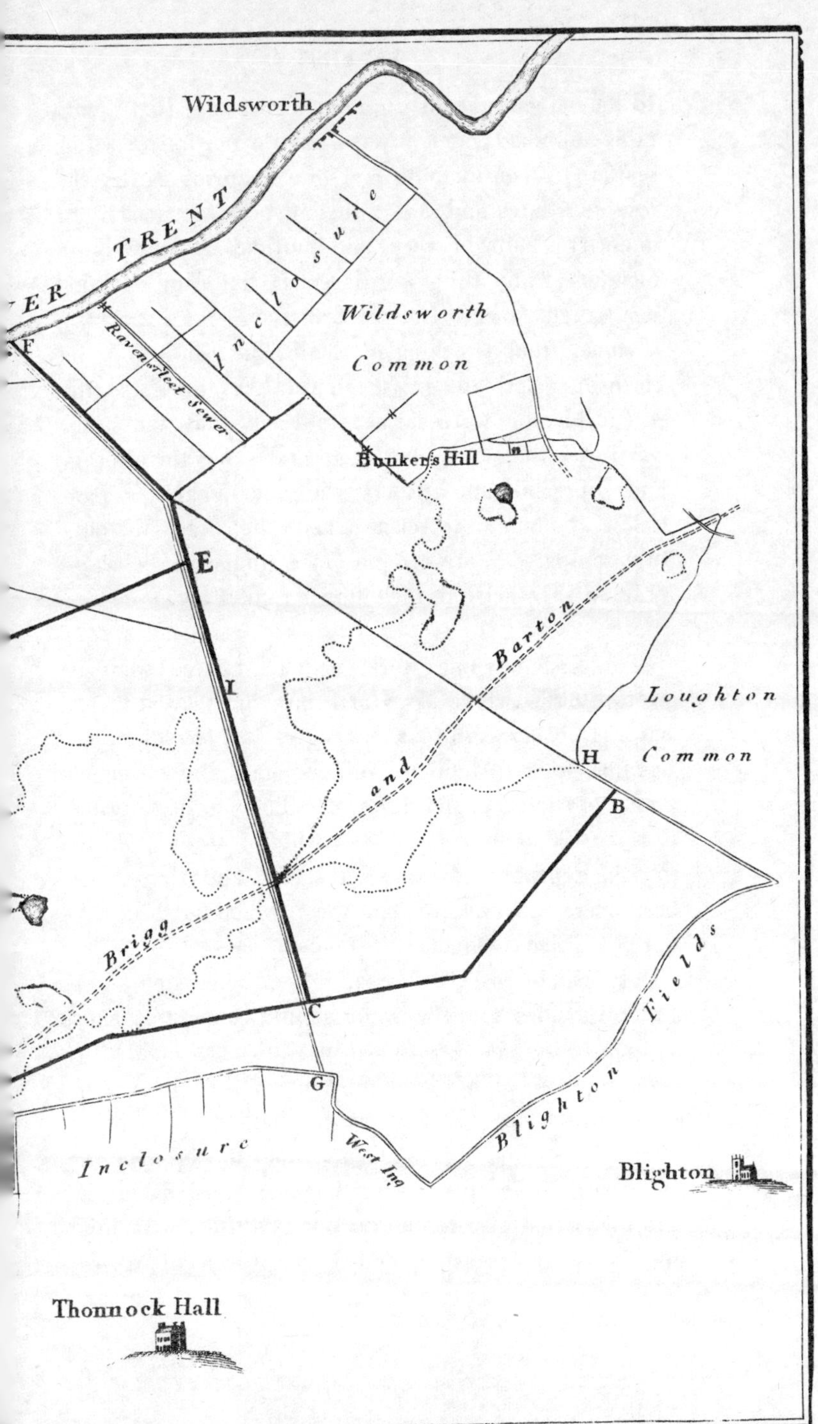

Wildsworth
ER TRENT
Inclosure
Wildsworth
Common
Ravensfleet Sewer
F
Bunker's Hill
E
I
Barton
and
Brigg
Loughton
Common
H
B
C
G
Blighton Fields
West Ing
Inclosure
Blighton
Thonnock Hall

to an eminent chemist; whose report was, that it contains mucilage, and a very minute portion of saline matter; a considerable one of calcareous earth; the residue is mica and sand; the latter in far the largest quantity; both in very fine particles. Here is no mention of any thing argillaceous; but from examining much warp, I am clear there must be clay in some, from its caking in small clods, and from its cleansing cloth of grease almost like fuller's earth. A considerable warp farmer told me, that the stiffer warp was, the better; but in general it has the appearance of sand, and glitters with the micaceous particles. So much, in general, as to the effect: the culture, crops, &c. are circumstances that will best appear, with others, in the following notes taken on the spot.

The first warping works which I viewed were at Morton-ferry, where Mr. Harrisson, who shewed them, has a large corncern in a very great undertaking, no less than to warp 4260 acres of commons, by means of an act of enclosure and drainage. They are attempting to warp 400 acres in one piece, which is to be sold to pay the expense of doing all the rest, and they have been offered 30*s*. an acre rent for it, when finished. A double sluice is erected to take the water from the Trent, which cost 1200*l*.; and a double canal, cut under the idea that the water should come in by one, and return by another; this apparently has created a great expense. They have used fifteen tides over 200 acres, which has raised about six inches of warp in some places, but not uniform: and the opinion of the best informed persons is, that they must divide it into fifty-acred pieces, and do one at a time. All this may be easily corrected, and the improvement will be amaz-

amazingly great. The common is worth nothing, as it has been hitherto fed.

"*To the Proprietors of the Commons and Waste Lands in the Parishes of Morton, Walkerith, East Stockwith, Bliton, Wharton, Pilham, and Gilby, in the County of Lincoln.*

"GENTLEMEN,

"In conformity to your order of the last meeting, we have taken a survey of the above common and waste lands; and find the quantity of land to be about 4260 acres, 2600 of which are low land, capable of being warped, the remaining 1660 acres high land.

"We have taken levels from the lowest land in the commons to Surworth Sluice, and find the fall very inconsiderable, when compared with the expense and inconveniences that would necessarily arise in cutting through so many townships.

"And having also taken levels from the lowest land in the commons, to the Trent at Ravensfleet, we find a fall of two feet to low water-mark; and the lowest land lying so very near the Trent, we think the fall sufficient to make a good drainage, if a provision be made to take off the upland water into the Trent at a high level, which may be effected as follows:

"A catch-water drain should be made from Morton, to skirt the common to G, another from H, to form a junction with the other at G; from thence to be conveyed under the hereafter proposed warping-drains at C and E, and from thence to the proposed outfall at F.

"And considering that the aforesaid low lands, by means of warping, may be considerably raised above their present level, we should recommend a warping sluice to be built at A, near Morton, with two apertures

tures of eight feet wide, and ten feet high each, and a drain from thence to C, and from thence to E, as described by the blue line on the plan.

" Another warping sluice at D, near Walkerith, of the same dimensions as the other; and a drain from thence to E, to communicate with the other drain.

" The aforesaid warping drains to be 18 feet wide at bottom, 26 feet wide at top, and four feet deep; and to have a foreland of four feet, with banks on each side, of 14 feet base, six feet top, and five feet high each.

" Another drain from E to F, the proposed outfall at Ravensfleet, with a 24 feet bottom, 32 feet top, and four feet deep, with forelands and banks as aforesaid.

" The outfall sluice at F, to have three apertures of eight feet wide, and ten feet high each; one for the catch-water drain, and the other two for the purpose of draining the commons, and warping also.

" All the sluices to be laid two feet below low water-mark.

Estimate of the Expense.

Cutting the catch-water drain, 400 chains, or 3696 floors of earth, at 3*s*. per floor	£.554	8	0
Cutting a main drain, or warping drain, from A to C, and from C to E, 258 chains, or 3746 floors of earth, at 4*s*. per floor	749	1	0
Cutting a main or warping drain from D to E, 276½ chains, or 4015 floors, at 4*s*. per floor	803	0	0
Cutting a main drain from E to F, 100 chains, or 1848 floors of earth, at 4*s*. per floor	369	3	0
Carry forward	£.2475	12	0

Brought

	£.	s.	d.
Brought forward	£.2475	12	0
Warping sluice at A, near Morton	400	0	0
Ditto, ditto, near Walkerith	400	0	0
Outfall sluice at F, near Ravensfleet	600	0	0
Road bridge near Morton	150	0	0
Ditto, ditto, at Swansea bridge	180	0	0
Two culverts under the warping drains, at 100*l*. each	200	0	0
	£.4405	12	0
Contingencies 10*l*. per cent.	440	10	0
	£.4846	2	0

"A. Bower.
"J. Dyson.

"*Gainsborough, 4th Jan.* 1796."

At Althorpe, Mr. Dalton is warping 300 acres, which will be converted from a very inferior state to 30*s*. an acre. At Knaith he manured a piece with it for turnips, on a sand soil; the rest of the field with dung; the warp equalled the dung.

At Amcots, there are other undertakings of the same sort.

At Gainsborough, Mr. Smith shewed me a spot that was warped to the depth of ten inches in eight hours; and as I was on the Trent, in Mr. Dalton's boat, I was shewed the way of repairing a breach when a bank breaks: they surround the spot with a new semicircular bank, in order to let in the warp, which fills it up presently; then the new bank may be removed if wanted; but the spot itself of the breach cannot be repaired without a greater expense; the warp forms the junction intimately.

A

At Haxey, in Axholm, viewed some pieces that were warping on the participant's lands; some were done the summer before I travelled, but did not seem well effected. I remarked, that where the warp first came into the pieces, the rushes were clean destroyed. The works seem to be all at a stand.

Mr. Webster, at Bankside*, has made so great an improvement by warping, that it merits particular attention. His farm of 212 acres is all warped; and to shew the immense importance of the improvement, it would be necessary only to mention, that he gave 11*l.* an acre for the land, and would not now take 70*l.* an acre; he thinks it worth 80*l.* and some even 100*l.* Not that it would sell so high at present; yet his whole expense of sluices, cuts, banks, &c. did not exceed 2500*l.* or 12*l.* per acre; from which, however, to continue the account, 1500*l.* may be deducted, as a neighbour below him offers 5*l.* an acre for the use of his sluice and main cut, to warp 300 acres, which will reduce Mr. Webster's expense to 1000*l.* or about 5*l.* an acre. Take it, however, at the highest, 12*l.*, and add 11*l.* the purchase, together 23*l.* an acre; if he can sell at 70*l.* it is 59*l.* per acre profit. This is prodigious; and sufficient to prove that warping exceeds all other improvements. He began only four years ago. He has warped to various depths, eighteen inches, two feet, two feet and a half, &c. He has some that before warping was moor land, worth only 1*s.* 6*d.* an acre; now as good as the best. Some of it would lett at 5*l.*

* This is within the line of the county of York, as well as Rawcliff; but as warping began there, and has been very largely practised, I thought it would contribute to rendering this account more satisfactory, and therefore viewed the works. No mention is made of it in the Reports of that county.

an acre for flax or potatoes; and the whole at 50*s*. He has twenty acres that he warped three feet deep, between the beginning of June and the end of September; and eighteen acres, part of which is three feet and a half deep. This is the worst year he has known for warping, by reason of wetness. He has applied it on stubbles in autumn, by way of manuring: for it should be noted, as a vast advantage in this species of improvement, that it is renewable at any time: were it possible to wear out by cropping, or ill management, a few tides will at any time restore it. As to the crops he has had, they have been very great indeed; of potatoes from 80 to 130 tubs of 36 gallons, selling the round sorts at 3*s*. or 3*s*. 6*d*. a tub; and kidneys at 5*s*. to 8*s*. Twenty acres warped in 1794, could not be ploughed for oats in 1795, he therefore sowed the oats on the fresh warp, and scuffled in the seed by men drawing a scuffler; eight to draw, and one to hold; the whole crop was very great: on three acres of it measured separately, they amounted to fourteen quarters one sack per acre. I little thought of finding exactly the husbandry of the Nile in England. I had before heard of clover seed being sown in this manner on fresh warp, and succeeding greatly.

He warped twelve acres of wheat stubble, and sowed oats in April, which produced twelve quarters an acre. Then wheat, 36 bushels an acre. His wheat is never less than 30.

Six acres of beans produced 30 loads per acre, or 90 bushels; one acre, measured to decide a wager, yielded 99 bushels. Has had 144 pods from one bean on four stalks; and Tartarian oats seven feet high. One piece warped in 1793, produced oats in 1794, six quarters an acre; white clover and hay-seeds were sown with them,

them, mown twice the first year: the first cutting yielded three tons of hay an acre; the second one ton; and after that an immense eddish. Warp, Mr. Webster observes, brings weeds never seen here before, particularly mustard, cresses, and wild celery; with plenty of docks and thistles.

Courses pursued on Warp Land.

1. Beans,
2. Wheat; and this the most profitable.

1. Potatoes,
2. Wheat,
3. Beans,
4. Potatoes,
5. Wheat.

Also,

1. Beans,
2. Wheat,
3. Flax,
4. Wheat.

Flax, 40 or 50 stone per acre.

A sluice for warping, five feet high, and seven wide, will do for 50 acres per annum; and if the land lies near the river, for 70. Costs from 400*l.* to 500*l.*

At Reeveness, warped land has sold for 100*l.* an acre.

Lord Beverley has six or seven sluices going; and has warped so far as 300 acres in one year.

Provision is made for warping a great extent of country by a navigable canal, 40 feet bottom near the Trent, which is making at present from the Trent near Althorpe to Thorne, &c. by which extensive tracts will be done. 24,000*l.* is expended; a branch to Crowle is marked out; and another from Thorne to the river Dun: these for navigation. But it is not by the canal that the warping is done, but by a soakage drain on each side of it, which drains the country, and at the same

same time is capable of admitting the tides to deliver warp to the whol country for twelve miles, by cuts at right angles; and to sell warping on either side. The price talked of is from 4*l*. to 5*l*. an acre And in case the drains should warp up at any time, provision of sluices is made to let water out of the canal into either, to scour them out clean.

Mr. Nicholson, at Rawcliff, takes the levels first; builds a sluice; if a quarter of a mile or half a mile, 60 acres may be done the first year; the drier the season, the better. The clough or sluice 400*l*. eight feet wide, and five or six feet high: a drain fourteen feet at bottom, and as much more at top: 30*s*. to 40*s*. an acre, of 28 yards: banks four to eight feet high, and expense 7*s*. to 20*s*. an acre of 28 yards. Begin at Lady-day till Martinmas; but all depends on season; the depth will depend on circumstances. If a landlord warp, it should be deep at once; if a tenant, shallow, and repeat it; as good corn will grow at six inches as six feet; at three inches great crops; the stiffer the warp the better. Some seasons, sow corn the year after. Warp is cold, and if deep, takes time; a dry year best: great seeds. Crops ought to be, beans twenty loads; wheat ten or twelve loads; oats ten quarters; never barley. After six years potatoes, and good flax: he makes it worth 40*l*. to 50*l*. an acre

1. Oats,
2. Wheat,
3. Beans,
4. Fallow,
5. Wheat,
6. Beans,
7. Wheat,
8. Beans, till it wants a fallow; it will go four, five, six years without a fallow.

Turnips bad; tread and daub too much. Has had it

it twelve or thirteen years without any manure. Mr. Walker, steward to Mr. Twistleden, 40 years ago began this practice, but it dropped for 20 years, till Mr. Fareham, another steward, took it up: many hundreds of acres have been done. It is full as good for grass as for tillage, and made capital grazing land by it; an acre will carry a good bullock, and some two sheep an acre; none in winter till after many years. A kid full of the thick water will deposit an inch in a dry time. Certain that it does not come from the sea, or from the high country, but from the Humber itself. This is on the river Dun.

By keeping up the sluices, and drains, and banks, the land can be refreshed at any time.

Warp land has had crops of flax sold for 10*l*. an acre as it stands; and then they sow rape on good tillage.

I viewed Mr. Nicholson's warped land with much pleasure, and found his warp in some fields to have been deposited from two feet deep at the bottom, gradually shallowing up a slope to five or six inches at the top, forming a level. Mr. Harrad warping on the other side the bank; the tide was in, the morning I viewed it, and a fish-pond and holes were filling up rapidly.

Sand land at Snaith has sold for the plough at 100*l*. per acre.

Mr. Wilson's idea of warping very just; to exhaust the low lands in favour of the hills, then to warp six inches deep, to exhaust that to make the hills; then to warp again; and by thus doing to keep the warp land in the highest order, and at the same time work a great improvement to all the higher grounds.

Note by a Commissioner employed in Warping.—

"Warp

"Warp leaves one-eighth of an inch every tide, on an average; and these layers do not mix in an uniform mass, but remain in leaves distinct.

"If only one sluice, then only every other tide can be used, as the water must run perfectly off, that the su face may incrust; and if the canal is not empty, the tide has not the effect. At Althorpe, Mr. Bower has warped to the depth of eighteen inches in a summer.

"Ten quarters an acre of oats, on raking in the seed on warp; the more salt in it the better; but one fallow in that case necessary, to lessen the effect, or it hurts vegetation."

A very great object in this husbandry of warping, is the application of it in other districts. They have much warp on all the coast from Wisbeach to Boston, &c. and though a long succession of ages has formed a large tract of warp country, called there *silt*, yet no attempts that I have heard of, have been made to warp artificially there. How much the tides abound with warp, may be learned from a remark of different application by Major Cartwright; he observes:

"It is true, that immediately below the sea doors, the rivers warp up in dry seasons to a great height, with a muddy sand or silt, which the tides deposit. The Witham, for instance, sometimes warps up ten or eleven feet on the lower side of the sea doors at the grand sluice; but the first freshes in the fall of the year have always, hitherto, made an early breach, and soon swept this mud bank into the sea. Apprehensions have sometimes been entertained, that in case of a very sudden, and very great downfal, this mud bank might withstand the stream until the banks of the river might give way, and leave the country a prey to inundation. A small portion, however, of engineering

gineering skill seems sufficient to avert such a danger; and perhaps it may in time be found, that the mud so deposited may prove a treasure to agriculture, which it would be bad economy to wash into the sea. Two years and a half ago, I laid several hundred loads of it upon my fallows. I perceived little effect from it in the rape; but the barley and the clover have been as good as that which had the benefit of stable dung. Was I to use it again, it would be in compost; but a most improvident clause in what is called the Witham Act (2d Geo. III. c. 32.) will in future prevent my using that silt, unless on the other side of my farm, to which there is access by another navigation, especially since I have learnt the use of the saline silt of my own land."

Such are the principles and practice exerted in this greatest of all improvements, in which the county of Lincoln is rapidly advancing, greatly to its honour, and most solidly to its profit. I never heard of this husbandry in any oth r part of the kingdom; and if it is considered that so many years have elapsed since its first discovery, it will appear extraordinary that it has not been fully described and explained by our writers and re orters of agriculture. And it might have co tinued to remain in obscurity, like other local practices, had not the Board of Agriculture undertaken the Survey of the ki gdom. But from this time, assuredly, the proprietors of low lands on other muddy rivers will open their eyes to such enormous profits. On the Wye and the Severn, I conceive that such might be found, on which the improvement would be equally practicable; and probably on many other rivers.

CHAP.

CHAP. XIII.

LIVE STOCK.

HERE we enter on the subject which has engrossed more attention in this county than perhaps any other; and one upon which opinions are more divided. Before I examined the county, I determined to keep my mind free from every bias, and to report the facts procured, and the ideas current, with as few comments as possible; concluding that the Board is solicitous to discover, not the opinions of a Reporter, but the practice of a County.

SECT. I.—CATTLE.

ALL round Spalding there are many good bullocks grazed, and in Deeping Fen also; they give from 14*l.* to 20*l.* a head; keep them in winter in stable, on cake at 9*l.* per 1000; making no more than the manure.

Lincoln oxen about Boston, 60 or 90 stone, 14 lb.; they are kept on some lands a bullock an acre, on others two to three acres; on others, one on two acres, all besides sheep. A bullock and six sheep to one acre and a half not uncommon.

About Swineshead, the grazing lands fed with bullocks and sheep; the former bought in at Boston fair, 4th May; and at Lincoln, in April, on an average of seven

seven years, 12*l.* to 12*l.* 12*s.*; sell at 15*l.* after keeping six months.

Mr. Cartwright procured a bull from Mr. Collins, of Durham, in the spring of 1794, being then two years old. I say nothing of the merit, as I have seen very few of these cattle yet.

The Major remarked to me, "that Mr. Thomas Tunnell, of Reesby, near Wragby, has a breed of cattle which are not surpassed by any in the county for points highly valuable, or their disposition at any age to fatten rapidly. His bull covers at a guinea, and has many cows sent to him. The breed originally came from the neighbourhood of Darlington. From two celebrated breeders there, Robert and Charles Colling, breeding stock has lately been brought into this neighbourhood by Mr. Mudd, and the Messrs. Artons, near Lynn; and I also have six heifers and a bull, bought of the Messrs. Colling. I have also procured heifers of Mr. Tunnel's breed. In my choice of this stock, I was induced, from a peculiarity in my grazing land, to prefer animals of *a medium size*, to larger ones. My observations upon stock have strongly persuaded me, that the preference so generally given to *great size* in feeding cattle, is a radical error, and that magnitude becomes a defect instead of a perfection, much sooner than graziers are aware of. The perfections of the animal seem to lie in a healthy constitution; a disposition to feed rapidly *at any age;* a capacity of fattening upon land *more or less rich by many degrees*, in proportion to the value of such land; light offal; the most delicate in grain and flavour; and most abundant meat on the most valuable parts. Although *shape* will be found essential to much of this merit, *great magnitude* can scarcely be supposed necessary

cessary to any of it; and must evidently counteract it in points of consequence. In such cattle as I speak of, the grazier has many advantages. On very moderate land, he may get them fat; and *on the most powerful land*, he will convert a given quantity of herbage into as much beef, as by means of the largest animals, but I imagine more; he is better insured against loss by accidents and disease, from having that risk more divided; and he has a greater choice of markets."

The Rev. Mr. Berridge has a cow which I take to be also of the Durham breed, which is a very fine one of the sort; and if he gets a bull equal to her, he is like to have good stock.

Mr. Tyndall, of Ewerby, has been long celebrated for his breed of cattle; he found them many years ago upon his present farm, which he first occupied, and then purchased; I viewed them with pleasure; for though he has in a very great stock (breeding forty to fifty calves every year), many very unequal, yet some are capital, and merit their reputation. The grand-daughter of the Two-pap cow; the daughter of Bald-face; the red cow; the grand-daughter of the old Blue; and the cow called Wide Hips, are all very fine beasts: the last he thinks the best, and would sell at no price; he would not sell the three former under 50*l.* each, valuing them equally. Apparently they have Durham blood in them; but having been long here, and bred from very old cows, they are called the true Lincoln breed, and may be pure for what I know; supposing these breeds are not originally the same, which there is great reason to believe they are. These cows would any where be esteemed well-formed beasts: they are wide on the hips and loin, have good quarters, clean light bones, thin horns, light dew-

lap,

lap, neat throats, and pretty full in the bosom, with middling spring of rib; and at the same time they shew good milk veins. Wide Hips is $21\frac{1}{4}$ inches from centre to centre of hip-bones, and her quarters the same; length of carcass, from hips to withers, three feet. As to the quality of flesh, and disposition to feed, they appear on feeling to be inferior to several other breeds; I could, however, form in this respect but a very insufficient idea, for of all Mr. Tyndall's cattle, I could feel only these three cows, and that not without danger: they are never handled, and so wild as no approaching them; for a full and satisfactory judgment, you might as well pass over the country in a balloon, as to go into the pastures. No good sign this of any breed; fatness in animals is generally the reverse of wildness. Habit of management will, however, do much in this respect. Mr. Tyndall shewed me a couple of bulls, which I thought very inferior to those three cows; and it is to be noted, that most of the capital stock now upon the farm, was got by a bull that died twenty years old; and some out of cows twenty years old; and a cow now upon the farm, of the same age, is not in the worst class of cattle, and spoken of as having been one of the best. This appeared to me to be remarkable, for it implies that there has, in that period, been but a small, perhaps no improvement; which is what I cannot understand, with a man of Mr. Tyndall's knowledge and experience: I started this observation in company, and was told, that *when cattle are in perfection, they cannot be improved.* Mr. Tyndall shewed me also two oxen of very great size, and a high degree of fatness; one in particular is remarkably fat, especially on the ribs and fore-flank, and quarters, as well as could be judged by the eye, for we could not feel

feel them. This beast was guessed last year at 120 stone; apparently he may weigh now 120 stone; and a very extraordinary beast he will be, if a ton of oil-cake is given him next winter. Colour, white, which Mr. Tyndall prefers. They are six years old, are very wide in the hips; and for so large a beast, bone small.

Several black and white cows of Mr. Tyndall's breed seem to class high for cleanness of leg, throat, and horns; very neat; with light offals.

The system of breeding pursued by Mr. Tyndall, is to keep all his calves; they run with the cows all summer; but many cows have two, and to let the other added have a fair chance, as well as her own, they are coupled together till the cow admits both equally; this leaves a few in milk for a small dairy; for butter and cheese are no objects in this country*; cows seem to be kept chiefly for the sake of breeding; and by this means the calves are pushed on for size as the material object. In winter as well as in summer, all run in the pastures, only they have hay given occasionally, according to weather; and the cows straw in the yards. Oxen sold fat generally at four years and a half old; but they pay well when kept to five and a half. His bulls leap at 5*s*. a cow.

Mr. Hoyte, of Osbornby, is in the same breed as Mr. Tyndall, having had cattle from him; also in the

* There are very few farms in this county where the tenants profess keeping cows as a principal profit, but only for the use of their families, and a little butter for the market; and therefore as the cheese they make is, for the most part, consumed in their own houses, they are not so very careful in the making of it; and though its quality may have suffered by the high price of butter, the pence in the pocket counterbalances any ill cheer in the eating.—*MS. of the Board.*

dun

dun French*. I do not admire the flesh of his Lincoln bull; but a dun cow is far superior. I took the measure of some points of this cow: hip to hip 21 inches; quarters long 22; length of barrel, from the withers to the centre between the hip bones, 36; girt at the chine seven feet one inch; girt at centre eight feet two inches; girt of the neck at middle, three feet three inches; she feels mellow; broad in the nache, or breech, as called here; six years old. I think Mr. Hoyte will pursue this breed; and if he does, I have little doubt, by making proper selections through the neighbourhood, but he will get a very superior stock to any thing common in this country. I was glad to see one Devonshire cow on his farm, which, though too small, is enough to speak to the hand what an ordinary specimen of that breed shews.

Uncommon as dairies are in general, it is not universal; Mr. Grundy, of Heath-hall, near Grantham, has forty cows for making cheese, which he manufactures of various sorts, and with much success.

Viewed Mr. Hough's cattle, of Threckingham, amongst which there is nothing comes up to the dun breed, or French ones; in 1789 he killed an ox of this breed that weighed 116½ stone, at seven years old, and measured two feet seven inches from the outside of one hip to the outside of the other; and he has now a three-

* In the vicinity of Folkingham, a dun coloured breed of beast has of late years been much attended to by several graziers, and though they may not equal Mr. Tyndall's, &c. in size, or symmetry of shape, yet their propensity to feed renders them a valuable acquisition to the grazier; they are said to have been originally brought from the Isle of Alderney, near the coast of France, by the late Sir Charles Buck, Bart. of Hanby-grange.—*MS. of the Board.*

year

year old cream-coloured heifer of that breed, but with a small cross of the Alderney in her, which is remarkably wide, and feels vastly more kindly and mellow than any Lincoln beast I have yet handled. This dun breed of cattle was introduced above twenty years ago, by Sir Charles Buck, from France; they were not originally larger than Alderneys, but they have improved here so much in size, that they are now nearly, if not quite, as large as the more common sorts of the country. In this yellow cow the French blood was a little restored by a cross of a yellow Alderney, and it is singular that this cow was admitted, by several considerable breeders, to feel remarkably well, and to have otherwise great merit; yet as a breed, it has been entirely neglected, no person whatever having taken them up to form a breed from them, *in and in*, to see what they would come to by a good selection of them. I advised Mr. Hoyte to do it; and he is the more likely, as he has a very good opinion of them, and Mrs. Hoyte urged also their having been their best for rich milk, and fat calves.

About Belton, cows that are not bad give six or seven pounds of butter a week.

Devons have been introduced by Mr. Cholmondeley at Easton, near Closterworth, and by a gentleman at Westby.

Lord Brownlow is in the common Lincoln, and has a very large bull. I think he will change his stock.

Mr. Bestal, at Leadenham, has a dun bull of six years old, got by Mr. Hough's, of Threckingham, which, from feeling, I judge to be well inclined to fat, and to get stock with fine flesh. But in his points he is not capital; clumsy and projecting in the shoulder, and falls in too much below the chine. The Rev.

Dr.

Dr. Ellis here, informed me of a Lincoln cow, that was in the possession of the Rev. Mr. Hec et, of Beckingham near Newark, that produced 19 lb. of butter in one week; but at Leadenham six, seven, or 8 lb. are common for good ones.

Mr. Chaplin has, at Blankney, a fine bull of the Lincoln breed, belonging to his relation, four years old, very large, and free from any gross fault in his shape; he would be better if his hips laid higher and rounder, and if his shoulders were rather cleaner; but his flesh is good and mellow. This gentleman has also got a couple of Devonshire cows, which he procured to cross with the Lincoln breed, as he thinks, and justly, that the mixture will be an improvement. They are not so large; but he thinks this no disadvantage on land not of the first quality.

About Hackthorne, &c. the larger farmers buy in beasts in autumn; put them to eddish, and then feed with cake; sell from Christmas to May-day. This is done for the sake of the dung; and thought if that is cleared, that it answers well.

Mr. Thorpe, at Kirton, fattens many beasts every winter on cake; his landlord, Mr. Harrisson, having built him for that purpose very convenient stalls, in a double range, with a gangway between their heads. They are in the Hereford style; the beasts may be loose or tied: a pump supplies water by troughs to cisterns; the whole well executed. He has sold beasts from these to 38*l.* a head, and fats 40 in a season. The same farmer has on his farm at Owersby, Lord Monson the proprietor, another bullock-house, in the same form nearly; here he fats also on oil-cake; but the dearness of it induced him to substitute lintseed, boiled and mixed with barley-meal; two quarters of barley, four bushels of lintseed

lintseed; and mixed to give cold, in the form of a rich jelly; this quantity will go as far as half a ton of cakes, costing less, when barley is not extravagantly high, that is, 24*s*. a quarter; half a peck of lintseed is boiled in four gallons of water I inquired of Mr. Thorpe particularly if he had reasons adequate to the expense, for not tying beasts in their stalls, instead of giving them so much room separately; and he is clear they fatten much better: this *necessity*, however, is not ascertained; for the question can hardly be considered as answered, in any case where a farmer builds, and a landlord pays. Mr. Thorpe buys his beasts at Lincoln; he thinks the Holdernesse too big for his purpose; but there is a very good cross of long and short horns about Spilsby, which fatten kindly, and which he likes to buy. Is of opinion, from very considerable experience, and speaking of grazing in general, both summer and winter, that middling-sized beasts will pay better than large ones; for instance, two of fifty stone will answer better than one of 100; they do not take so much food to bring them to their weight; and will do on worse pasture.

At Knaith, where the pasture is not of the first quality, Mr. Dalton has fatted Teeswater beasts to 130 stone, at seven years old, and gave only half a ton of cake to each. He prefers this breed to any other he has tried. His beasts of eighty stone will be fat at five years from grass, without any cake; and his regular return is seven a year, at four years old The cows are good milkers in their own country, but here are not equal to Lincolns. He is of opinion, in relation to the size of fatting animals, that an ox of 80 or 85 stone will not eat more than one of 50, and his bailiff thinks he will not eat so much.

At

At Haxey, in the Isle of Axholm, they have an odd way of ladling the milk when it comes from the cow, till it is cold, before they *set* it for cream. Experiments of comparison should be tried, to see if they are right in this, or if wrong, in what degree. Mrs. Lambe, I hope, will try it carefully.

At Bankside, Mr. Webster feeds his cows and his team-horses with steamed turnips and cut chaff, with great success.

About Normanby, Burton, &c. it is a great breeding country: they wish some of their cows to calve the latter end of the year, in October or November; then they let them run with the cow all winter, in the fields generally, but this is only in singular cases; and are fond of autumn calves; but in general the calving-time is in spring; suck ten or twelve days, then weaned; what butter they make goes to Hull; but in general breeding the calves is the great object; dairy no where the first aim. Suck a great while; by this means the dairy is sacrificed to the breeding; when they wean, they do it with porridge. They sell fat at six years old; heifers at three years spayed; but the quantity of oxen grazed, few; generally sold into the marshes to the graziers; yet 12*l.* to 16*l.* for them lean, at five years old.

They have for some years crossed the Lincoln short horns with the Craven long-horned bulls; and Mr. Goulton, of Walcot, has found them much better than either; four beasts of the half breed were sold by Mr. Sutton at Leeds, 84 to 92 stone each; four years old off; one cross only, for by going further, the improvement ceases: prefers this cross to the short-horned breed. Mr. Skipwith breeds many calves, and the cows

cows suckle three calves, kept in the house, and even five to a cow; buys calves for this purpose.

Mr. Uppleby, of Barrow, rears many calves, some run with the cows coupled together; and a cow will bring up four in the summer: has known more. Others he brings up by rearing at about six weeks, and gives first new, then skim-milk.

He has some Alderneys, and I could not help pointing out to Mr. Uppleby the superiority of their form, their smallness of offal, and kindly feeling flesh, for a comparison with the Lincoln.

Mr. Lloyd, of Belesby, has 100 head of horned cattle in all, breeding 20 calves a year; he keeps all his labourers' cows, and buys their calves, milking only four or five himself. Sells at four years old fat; and spays about half the heifers. These at four years old, weigh in June 54 to 60 stone; and the oxen by Christmas 60 to 70 stone. They are all of the long-horned breed, which he has been in since 1788, when he was at Mr. Fowler's, from viewing his stock then, and taking a bull. He was in the short-horned breed, and had good ones. He is convinced they are preferable to the short horns, better feeders, and lay most beef on the best joints. Those he has bred in and in are very tender, more so than the short horns; he will therefore breed in and in no more; but he observes nothing of this in the Leicester sheep. He thinks the long horns as saleable as the short horns; keeps as many on the same land as the short horns, but not more. Has killed to 100 stone, and Mr. Skipwith the same breed to 128. They joined with Mr. Ostler for the bull: but the latter is got out of the breed, not liking them. That gentleman killed a short-horned ox of 150 stone 9 lb. six years old, cake-fed the last winter. For the

 weights

weights above given, Mr. Lloyd never cakes, but for large ones he does. I felt of Mr. Lloyd's two bulls, the long and the short-horned ones; the latter is by far the best; I have not often touched a worse for feeling than the former. This breed, I apprehend, will not be kept much longer by so skilful a stock-master as Mr. Lloyd. What pity, when he made the trial of a change, he did not take Devon, Sussex, or Hereford!

Mr. Skipwith, of whom I made inquiries concerning the long-horned breed, informed me, that he kept both breeds distinct; but that he had not possessed the new sort long enough, to have made up his mind on the comparative merit.

About Humberston, the breed is mixed with long-horned. Mr. Tomlinson, who came from the East Riding of Yorkshire, has the Holdernesse, as he does not approve of the long-horned. They do not regard the dairy further than what is sufficient for the family; but rear many calves, and sell lean at three or four years old; most farmers fatten a few, as from four to six, giving cake in the winter, especially to the beasts that have been worked; but it is not general. Heifers sell at 13*l.* or 14*l.* at high rates; oxen 15*l.*

Mr. Bourne, of Dalby, breeds a mixture between long and short horns, which he thinks better than either of them distinct; they are kindly feeders, and not being so large as the short horns, better adapted to the soil; he sells them fat at London, at three and four years old, from 15*l.* to 18*l.* each, including both heifers and oxen.

Mr. Wright, of Spilsby, has had cattle from Durham, as a purer breed than the same sort in Lincolnshire; but six or seven years ago has had a long-horned

horned bull; they do not come to the weight of the short horns by ten stone in eighty; not so saleable as the long horned at Smithfield; but the butchers here like the short-horned best. Equal in hardiness. Good short horns will fat as quick. Sell at three years old in June or July, 56 to 60 stone. Keeps 150 head; rears above forty in a year; but milks only six cows. Couples them, two to one cow. No cake.

Sir Joseph Banks had the goodness to shew me, at Boothby, in the Middle Marsh, in company with the Rev. Mr. Walls, of Spilsby and that place, two beautiful short-horned heifers, Spot and Gypsey, bred by His Majesty, and now extremely fat, at four years old; the smaller of the two of the more correct form; but both are beautiful. Measure of Spot:

	Ft.	In.
Across from the centre of one hip to the centre of the other	2	1
Length in quarters from centre of hip	1	10
Breadth of nache, eight inches below the tail setting on	1	6
Girt chine	8	0
—— centre	9	2
Length from withers to rump-point	5	4
Height at rump	5	0
Girt neck	3	7
Horn to withers	2	8

Of

Of Gypsey:

	Ft.	In.
Width hips	2	2
Nache	1	3
Quarters	1	11
Length to withers	4	7¾
Girt chine	7	8½
—— centre	9	0
—— fore-leg	0	8

They have one cake, and half a peck of beans split each *per diem*. They are called Holdernesse; but as that is the same as the true Lincoln, I may observe, that Gypsey is the best Lincoln beast by far that I have seen.

Weight at London:

Spot alive, 155 stone, at 8 lb.
Dead, 100 stone.
Gypsey alive, 127 stone.
Dead, 82 stone 4 lb.
Born in May, 1793.
Sold for 70*l.*

Mr. Parkinson, of Asgarby, works oxen, and is very fond of them; I saw two and a horse draw home in a waggon, as good loads of corn as are common in Suffolk with three horses.

In the whole hundred of Skirbeck, there is very little in cattle that deserves attention; they have not in breeding been at all attentive, nor is the scale any thing considerable; but the breed in general is mostly short-horned. Mr. Linton milks three or four cows, and rears six calves every year, which he fats and sells at four years old, for 16*l.* to 25*l.* each, average 19*l.* And

And this he thinks a very profitable system, connecting well with his straw-yard. He sometimes turns them on the fen.

Mr. Loft, at Ranby, uses a long-horned bull from Mr. Stone, introduced here by Mr. Codd, to cross the short-horned, which are better in the cross than either separately; better flesh, and fatten kindlier.

Mr. Thomas Tannard, of Frampton, prefers the true short-horned beasts as the best for the Lincoln grazier. He has tried Fifes, Northumberlands, and Lancasters, which do very well, provided they are wintered; but to sell all by the 4th of December, nothing like the short-horned.

The prices of cattle were long ago very high in this county. The father of Mr. Loft, of Marsh Chapel, 50 years ago sold a cow and a ewe for 40*l.*

This gentleman has a high opinion of the half breed between long and short horns: he has a very fine long-horned bull from Mr. Stone, of Quarn. Stock got by him out of short-horned cows, have at four years old been sold from 25*l.* to 30*l.* And he saw a cow of the half breed at eighteen years old, that weighed 95 stone. He sold four half-bred at 27*l.* 10*s.* each; one three years and a half old, and three years old. He gave 9*l.* each for these three, and had them only nine months, yet trebled their value without cake or corn. He has also been very successful with short horns, unmixed; he has fatted an ox at four years to 119 stone, that never ate any thing but grass and hay.

Mr. Smith, of South Elkington, finds the long-horned breed more thrifty on poor land than short horns. He breeds 20 a year, selling fat at four years old, 60 stone; at five or six years they come to 80.

Mr. Ellison, at Sudbrook, buys in about 30 bullocks

locks annually; from April to Midsummer puts to grass till a fortnight after Old Michaelmas; then puts them part in stalls, and part remains in grass till near Christmas. In the stalls, feeds with cake and hay; they eat about two cakes and a half a day, at 7 lb. each, and about half a ton of hay each beast; and are up about ten weeks, some twelve. They were bought in at 15*l.* each last year; and sold at about 6*l.* In general, reckons them to pay 10*l.* each, which answers well. Prefers the short-horned breed; has tried long-horned Cravens, but they did not answer at all. His bailiff chooses the smallest boned ones he can get; clean heads and muzzles, wide in the hips, out in the ribs, and deep in the fore quarter. The greatest fault in the Lincoln short horns, is being thin in the backs and chines; it is not universal, but very common; but upon the whole, they fatten kindly. Observes, that the oil-cake dung is uncommonly rich, so as by mixing to make the straw dung excellent.

Mr. Moody, of Riseholm, fats many beasts upon oil-cake, even as far as buying 100 tons of cake in a year. He keeps them loose in a straw-yard, and finds they do well without any hay, giving straw only in addition; and has sold beasts thus fed at 40 guineas.

Mr. Hebb, of Claypool, breeds many cattle, all short horns, which he prefers much to the long-horned kind. He approves very much of all the Devonshires he has seen, but never tried them. The dun breed about Folkingham good, but likes the true Lincoln better. He shewed me two cows of this kind, which give each seven gallons of milk a day, yet are at the same time inclined to fat.

Mr. Walker's stock of cattle are chiefly short-horned, of Mr. Tyndall's sort, which he prefers to the long-horned;

horned; he breeds a score a year. He had once many long-horned ones; but the best bred ones proved unhealthy, and he was forced to change the stock. He found them tender when young, and very apt to scour.

The Duke of Ancaster fattens many beasts; he buys in from Candlemas to Midsummer, generally Scotch and Welsh bullocks of 34 to 50 stone, sometimes larger; sells fat from Midsummer to December. Gives on an average for the two last springs, 8*l.* 8*s.* or 9*l.* each, and sells at 13*l.* to 17*l.* They are kept through the winter in the park, and go off at Midsummer twelve months after. Have no fodder, except in a blast. North Wales, Pembroke, and Highland Scots, and very little difference in advantage; the Welsh grow rather more, and come to greater weights. The Fifes grow more than any, but they require foddering.

Mr. Parker remarks, that there is little attention paid to the breed of beasts in this country. In the open field towns the breed is wretched: they all run together on a pasture, without the least thought of selection. At three years old, they are worth about 7*l.* or 8*l.*; and if they would pay the same attention that is paid elsewhere, instead of that, they would be worth 12*l.* or 13*l.*; and all this result is from being open and unenclosed; they will breed four or five calves from a wretched cow before they sell it, so that a great quantity of food is sadly misapplied.

I have very little to observe upon the preceding notes: it is evident that the Lincoln breed of cattle, upon Lincoln pastures, are profitable; and it appears evident, from the general colour of the comparisons made

made with the long-horned breed from Leicestershire, that their own short horns are superior. In the next article, on sheep, it will appear that the breeders and graziers of this county are by no means to be accused of that sort of prejudice, which will not give a fair trial to the introduction of a new sort of live stock; but that on the contrary, they are most ready to make experiments; the long-horned breed having therefore been tried, and given up by so many, even by a member of the Leicester Tup Club, shews clearly that it was an attempt to introduce an inferior breed; and the result has been such as it ought to be, amounting in the whole to a considerable and varied experiment. As this famous breed of Leicester has failed so greatly on comparison with the Lincoln, it surely deserves the attention of breeders in other counties (if any such there are) who are trying to introduce that stock, which is thus proved to be so inferior to one that is not supposed to be the best in the kingdom, but which, in the opinion of many excellent judges, is on the contrary inferior to several others. I scarcely know an experiment more wanting, than that of planting a colony of good North Devons in this county, for breeding, working, and fatting.

SECT. II.—SHEEP.

I HAD made but little progress in the county, before it was evident that the information I should receive under this head would be considerable; I had therefore planned a regular arrangement of the subject, so classed as to present under every head the respective circum-

stances

stances procured; but upon further consideration, I found that more would be lost in accuracy by this method, than was gained in clearness. Every breeder that offers various facts upon the same topic, of course throws out circumstances, which in union may give a light to each other. If, upon the general colour of each person's information, there is an air of accuracy, or on the contrary, of too free *assertion*, such should appear, that the reader may give that degree of confidence which the particulars seem to merit. But all this satisfaction would be lost, if every article was not given as received. Upon common subjects which do not excite a spirit of emulation and discussion, the necessity is not equally apparent; but in the present temper of the breeding mind in Lincolnshire, it appears to be the only method of enabling the reader to have the full information necessary.

The system at Long Sutton, upon their rich lands, once common, is to buy shearling wethers at Boston, in April or May; the price in 1796 and 1797, from 40*s*. to 3*l*.; they keep them one year to shear, and sell some at 4*l*.; but in general, buy at 36*s*. to 42*s*. and sell at 3*l*. besides two fleeces, which are worth 10*s*. to 12*s*. The profit may therefore be laid at about 30*s*. a head, which is very great.

Wool in 1796, 21*s*. 6*d*.; was once 27*s*. It will not keep more than a year without some damage. All true bred Lincoln.

Mr. Graves, of Spalding, buys for Deeping Fen, shearling wethers in the spring, at 35*s*. each, which after clipping three times, he sells at 45*s*.

Mr. Graves had a true Lincoln sheep, that clipped, the first year 23 lb. of wool, and the second year 22½ lb. and was sold at Smithfield at Christmas, and weighed

40 lb.

40 lb. a quarter. Of this sheep Mr. Bakewell said, that he ate as much as three; but that was mere assertion. Mr. Graves thinks that the New Leicesters are an improvement, in fattening sooner, but likes the first cross best; a Leicester tup and a Lincoln ewe; and these will give 10 lb. of wool.

This gentleman's sale in 1796, from the fen and marsh, was 40 at 58*s.*—35 at 70*s.*—60 at 50*s.*—60 at 54*s.*—44 at 69*s.*—70 at 55*s.*—8 at 75*s.* 6*d.*—100 at 59*s.* 3*d.*—70 at 53*s.*—81 at 54*s.* 6*d.*—72 at 54*s.*—Many of them two shear, some three. Had two fleeces from them, worth 17*s.*

In 1796 he sold 3568 tod of wool, at 23*s.* Has kept wool four years, and lost nothing, neither by waste nor moth; but it was kept next the tiles. It will not do on a ground floor. Price in 1797, 18*s.* to 19*s.*

The Mr. Fishers, at Weston, have New Leicester sheep, and answer very well; have sold two shears at 3*l.*

Two sheep an acre in winter, on the rich land near Boston. In summer three or four, besides bullocks.

Two shear sheep about Boston, not common; in general three shear. Price in 1797, 56*s.* for shearlings; two give a tod of wool. Mr. Fydell of this place, who has been one of the greatest graziers in this county, made a fair trial between the New Leicester and Old Lincolns, in which the latter turned out best; and in some of them which he killed, the comparison as to offal, was very much in favour of the Lincoln; which he thinks will, on the rich lands in that vicinity, answer much better than any other breed of which he has had experience.

Mr. Charles Trimmell, of Bicker, near Boston, has sold Lincoln shearlings at 42*s.* each, at Michaelmas, without

without having any cross of Leicester blood in them; and killed a wether of 67 lb. a quarter, four years old; never had any cake, but was made up with sow-thistles for two or three months. This sheep was bred by Mr. Hutchinson, in Hail Fen, from a ram bred by Mr. Robinson, of Kirby, near Sleaford, or Mr. Fisher of the same place, and fed to this amazing size by Mr. Trimmell, of Bicker Fen, near Boston, Lincolnshire, upon fen land.

He never ate any corn, oil-cake, &c. but fed wholly upon grass and herbage. Being turned with many other sheep, into a field of clover, this sheep was observed first to search for all the sow-thistles, and would eat no other food whilst any of them could be found in the part of the field that was hurdled off successively, a little at a time. A kind of hut was erected for him in the field, to repose under in hot weather; and when the part that was hurdled off became bare of food, the shepherd, being guided by his propensity for sow-thistles, gathered a quantity for him, at stated hours, three times a day, from 2 lb. to 5 lb. at a meal.

Standing on his feet he measured only two feet six inches high; he was weighed once a month, and weighed alive 26 stone, at 14 lb. to the stone; he gained only 1 lb. the last month; and then thinking he had got to the top, and quite ripe, and might possibly lose 3 lb. or 4 lb. the next month, he was killed on the 13th day of October, 1791, by Mr. Isaac Lumby, of Bicker, being then a four-shear, or four years old sheep.

The skin hung up by the nose, measured ten feet two inches from the point of the nose to the tip of the tail, and was sold for 7*s*. 6*d*. in the common course of business.

The carcass measured five feet from the nose to the tail;

tail; its rump or cushion eight inches and a half in depth; plate or fore flank the same thickness; breast end seven inches, one yard five inches and a half round the collar, and weighed 67 lb. a quarter.

The legs were estimated at 40 lb. weight each, but if cut haunch or venison, fashion would have weighed 50 lb. each; which the proprietor, Mr. Lumby, sold at 2*s*. a pound, so the two legs brought 10*l*.

The progress of this sheep was as follow:

	St.	lb.
Weighed alive the 18th Feb. 1790	19	2
April 15	19	9
May 20	20	9
June 5	21	1
July 16	20	7
Sept. 9, ...	21	10
Nov. 9	23	3
Dec. 6	23	10
Oct. 13, 1791	26	0

Girt six feet six inches.

Length five feet.

If 26 stone gives 268 lb. (67 lb. per quarter) what will 20 give?

Answer, $14\frac{3}{4}$ lb.

Mr. Watson informed me, that buying 200 sheep that came to 24 lb. a quarter, one among them came to 41 lb. a quarter, and fattened soonest and kindliest, and apparently did not eat more than the others.

In Holland Fen two fleeces and a half to the tod; on the Wolds three. Three-shear sheep, average two guineas and a half. Two shear, 35*s*. to 40*s*. by John Cartwright, Esq.

Mutton

Mutton uncommonly marbled, and the best feeding sheep Mr. Cartwright ever had; a cross, a ram half Lincoln half Spanish, and the ewe Lincoln; the lamb of that cross well fed, was this.

Viewed a two-shear tup of the Old Lincoln breed, belonging to Mr. Bartholomew, on the farm of Mr. Thacker, of Longrike ferry; his neck was two feet eleven inches girt; his fore leg five inches and a half; yet the loin only eight inches and three quarters. Great weight of bone, and heavy offals; an appearance of immense wool, but coarse on the breech. Another of the same breed, better made and woolled.

In Holland Fen, generally rear a lamb or something more to every ewe.

About Swineshead, the rich grass grazed with sheep and bullocks. They buy in for stock, hoggets and shearlings at Lady-day; hogs at 30*s.*; shearlings 40*s.* to 45*s.*; the shearlings kept a year, take the fleeces, as they clip when they sell, though before the common time; last year sold at 50*s.* to 60*s.* but very high; average for seven years, hogs bought at 20*s.* and kept two years; shearlings bought at 32*s.* sale 40*s.* All clipped thrice; the three fleeces, 1st, 9 lb.; 2d, 11 lb.; 3d, 9 lb.; in general the three a tod of 28 lb. Leicesters go at two shear.

Mr. Cartwright thinks that adopting a breed between Lincoln and Leicester, would be better for Holland Fen, than to introduce all Leicester blood; to preserve the Lincoln skin and wool of a good quality, for there is some very coarse and bad Lincoln wool; but with the improvement of the carcass, especially in the fore quarter, by means of Leicesters, thus a breed might be raised, the larger the better, which would perhaps answer the purpose better than either breed pure.

pure. Mr. Tyndall, in conversation, admitted that the Leicesters are more tender in winter than the old Lincoln, demanding a drier layer. In combining the two breeds, therefore, here is wool, carcass, a quick return (if more profitable than the third year of the Lincoln) and hardiness, all to be taken into the account.

Mr. Cartwright had for several years Northumberland ewes, larger size than Leicester; fuller in the fore quarters than Lincoln; a good disposition to feed; wool finer than Lincoln, fleece six or seven pounds; covered with well selected rams from Mr. Bartholomew and Mr. Chaplin, but latterly from Mr. Codd, of Ranby, who was deeper in Leicesters; the effect improved the carcasses gradually, and kept up the wool tolerably in weight, but much improved in fineness.

Mr. Hoyte, of Osbornby, has been seventeen years in the New Leicester; he has had tups from Mr. Buckley, Mr. Breedon, and of the late Mr. Walker, of Woolsthorpe. I viewed his stock with pleasure; he has some shearling tups, and two shear that are good; but his lambs promise to be the best on his farm, which shews a right progress of improvement. He has a two-shear with a loin nine inches and a half wide, and only four inches difference between the chine and centre girt; leg four inches circumference. A three-shear wether, leg three and a half; difference in girt only three; and loin nine and a half; very broad in the chine; fat and heavy fore-flanks.

In 1796 there was a new Tup Society established at Lincoln, for the encouragement of breeding; a sort of offset from the famous Club of Leicester. Ten original members; the chief object is to promote the

the spirit of breeding in this county. By the rules of the Society, in union with that of Leicester, it was agreed, that the Leicester breeders should show their rams two days previous to the letting day; that they should lett no ram to a wether breeder in the county of Lincoln under thirty guineas; that they should give the preference, in letting rams into Lincolnshire, to the Society; and in return, agreed, that no ram in Lincolnshire should be taken to market, or lett under five guineas; and to sell no ewes, but what is to go to the butcher. The Leicester folks have been so badgered for their Tup Club, that they have persuaded their Lincoln brethren to form another, to divide the odium. The Leicester motto is, *Let those laugh who win.*

Mr. Tyndall, of Ewerby, has been seven years in the New Leicester blood, and has some good stock, but capable of improvement; he is however one of the most considerable breeders and graziers of sheep in this country. June the 29th, 1797, he sold his wool of the preceding year's crop, 1518 fleeces, 465 tod, at 21*s.*: this is eight pound and a half per fleece. This gentleman observed an article of management to me, which, though it may be well known here, is not generally so elsewhere; that in weaning lambs, they should not be drawn off from the sheep, but the sheep drawn off from them; by being left in the pasture they are more quiet, not apt to be equally disturbed, and generally do better. In discourse with him upon the introduction of the New Leicester breed, to which he is now a great friend, though once an enemy, he candidly admitted, that being a tenderer breed than the old Lincoln, they will not pay, when at two years and a half old, for keeping another winter like the Lincoln, therefore

therefore it is more advantageous to sell them a year sooner than was formerly the custom with the old breed.

It is said that the late Mr. Chaplin took a cross of New Leicester 25 years ago; mentioned as a proof of the difficulty of finding the true Lincoln blood unmixed. Mr. Bourne, of Dalby, also had a Dishley sheep so long ago as Mr. Bakewell's failure; above thirty years*.

Mr. Wetherel, of Hackington, informed me, that of what was called Lincoln sheep, he todded all threes; and now under New Leicesters, half threes and half fours. Keeps the same number, but fatter. This gentleman gave as his opinion, that on the rich land of Holland Fen, and about Boston, the last year of keeping from two-shear off to three-shear off, pays better than any other year.

In conversation at Mr. Tyndall's, in company with many eminent breeders, the following table of the value of New Leicester sheep, at various ages, was taken:

---

* An idea is current in this country, that Mr. Bakewell derived his breed originally from Lincolnshire. On this supposition a correspondent remarks: if Mr. Bakewell derived his breed originally out of Lincolnshire—if Mr. Walesby, and many others, have improved the breed of the county *since* Mr. Bakewell set about perfecting the ovian race—there must be something radically good in the sort, something worth mending, something well suited to the county, worthy the attention of the Honourable Board. Indeed, to encourage the breed of the best sort of sheep that will suit the soil, is highly laudable; to point out the quality of the wool each district ought to produce; to encourage an excellence in that most valuable article, in a county where so much of it is grown, would be a great benefit.—*MS. of the Board.*

Wether

		s.
Wether lambs,	at six months, worth	17
———————	at 12 months	30
———————	at 18 months	35
———————	at 24 months	45
———————	at 30 months	45
———————	at 36 months	55

According to this table the scale of receipt is,

For the first summer	£.0	17	0
For the first winter	0	13	0
For the second summer, including 8 lb. wool at 9*d*.	0	11	0
For the second winter	0	10	0
For the third summer, including wool	0	6	0
For the third winter, including wool	0	16	0
	£.3	13	0
Three fleeces	0	18	0
As above	£.2	15	0

At 73*s*. they pay per ann. 24*s*. 4*d*.

At these prices the last half year pays better than any; if this is just, there is a great loss by selling at two years and a half old, for it is just at the conclusion of the worst half year there is.

Mr. Dawson, of Berthorp, has been ten years in the New Leicester; he did me the favour of shewing me a very fine parcel of two shear-wethers: capital sheep indeed; bred from Mr. Dalby's tups. Last year he sold 200 two-shear ones at 3*l*. round. The following is his table of sales for seven years, of wethers of that age.

		s.
1790 average,	....	35
1791 ———	....	35
1792 ———	....	43
1793 ———	....	38
1794 ———	....	44
1795 ———	....	50
1796 ———	....	60

He tods threes.

Average 2*l.* 3*s.* 6*d.*

And at this average he would thus divide it, by supposing the proportion to be,

		£.		
At six months	....	0	17	0
At 12 ditto	....	1	7	0
At 18 ditto	....	1	12	0
At 24 ditto	....	2	0	0
At 30 ditto	....	2	3	6

Mr. Thomas Parkinson, between Doncaster and Rotherham, has often bought Mr. Dawson's wethers of this age, in order to graze on turnips, getting some off in spring, and the rest early in summer at very high prices; and Mr. Dalby bought three of him, which after a year's keep sold at Rotherham for 5*l.* 10*s.* each. Mr. Tyndall on this observed, that old sheep will stand the winter better, and pay better for keeping than young ones. Surely all this takes off much from the advantage said to be the great merit of the modern improvement, which magnifies the benefit of what is called the quick return.

Mr. Hough, of Threckingham, has a few two-shear, three-shear, and four-shear favourite wethers of the New Leicester

Leicester breed, which are fine sheep, and very fat; they are supposed to weigh 36 lb. a quarter. This gentleman shewed me a Smithfield salesman's bill of three New Leicesters, two-shears, and one Lincoln three-shear; the former sold at 65*s*. and the latter at 46*s*.: yet this Lincoln, when a hogget, was worth more than either of the Leicesters.

The following is a series of the prices of wool per tod of 28 lb. sold from one farm near Folkingham in this county, from A. D. 1758 to 1794.

Date.	Price.			Date.	Price.		
	£.	*s.*	*d.*		£.	*s.*	*d.*
1758	1	0	0	1777	0	18	6
1759	1	0	0	1778	0	14	6
1760	0	19	0	1779	0	12	0
1761	0	16	0	1780	0	12	6
1762	0	17	0	1781	0	12	0
1763	0	18	9	1782	0	11	0
1764	0	19	6	1783	0	14	0
1765	1	0	0	1784	0	15	6
1766	1	1	6	1785	0	13	0
1767	0	17	6	1786	0	16	6
1768	0	15	0	1787	0	17	0
1769	0	15	0	1788	0	17	0
1770	0	14	6	1789	0	18	6
1771	0	15	0	1790	0	18	6
1772	0	15	0	1791	1	0	0
1773	0	15	6	1792*	1	3	6
1774	0	18	0	1793	0	17	0
1775	0	17	6	1794	0	18	0
1776	0	17	6				

Besides

* In this year the same sort of wool was sold as high as 27*s*. per tod; a price that wool of that description was never sold at since the year 1728, when, by reason of a very extraordinary rot amongst the sheep (in two preceding years), it was sold at 30*s*. This information I had from the

Besides Mr. Hoyte, Mr. Hough, and Mr. Dawson I called on Mr. Byshe, but he was absent.

Lord Brownlow's flock at Belton, managed in the common method of the country, consists of,

Breeding ewes	240
Rams	4
Culled ewes; *drapes* two, three, four, five, and six year	100
Shearling wethers	100
Two-shear wethers	100
Theaves; ewe hogs	100
Lambs	240
	884

Value of his Lordship's wethers at various ages, on an average of seven years:

	£.	s.	d.
At six months	0	12	0
Twelve ditto	1	0	0
Eighteen ditto	1	5	0
Twenty-four ditto	1	15	0
Thirty ditto	1	15	0
Thirty-six ditto	1	15	0
Forty-two ditto	2	0	0

First fleece of wool 8 lb.; second 8 lb.; third 7 lb. This is Mr. Abbot's account; but I cannot understand their remaining at the same price three years together.

Mr. Betsal, at Leadenham, keeps 100 breeding ewes of the New Leicesters, and has 100 lambs on an average;

---

the ate Mr. Metheringham, of Spanby, county of Lincoln, who died in 1796, at the great age of near 100 years, and retained his faculties in a wonderful degree to the last.—*Mr. Cragg. MS. of the Board.*

rage; 100 shearlings, and 100 two-shear; half wethers sold at that age, at 40*s*. to 55*s*.; and his four or five shear ewes at 58*s*.; the wetheıs are bought of him to put to turnips. At Bruton, in the Vale, they have begun to clip lambs.

On the Wolds, large flocks. They do not commonly sell lambs, but having marsh land, keep them till shearlings, then sell them to butchers, and also to other graziers, to carry on. Three to a tod, the outside of wool. Never fold; the sheep will not bear it.

Mr. Chaplin, at Blankney, sells his shearlings from 30*s*. to 38*s*.; and have been re-sold at two shear at 60*s*. Last year his shearlings were 36*s*. His breed has a good deal of Leicester blood in it.

At Hackthorne, &c. the heath farmers keep breeding flocks; and sell the lambs in April, hoggets in the wool; the wethers, and the culled ewes; price of the former 37*s*. or 38*s*.; about 30*s*. the average; for the culled ewe hogs about 20*s*. Fatten the old *drape* ewes on turnips; and the wether lambs the first winter are on the same food.

Mr. Harrisson, at Norton-place, keeps breeding ewes of the New Leicester sort, and has some very handsome ones; he sells the produce shearling wethers in November, at 40*s*. or 41*s*. times being high, but less when prices are not equal. They clip half threes, half fours. Hogs will sell 28*s*. to 30*s*. in April, turniped. Mr. Thorpe, at Kirton, has a very fine arable farm, on which there is a good crop of lambs of the same breed; but as he has another where he resides, his best are at home; he goes into Leicestershire every year, and gives as high as 130*l*. for a tup; letts his own rams up to fifty guineas. I viewed his tups at Owersby, and think he has some which will do him credit. But

he

he is now breeding, if I am to judge by comparing his two and three-shear tups with his lambs, in a manner that will make a great change in his stock for the better. Very few, if any, of the breeders I have seen in this county, seem, however, to be sufficiently impressed with the idea of *raising a peg*, to use Bakewell's expression, every year; on this principle, the youngest tups of a farm ought always to be the best.

In discourse with Mr. Thorpe, on the advantages of changing the old long-woolled breed of Lincoln for New Leicesters, I wished to have them clearly ascertained. He remarked, that he was for many years in that breed, and sold his wethers then at the same age as he does now, but not fat; if he would reach the same price, he must keep Lincolns to May or June. At Wakefield market he has had both, and his Lincolns did not sell for so much as the Leicesters, by 10*s*. a head. Shearling Leicesters have sold as high as two-shear Lincolns. But, on the other hand, the difference in wool has been as much as 8*s*. to 16*s*. He has got off shearling wethers in February, at 51*s*. each. In point of stocking, he runs Leicesters thicker by one in five. He admits, however, with all I have conversed with, that the Leicesters are tenderer in winter. Bring all this to a balance, and the question does not yet seem decided, for obvious reasons.

H. Dalton, Esq. at Knaith, has had New Leicesters for two years past; sells the wethers at two shears 48*s*. to 50*s*. Last year his culls at 50*s*. He finds that the New Leicester sheep do not *clot* their wool so much as the Lincoln. He has given wethers oil-cake while on turnips, 1 lb. each *per diem*. They did well, and fed more profitably than they would have done on turnips alone.

Whenever

Whenever sheep have cake given them in this part of the county, it is in troughs in the turnip field.

About Normanby, Burton, &c. the New Leicester has been introduced six or eight years; and have made yet no great progress: they may be said to be only coming in. The old breed was considerably larger than the new; the wool much longer, and heavier by 2 lb. The great advantage urged is, that the Leicester can be got off shearlings, whereas the Lincoln require to be kept to be sheared twice, and to be in full perfection thrice. The Leicesters are finer grained mutton. It is asserted, that they are also kept rather thicker on the land. The system here is a flock of breeding ewes, and to fatten their own wethers. William Potton thinks that he can have as much wool per acre from the Leicester as the Lincoln. Mr. Robert Holdgate thinks that the Lincoln sheep pay well for being kept till three shear.

Mr. Sutton, of Walcot, and a relation, carried wool to Wakefield market; his relation the Lincoln breed, himself the New Leicester; the Lincoln fleeces eight ounces one dram more per fleece; but his sold for 2½*d.* each more money. He clips 500, having 200 breeding ewes, ten to fifteen die an acre.
200 lambs,
100 shearlings,
100 two-shear.

Sells 100 wethers two shear; loses 50 or 60 every year; full bred sheep are here very rare, for they are merely coming in.

Never give turnips to tupped ewes, and the stock in general eat but little hay, merely in a blast, as it does but little good; the lambs and shearlings have turnips. An

An acre of good turnips will keep ten sheep from Martinmas till Lady-day.

Mr. Skipwith, of Alesby, tups 1400 ewes.

Mr. Goulton, of Alkborough, has 103 ewes, 137 lambs; clips 310; and has 207 shearlings and two-shear, and three rams. He sells his wethers fat, at two shear, as soon as clipped; ewes and culled wethers 1797 at 45*s*.; in 1796, 40*s*.; the year before 34*s*.; average 40*s*.; two fleeces 12*s*.; in all 2*l*. 12*s*. a head; there is very little Leicester blood in them: his wool 77½ tod, at 21*s*.

Mr. Graburn has a flock that have been four years crossed with Leicester: finds that they are more thrifty; used to sell his shearlings lean, two years old, but now sells them fat; used to sell in April in the wool at 25*s*. old breed, no Leicester blood; now has sold at 36*s*. to 40*s*. the same age; average and old breed, ten or twelve years previous to 1797 25*s*. to 30*s*. Does not find ehtm tenderer in winter than the old. No difference in number on the same land. Old breed gave 6 lb. or 7 lb.; the new the same; but Mr. Graburn keeps better now than he did before. Some persons have cake-fed sheep while on turnips, and they throve exceedingly well.

Mr. Graburn has seen the flukes of rotten sheep on water-cresses in March, which he remarks as a fact which may lead to a right theory of that distemper; for by similar observations of other plants, the same thing might be found.

Mr. Goulton, of Bonby, thinks that the New Leicester will come to sale sooner than the Old Lincoln, and are likely to answer better; but that they will not bear cold wet land so well in winter as the Lincoln, nor

nor will they after shearing bear either hot or cold weather so well.

George Uppleby, Esq. of Barrow, was in the Lincoln breed for six or seven years before he took any cross of Leicester; during that period he sold his wethers at three shear, soon after clipping, and so as they came fat through summer; sold at from 30*s*. to 35*s*. getting at the three clippings 27 lb. of wool, or 9 lb. yearly; some of them two to a tod. Since he has been in the Leicester he has sold the produce fat at two shear, at 40*s*. on an average; getting as the two clippings 14 lb. of wool. It is always in such comparisons to be recollected, the rise in the price of sheep which has in general taken place. He is also clear that, in his opinion, he can keep five Leicesters where he before kept four Lincolns; and further, that upon the worst land he has, the Leicesters have done better, that is, have resisted hardships better than the Lincolns. Sells them sometimes at Rotheram, where graziers buy them to carry on further. Mr. Uppleby thinks, that if his farm consisted of better land, any thing like marshes near Boston, that it might be more profitable to keep his sheep longer, and also to have a larger size; but that upon such a soil as his, the quick return of Leicester is more beneficial. In respect of wool, Mr. Uppleby is clearly of opinion, that if you will have a very weighty fleece of wool, not taking into account exceptions which will now and then happen, you cannot have such a fleece from a well made carcass; not that wool need be entirely neglected, for he has observed that for three years past, the Leicester men have provided some rams, carrying more wool than before common with their breed in general.

Mr. Skipwith, 1000 guineas this year by rams.

Lord

Lord Yarborough puts 450 ewes to tup; has 216 ewe lambs, and 226 wether; besides which he has 213 shearling wethers *(heeders)*, and 196 *gimbers*, 123 culled ewes. Has sold 100 two-shear wethers at 46*s*. His whole flock 1068.

Upon the much agitated question in this county, of the comparative merits of the Old Lincoln and the New Leicester sheep, I wished to know of Mr. Dickenson, of Brocklesby, what appeared to him from the opportunity his situation, as steward upon so large a property, gave him of forming ideas from the conversation and characters of the farmers as careful or sanguine men: and he said that many farmers who are supposed to manage very much to their advantage, are clearly of opinion, that the New Leicesters are not so profitable as the Lincoln; and this from some who have tried the Leicester. Their system is this, according to Mr. Richardson:

300 breeding ewes.
300 lambs doubles making up for loss.
4 rams.
145 wethers, } shearlings.
145 *gimbers*, }

To sell every year,

100 *drope* ewes at Michaelmas.
145 shearling wethers; turniped by many, and sold in the wool, as store sheep, at Boston.

Drapes sold on the average of the last three years at 25*s*.; before that at 15*s*. 6*d*. Wethers for the last three years 36*s*. 6*d*.; before that 28*s*. This will be the way where there is much Lincoln blood left; for few that have much Leicester sell stores, but fat, within two months after clipping. Mr. Richardson thinks, that

that if a man can fatten at an early age, he should breed all Leicester blood. But if so circumstanced as to be able to keep them till three shear, by means of marshes, then the true Lincoln; or if with a small mixture of the New Leicester not worse. The graziers prefer the Lincoln breed, and declare so openly. He does not think, that upon the same land more sheep are kept because of Leicester blood, though some will say so. In point of wool, the full bred Leicester sells at 1*s*. a tod more than Lincoln: for weight, three Lincoln to a tod, and four and a half Leicester. The latter breed is found much more liable to the fly, so that they are kept in caps, but not the Lincoln; at first shearing also, some have flannel jackets. They are also objected to for not being so hardy as the Lincoln, from thin pelts and less wool. Lincoln tup men give high prices in Leicestershire, it is said so high as 200 guineas by Mr. Skipwith, who lett, as report goes, last year to the amount of 1000 or 1200 guineas.

Mr. Richardson, sixteen years previous to 1797, sold shearlings in April at 18*s*. Michaelmas 1796, he gave 30*s*. 6*d*. for drape ewes; and sixteen years before sold his own at 8*s*. 6*d*.

Calling on Mr. Edlington, at Cadney, to view his Lincoln breed of sheep, having been often informed that he held the New Leicester as a breed much inferior; I was informed by a butcher who happened to be there, that Mr. Euston, at Manby, near Brig, sold 40 two-shear Lincolns of pure blood, in June, as soon as clipped, half at 2*l*. 12*s*. 6*d*.; and the other 20 in August, at 3*l*. each; which was mentioned as a proof that the Old Lincoln would come to a great value at an early age. Mr. Edlington has bred his flock by hiring tups from the men supposed to have the pure Lincoln

Lincoln blood, such as Mr. Onnley and Mr. Dun, of Holdernesse, Mr. Preston, by Louth, Mr. Chaplin, at Tathwell, and Mr. Johnson, of Kermond. He sells at two and at three shear; two shear as soon as clipped as high as 50*s.*; three shear to 3*l.* 3*s.*; these prices for a few; but in general two shears at 42*s.* with some three shears among them. For wool, he runs, at an average, three to a tod; some two, some three, and a few four. He informed me, that Mr. Johnson, at Kermond, kills at both Caistor and Lincoln, and beats the New Leicester in weight at the same age. He complains of Mr. Bakewell buying of him the ugliest, worst Lincoln tup he had at the time, and shewing it as a sight at Dishley. This anecdote, however, proves that Mr. Bakewell considered this as a good shop to get Lincoln blood *for his purpose.* It cuts both ways: if it is said that Mr. Bakewell would go on such an errand, where he could find the worst; then it may be replied, that if the worst will do, what is here noted, what would the best come to? Having examined the tups, and adjourned to Mr. Edlington's tankard, and discoursing on the two breeds, he dropped the observation, that if he bred for feeding only, and lett no tups, he would have *a little touch* of the Leicester.—How so, Sir, when Lincoln will come to such prices at such an age?—*Why, they will feed a little bit quicker, and run a little bit thicker.* If this is so, he is breeding sheep to answer some purpose not well understood by those who hire them. But I must suspect, from the countenance of some of his lambs, that he has, somehow or other, already got a *touch* of the Leicester.

Mr. Mallis, of Lumber, in 1797 sold 100 shearling Leicesters, in April, at 50*s.* each, having drawn a

score

score at 36*s.*; these were all in the wool, and had had only turnips and grass. Never sold Lincolns higher than 39*s.* The first fleece, Leicester, 8¾ lb. I asked his opinion in general, and found him wholly for Leicester.

Mr. Loft, of Marsh Chapel, five years ago, clipt from Lincolns 12*s.* a head.

Mr. Lloyd, of Belesby, was in the Lincoln breed, for 27 years: has had New Leicesters for seven years, and thinks them much the better. Keeps one in six more on the same land; but admits, that not all this is breed, as the land is improved; but on breed account cannot reckon on less than one in seven. He sells the wethers fat at two-shear, in harvest, and all gone by Michaelmas; and he did the same when he had Lincolns, which were not more than 20 lb. a quarter; his Leicesters 18 lb. to 24 lb. a quarter, and fatter than the Lincolns. Both breeds four to a tod; so no difference in wool. This year he had fleeces from 5 lb. to 15 lb. The Leicester breed is much hardier, some few individuals excepted, that are deficient in wool. Even on wet land, there is no difference; and will be in condition much sooner than Lincoln. They have also less offal; in tallow equal; and the wool a higher price. And he is of opinion, that in all these points he should think the same if he was on very rich land. He hires tups of Mr. Skipwith, and letts himself up to ten guineas. He has not observed them to go barren more than other breeds; tupped 400, and had only nine missed. He sells his wethers on an average of 1795, 6 and 7, at 45*s.*; some as high as 50*s.*; and he divides in supposition the 45*s.* in this manner:

Leicesters

	s.
Leicesters at six months old, worth	14
——— at twelve ditto	22
——— at twenty-eight ditto	28
——— at twenty-four ditto	35
——— at thirty ditto	45
——— and, if kept to thirty-six, would be	50

But if sold at a younger age than he does at present, he would make them worth more at those ages. Mr. Lloyd feeds sometimes with chaff and corn; observing, as I remarked, a parcel of troughs, that it would sometimes be necessary; but this he did not when he had Lincoln.

Mr. Skipwith, of Alesby, has been in the New Leicester breed twelve or thirteen years; and had been a Lincoln tup man sixteen years before: he prefers the New Leicester greatly; they feed quicker, have lighter offals; less wool per head of wethers and hogs; but the ewes equal to Lincoln; and upon the whole, yield more per acre, as he finds by his tod bill. The flock through, about 7 lb. on an average; the Lincolns about 8 lb. In winter they do not shrink like the Lincoln: the flesh is firmer, and endures better, and this even on wet land and bad keep; and they bear driving much better to market, to either London or the Yorkshire markets. In point of time of selling, his Lincolns went within three weeks of the same age, but the Leicesters fatter: he runs them also thicker on the same land, keeping five instead of four. Sells fat wethers at two-shear as soon as clipped; from 15 lb. to 40 lb. a quarter; average perhaps (but quite uncertain) 20 lb. In a word, he has no doubt of the superiority; and if he bred only to feed, without letting any

any tups, should adhere to this breed. He gets more than a lamb from every ewe tupped, on an average, on 1300 ewes. He used to lose many Lincolns in lambing, from the size of the head and legs, but the Leicesters come much easier. He letts rams from five to fifty guineas. His drape ewes he sells at Michaelmas, the lambs having been weaned at Lammas; last year none under 40*s.*; of some he knocks out the teeth, and puts them on turnips to eat the tops, and all gone by Christmas. This custom is common, but not too humane. Of Mr. Skipwith's sheep I did not see the best, for his shearling tups were not at Alesby; I saw some three, four, and five shears. Inquiring into the support in spring, I find they depend on turnips till the grasses are ready, and are consequently often much distressed: Mr. Skipwith observed that it is necessary to give corn.

At Humberston, all breed sheep, and are getting fast into the New Leicester. Mr. Tomlinson thinks, that the race formerly more common in the country with a larger bone, more wool and bigger in size, were a better breed, and more advantageous; his expression was, *there is more pride than profit in the new sort.* At Humberston, Waltham, Scarthe, &c. they sell their lambs at Michaelmas, or hogs in the spring; but down in the better marsh land they keep till two or three shear. Here they say, they have not land good enough, saying, that they are forced to sell their *heeders*, and joist their *sheeders* in the spring; and besides this, buy turnips, and run their ewes thin on the ground, as the east winds in spring cut them very severely. Sell the lambs from 10*s.* to 20*s.*; hogs in spring from 24*s.* to 28*s.* in their wool. Mr. Bee thinks a mixture of the New Leicester good, better than all Lincoln; but with the

the caution of not taking too much. Ewes give seven to 11 lb. wool; but the Leicesters 2lb. less than Lincoln, nor is the wool better. If any thing, they are run rather thicker on the land; one in ten for instance; but they are of a smaller size.

In discourse with Mr. Philipson, butcher and grazier at Louth, he gave his opinion, that the best stock was half Lincoln, half Leicester; this cross better than all of either. That the Leicester fed quicker, and had lighter offals than the Lincoln; and that the cross of half and half tallowed well; he thought as well as the Lincoln. That in respect of hardiness, he found no difference; for though the Lincoln had the thicker pelt, and more wool, the thickness and snugness of frame of the Leicester made amends. Mr. Blythe, butcher of the same place, was more cautious of giving his opinion; he seemed to recollect too much of Bakewell's conversations at the Blue Stone; and imagined, I apprehend, that if a stranger came with questions, they might be put from some interested motive; he was, however, very civil, and I afterwards found him very intelligent. Another butcher I met with at the same place, was of opinion that the Lincoln was the better breed, the meat as good, and as good a price, and much more tallow; and thought, that if a Lincoln and a Leicester of the same live weight were killed, the former would yield more money.

Mr. Pearson, at Haffham, near Louth, clipped above 100 tod of wool from 100 shearlings, and 100 two-shears; these sheep were bred by Mr. Paget, of Ludborough, true Lincoln; and they were sold fat out of their wool at 42*s.*; this was when mutton was 4*d.* per pound; 26 lb. a quarter.

Mr. Hyde, of Tathwell, bought about 70 acres of marsh,

marsh, and took the stock upon it, which were New Leicester sheep, to which some Lincolns were added, in the same condition; they were all taken away together, clipped, and sent to Smithfield, and the Lincolns sold for 4*s*. a head more than the Leicesters, and yielded 5*s*. a head more in wool. Mr. Hyde's ewes tod threes: his wethers twos and threes.

Mr. Whitworth, of Cookswold, near Louth, informed me, that in the rich marsh land the graziers prefer Lincolns greatly; so that when he has been there to sell sheep, he has been asked, if any cross of Leicester; and on his replying, none, they have said, if there is any Leicester blood in your flock, let it out as soon as you can. This gentleman's farm is like his immediate neighbours, who are in the Leicester breed, and he is confident, that they do not keep more on a given space of land than he does of Lincolns; and the weight of their wool is to his as seven to ten.

About Louth they are in the common habit of giving oats to their sheep in the spring, in case of turnips failing or running short. Mr. Allanby gave oats to 1000 ewes last spring, when turnips were done.

Mr. Clough, of Gayton, near Louth, puts 400 Lincoln ewes to tup, which bring him 370 lambs on an average; and he draws off 75 drape ewes at Lammas, and he keeps 120 shearling ewes to supply their place, and that of losses. Clips 480; that is, 360 ewes, and 120 shearling ditto. His lambs at Michaelmas go to his marsh farm at Alderchurch; but would then sell at 23*s*. to 30*s*. the price of 1796, and 1797; but before that usually at 20*s*.; five or six years before that, 12*s*. to 18*s*. Lamb hogs in the spring 1796, were worth 28*s*. to 40*s*. at Boston fairs; bought by marsh-men. His flock tods, on an average, half

 threes,

threes, half fours. His shepherd has 20*l.* a year, a house, a cow and pig, and land for potatoes. For his farm, of 450 acres, with a flock of 500 at turnips, 100 acres of that root should be provided, upon middling and bad soils. Nothing pays like breeding sheep; beasts never answer here on land that will do for sheep, only on low rushy land that will rot sheep; yet they must have some to tread their straw into muck.

Mr. Hyde, at Tathwell, without reckoning his marsh farm (which it may be supposed is considerable, as he fattens 500 wethers, and seventy beast annually, clipping 1150 sheep in all); puts 400 ewes to tup of the *true Lincoln breed*, no Leicester blood, which rear 360 lambs. The farm 450 acres, over which sheep go. Sends the lamb hogs to the marsh in May; could have sold them in 1796 at 35*s.* Sells fat at two-shear from April to October, some from 55*s.* to 4*l.*; some culls at 42*s.* to 45*s.*; the year before not so high. For three years before, the best marsh sheep 2*l.* 2*s.* and were as good as 55*s.* now. Clips half threes, half fours. Respecting the superiority of the Lincoln to the Leicester breed, supposing each thorough bred, it is, in wool 4 lb. per fleece, the Lincoln rising to 11 and 12 lb. if in good condition. In weight of carcass, the Lincoln will beat by 2 lb. a quarter in two-shear wethers, and at three-shear the superiority will be 5 lb. a quarter. In point of losses there will be no difference, nor in ewes going barren, nor in distempers. In tallow at three-shear there will be 6 lb. difference in favour of Lincoln; Mr. Pearson thinks more. In running number to acres, no difference. Hogs sold at Boston in May, Lincoln superior, being more saleable. In hardiness, on bleak hills and wet soils, the Lincoln will beat. The Leicesters must

must have sheds to run in, and jackets to cover them after shearing, a thing never heard of with Lincoln. Mr. Clough thinks the Leicesters lamb easier; Mr. Hyde thinks otherwise, and Mr. Pearson, of Haugham, agrees with him. Mr. Hyde assured me, that if his farm was on the very poorest soils there are on the Wolds, he would keep all Lincoln breed, and no Leicester blood, equally as on the richest land; for if a farmer is forced to sell lean and poor, Lincoln will certainly beat Leicester. Mr. Hyde seldom corn-feeds, unless turnips are rotten or snow deep. Last spring he gave oats; Mr. Pearson and Mr. Clough, both in Lincoln breed, gave none. I had much pleasure in viewing Mr. Hyde's tups, examining one by one, I believe three or four score of them; but all two, three, four, or five-shear: I saw no shearlings. They are by far superior to any Lincolns I have yet seen. Mr. Hyde has had them but two years; but the old shepherd, who has been on the farm thirty years, under Mr. Wall and Mr. Chaplin, assured me that there was not one drop of Leicester blood in any that I saw. Many of them have very thin pelts, full fore flanks and chines, and for their size, small bones. Mr. Hyde letts great numbers. I should give a more particular account of them, but I wish Lincoln breeders, in a question so much disputed, to speak for themselves, which will be more satisfactory to the reader than my personal opinion. It is proper to add to this account, that a few years ago, before Mr. Hyde took Mr. Chaplin's stock, he made an experiment of a cross of the New Leicester; and it was from the result that he has since been so decidedly in favour of the Lincoln breed: from the same land he had less wool, and less mutton, and therefore went back to Lincoln.

The

The Wold farmers have very generally pieces of marsh, which are overlooked by men who live there, called shepherds, who look at the stock twice a day, and for a few weeks before clipping, thrice; they are paid 1*s.* an acre. Much attention is necessary when heavy in wool, as the sheep are often found on their backs, and if not soon relieved, die. This is called *far wel tard*, or *lifting*, and they have dogs that will turn them. With Mr. Neve, in travelling to Alford, a dog of this sort *lifted* twenty-one sheep in the way.

Distempers in the Marsh.—1. The sturdy, or bladder on the brain. There is an old fellow near North Somercots, who trepans for it, and saves as many as he loses. He raises the skin with a sharp strong hooked knife over the spot affected, about the size of a crown-piece; he then raises nearly the same size of the skull bone, letting the piece hang as by a hinge on one side, then with a quill cut slanting to a point, like a spear, and barbed on each side, he fishes in for the bladder, and brings it out whole, putting down the bone again, and covering with a plaster. He has 2*s.* 6*d.* if he succeeds; if not, nothing. 2. The *meag* runs, or rickets, incurable. 3. The *rubbers*, a sort of itch; they rub themselves to death; no cure. 4. The *scab;* mercurial ointment; used to give 5*s.* a score for all infected, or likely to be so; now cheaper. 5. The *respe;* probably the red water, not peculiar to sheep feeding on cole or turnips; for they have it on grass feeding in the spring, when thriving fast. 6. The *rot;* very little here; in rotten years, the sheep that feed on the salt marsh ver which the spring tides come, sell very high, in confidence that they are safe. Upon this disorder it well deserves noting, that a shepherd,

herd, who when young was a shepherd's boy to an old man who lived at Netlam, near Lincoln, a place famous for the rot, told Mr. Neve, that he was persuaded sheep took the rot only of a morning before the dew was well off. At that time they folded, being open field; his master's shepherd kept his flock in fold always till the dew was gone, and with no other attention his sheep were kept sound, when all the neighbours lost their flocks.

It is observed in the Marsh, that nothing makes wool grow so fast as feeding upon oil-cake.

In regard to the New Leicester, Mr. Neve, from all he has observed in the Marsh, though he is of opinion that the breed feed kindly, and have great merit, yet wool is an object of such importance in the scale of profit, that it must not be lost sight of. When that is 9*s*. or 10*s*. a tod, the breed would probably be the best, but not at the present prices.

Mr. Bourne, of Dalby, is one of the most distinguished tup breeders in the county; his flock:

Breeding ewes 900
Tups .... 150; letts upwards of 100.

Clips about 2400: lambs as many hogs from turnips the succeeding spring as ewes put to tup; consequently the number of lambs considerably exceed that of ewes. But say,

900

Shearlings losses 5 per cent. 855 { half sheeders, half heeders, except the reserve of rams,
425 sheeders

of which 350 to ewe stock, and the remainder sold with the drape ewes.

Heeders

Heeders	425
Five per cent. less	21
	404
Of these, to add to rams instead of 70 draped off or worn out	70
Two-shear wethers	334

Of these, 150 are sent to London in autumn, fat; the remainder clipt early in the spring three-shears, and sent also to London.

Annual Sale.

	s.	d.			
150 two-shear wethers, sold in autumn or winter for 1794, at	44	0			
1795, at	48	0			
1796, at	50	0			
3)	142	0			
Average	47	4	£.355	0	0
150 three-shear wethers, 1794, at	45	0			
1795, at	48	0*			
1796, at	62	0			
3)	155	0			
Average	51	8	387	11	0
Carry forward			£.742	11	0

* After the severe winter, wool only gained.

Brought

	s. d.	£. s. d.
Brought forward		£.742 11 0
300 drape ewes; 100 of the best fattened at home, sold at London the succeeding summer, in 1794, at	34 0	
1795, at	38 0	
1796, at	40 0	
	3)112 0	
Average	37 4	186 13 4
200 at 20*s*.		200 0 0
50 old rams, at 40*s*.		100 0 0
Wool about 750 tods, price 1795, at	20 0	
1796, at	22 0	
1797, at	20 0	
	3)62 0	
Average	20 0	768 15 0
Rams about 700 guineas; of course will vary much; but in an account of this sort they are only to be reckoned as the very best wethers of the flock; say, therefore, 100 at 52*s*. 6*d*.		262 10 0
		£.2260 9 4

50*s*. per breeding ewe.

19*s*. per head clipped.

The flock has generally about 140 acres of turnips; and about 100 tons of hay. Seldom grows seeds, has none

none at present, what is laid not being to be ploughed again; and in all about 1400 acres, wood excluded, of which near 1000 are grass, and the rest arable; upwards of half of it indifferent land, and keeps, besides this flock in summer, 160 head of cattle, and in winter 110, besides near 60 horses of all sorts and ages

In relation to Mr. Bourne's breed of sheep, it is neither New Leicester nor Old Lincoln, but a mixture gradually formed with much attention by his grandfather, his father, and himself, from many improved kinds, particularly the Durham, the New Leicester, and the Old Lincoln; the objects he has had in view have been size of carcass, and length of wool; and in these respects, the breed is generally admitted to be of great merit, as indeed may easily be supposed by the request his tups are in, for he letts from five guineas to fifty, and has more than once had a greater demand than he was able to supply. And for wool, five fleeces of two-shear wethers, that is, the second clipping, will weigh 2 tods 29 lb. or above 11 lb. a-head. Of the portions of each sort of blood it is difficult to be exact; of the pure Leicester blood, the nearest approximation has been by a Leicester ram, but bred in Lincolnshire, covering not more than ten of his own ewes in 1782; but is not sure that he was a full bred one, as he came from Lincolnshire only. The Durham blood has not been renewed of twenty years or more. Mr. Bourne has more than once used a ram half Leicester; but upon the whole. it may be concluded, that this flock has vastly more Lincoln blood than any other; and from the general colour of the information which has been gathered from various facts and observations, he is of opinion that the breed thus formed has such a degree of merit, that he has no reason

reason to wish a change upon any other system than what he has pursued. In case of lambing, he does not sustain such losses as makes that an object to consider particularly. In hardiness he is well satisfied; he generally has 8 or 900 lambs on turnips, and they all run in one fold, which he conceives to be a proof of it, as they are never allowed any fodder, except in cases of absolute necessity, such as intense frosts, or heavy snows, when a little hay is given; they have very rarely run to corn stacks on such occasions; does not feed his ewes or tups with corn; the latter have a little hay with their turnips. He has been very free from the *respe*, &c. and on the whole, as healthy a breed as any in the kingdom. And lastly, that to have ewes go barren, is a rare thing with him.

Shepherd paid 12*s*. a week, a house, and four or five acres of land, and summering two cows; besides a few trifling perquisites, particularly 6*d*. allowed for every pair of lambs reared to May-day. Many farmers allow the lamb-skins; but this, for obvious reasons, much better.

At Partney-fair, Mr. Blythe, of Louth, had the goodness to introduce me to a breeder of sheep (I am sorry his name is obliterated in penciling), who from 54 ewes of the Old Lincoln breed, had in 1797 72 lambs reared; and 92 fleeces yielded him 33 tod, at 29 lb. per tod, or $10\frac{1}{2}$ lb. each. He has killed, of 25 lb. a quarter, ewes that gave suck at the time of killing. He has sold drape ewes at 56*s*. each. I was a little surprised, after such circumstances, to hear that he intended going for a cross to Mr. Johnson, of Kermond, to get a change: his reason was the gid, by which he had lost three in sixty: after deducting all losses, he seemed to have profit enough left for a reasonable expectant.

At

At this fair, stock sold lower in 1797 than in 1796; the highest price given for lambs was 28*s*. for Mr. Brook's (30*s*. in 1796). The champion's (Mr. Dymock) sold for 25*s*. 6*d*. and were the best I saw in the fair; very fine well-made lambs in every respect. An observation I made was, that in a very full fair for lambs, there was very little Leicester blood *clearly apparent*.

At Mr. Bourne's, at Dalby, I had the pleasure of meeting Mr. Bourne, his relation, of Haugh, and Mr. Kershaw, of Driby, who are both in nearly the same system of sheep, and their account is as follows: the former took an increase of the Leicester blood in 1792, by which he increased flesh, and lessened wool. Mr. Kershaw half threes and half fours to a tod, Mr. Bourne rather less.

Both are clear that they cannot keep more of one sort upon an acre than of the other, especially in summer, when alone the comparison can be fairly made. Mr. Bourne has had his flock very unhealthy, so that he has received more for skins than common in any flock; and this induced him to change to Leicester. The *respe* had been very fatal to him on turnips, cole, and grass. Mr. Kershaw has had the same disorder; but by taking them out of nights, lost fewer. Disturbing alone is serviceable, but not so good as taking out. They sell the 4th of May, two-shear in the fleece: 1797, at 42*s*. to 50*s*.; in 1796, at 46*s*. at a medium; in 1795, lower. Average for three years 42*s*. 6*d*. proportioned to which their value would be,

At

	s.	
At 6 months	20	
12 months	30	5 per cent. loss,
18 months	33	
24 months	46	5 per cent. loss,

this upon land at 40*s*. an acre.

Mr. Philip Wright, of Spilsby, has been in the New Leicester breed for fourteen years by tups, but had no ewes except of his own breeding; had been for many years in another cross of Leicesters; but much Leicester blood. He says, that if he bred and lett no tups, but depended on fairs, and on feeding what he bred, he would equally prefer New Leicester: and he prefers them because they will get fat at an earlier age than the true Lincoln; he thinks that the New Leicester will be as fat at Lady-day, coming two-shear, as Lincoln will at Lammas. Run as many of one breed as of another on the same land; two an acre in marsh of summer and winter, and a bullock to an acre and a quarter, rent 30*s*. Equal in hardiness and difficulties. Leicesters lamb easiest. No difference in the ewes going barren. The Leicesters run about three to a tod; the Lincolns higher.

Mr. Wright puts 500 ewes to the tup.

Clips 1400, rears 500 lambs.

Sells 100 drape ewes.
30 tups saved.
70 two-shears.
70 three-shears.
50 shearlings.

In 250 heeders, 20 will be lost before coming to market.

Drapes,

Drapes, 1797——28*s*.
1796——30*s*.
1795——25*s*.

3)83

27*s*. 4*d*.

50 shearlings, 1797——a score at 3*l*. 5*s*. rest 54*s*.
1796——56*s*.
1795——47*s*.

Two-shears, 1797——3*l*.—3*l*. 3*s*.
1796——56*s*.
1795——47*s*.

Three-shear, 1796——some as high as £.4 4 0

Other prices { 3 10 0; 3 5 0; 3 0 0; 2 18 0 }

1797——70*s*.
ditto——58*s*.
1795——55*s*.

The 1400 go over about 800 acres, 55 marsh, 40 or 50 of cole and turnips; gives oats to ewes with lamb: none to tups; oil-cake never. Letts rams from three guineas to thirty guineas. Has gone to Dishley every year from 1784, except one, and has sometimes had three or four tups in a season. Never jackets any.

If a three-shear sells for 3*l*. it will be worth,

At 6 months, 28*s*.
At 12 ——— 35*s*. Wool 9½ lb.
At 18 ——— 40*s*.
At 24 ——— 48*s*. Wool 9 lb.
At 30 ——— 56*s*.
At 36 ——— 60*s*. Wool 9 lb.

At

At Boothby, at the Rev. Mr. Wall's, I was on a sort of classic ground, for here were first reared that breed of true Lincoln sheep which afterwards became so famous in the county, under the names both of Mr. Wall (uncle to the present proprietor) and Mr. Chaplin, and which are now in the hands of Mr. Hyde, of Tathwell; there are some very good tups here at present of the same breed.

In the hundred of Skirbeck they breed two-thirds of what is fed in the district; chiefly the Lincolnshire, but are not very choice in the selection of rams; it is principally done by little farmers, who tup under 60 ewes. But some few have a slight cross of Leicester blood. Mr. Linton tup 110 ewes, of the Lincoln breed. He sends to Mr. Bourne, of Dalby, annually for a ram, which is chosen by himself; and Mr. Linton prefers this breed to those which have more Leicester blood. He reckons the profit of a breeding ewe thus: he rears 115 lambs from 110 ewes; the ewes yield 8 lb. of wool, and the lambs would sell for, at Michaelmas, 18*s*. each; the surplus will make this 18*s*. 9*d*. the wool is worth 7*d*. a pound, or 4*s*. 8*d*.; the drape being worth as much as a lamb there is no deduction; but 2*s*. a-head on the ewes may be reckoned for losses; deduct this from 23*s*. 5*d*. and there remains 21*s*. 5*d*. for the product of a ewe, four running upon an acre in summer, and the winter feed being made up by following other stock on eddish, and a few cabbages in the spring; a plant which Mr. Linton considers as the best crop he has for the support of cattle and sheep. He sells his wethers in Smithfield, at three-shear, from 45*s*. to 65*s*. each; having produced about 30 lb. of wool. The drape ewes being fatted, sell on an average at 40*s*. having ceased breeding; the wool worth nearly 20*s*.

20*s*. a tod in 1797. A wether thus pays in three years, reckoning the average at 50*s*. at least 3*l*. 10*s*. or 1*l*. 3*s*. 4*d*. per annum.

At the ordinary at Horncastle, I had pleasure, and what is better, instruction, in meeting many capital breeders; the conversation presently fixed to the question of sheep, and as opinions differed greatly, I shall note one or two prominent features. Mr. Elmhurst, of Stainsby, the chairman, declared, that "he knew no better rule for breeders to attend to, than to have or get such a breed of sheep, as have good and thrifty feeding carcasses; high-standing enough for Smithfield; *properly* lengthy; and above all, with good, wide, and well made loins. And also never lose sight of, but strictly attend to, *having* and *keeping* a good, long-woolled skin upon the whole of their flocks; and not to lessen the weight and well grown quality of the wool, by running into new-fangled fancies, and be *persuaded* thereto by all the rhetoric and well-placed speeches of all the upstart, new-fangled disciples of *any* man."

A better rule by half, replied another breeder, is to breed that sheep which will eat least food, and pay most money for what he does eat.

That breed, rejoined Mr. Elmhurst, must be the true Old Lincoln; and remarked, in a comparison of the two breeds of Leicester and Lincoln, that many years ago they had in this country a very excellent old, rough, red potatoe, but from an over eagerness to introduce new sorts, they had so mixed, adulterated, and changed the sorts, that an old, true, honest rough red of the right old sort, was no where to be found: just so it would be with the right Old Lincoln breed of sheep, if it was not for such men as himself to resist novel-

novelties. The Rev. Mr. Raucliff replied to this, that the admission proved the new introduction to be better, or the old rough red would not have been lost; and if the Old Lincoln sheep followed the rough red, it will prove no more than the superiority of the sort that prevails. Mr. Elmhurst then observed, that he had been above forty years in business, and from that experience preferred the Lincoln breed greatly; he clips many two to the tod, and not many less; sells three-shear wethers at *3l.* The introduction of the New Leicester he looks upon to be as much a matter of fashion as the ladies' feathers. To which Mr. Raucliff replied, that it was a good matter of fashion, which enabled farmers to sell their sheep fat from farms that never had fat ones on them till they were stocked with Leicesters; and then observing that Mr. Elmhurst himself was not absolutely free from Leicester blood; that gentleman answered, "I come as near to the Lincoln as I possibly can; as to pure blood, I know not where to go for it."

Mr. Raucliff, of Fallaby, is in the Leicester cross, and remarked at the same meeting, that he sold his two-shears the end of May, taking the wool at *2l. 2s.* and that *36s.* had been the price for several years; he produced his tod bill, by which it appeared that 890 fleeces produced 253 tods: and

Here also meeting Mr. Gay, of Wragby, I found that he always buys the sheep that have the longest wool, which breed he prefers.

Mr. Whalesby, present also, was of opinion, that more Leicesters may be kept on the same land than Lincolns, and that the difference is rather considerable.

Mr. Bonner, a butcher, being present, and applied to for his opinion, remarked, that he did not con ider selling

ing at two-shear altogether such an advantage, for that he would always give more for a three-shear than a younger sheep proportioned to the weights, because he was sure to find a hidden treasure in the older ones. Mr. Gay, of Goutby, confirmed this, and said that he had long sold two and three-shear for Mr. Vyner, and the three-shear have paid best. So much for a Lincolnshire ordinary.

Mr. Parkinson, of Asgarby, who shewed me some good Leicester tups, or rather a cross or two of Leicester, approves the breed on account of their being earlier fat than Lincoln; but still holds the Lincoln to be an excellent breed, and is of opinion that the great Leicester breeders have bred their sheep *too fine:* from those with fine heads he does not get so much wool as he wishes. What made him originally have recourse to the Leicester breed, was his picking out for his father the largest tup he could find at Mr. Bourne's, at Dalby, of the Lincoln sort; but when the produce came to Smithfield, he observed that the New Leicesters, which were at market at the same time, did not lose flesh, and sold, a year younger, at as high a price. But at the same time admitted, that a brother of Mr. Johnson of Kermond, having noted the food ate by two large sheep, being shearlings of 34 lb. a quarter, and by two other of 24 lb. a quarter, there was a very small difference, but not near the proportion of their weights.

Mr. Cracraft, of Keal, keeps 400 breeding ewes, and last year sold his shearling wethers at May-day, at 3*l.* each, for 80*s.*; the rest 50*s.*; the year before, all at 2*l.* 12*s.* 6*d.* except a score, which went at 3*l.* 3*s.*; all in the wool; and he reckons the annual product of every ewe at 1*l.* 11*s.* 6*d.* He is in the New Leicester breed; his

his drapes, on a medium of 1795, 6, and 7, 27*s.* each, 130 annually. He clips threes nearly, or above 9 lb.; rears as many lambs as ewes. He clips 800 on his farm, of 590 acres; but keeps besides, 90 head of cattle, 80 horses, 20 being breeding mares; from 30 to 40 of this stock run in the fen, but to sore loss, for he one year lost sixteen horses by the botts, a disorder very common there. He has 200 acres of corn; the stock of sheep is therefore considerable.

Sir Joseph Banks, on the sheep system of this county, gave me a general hint extremely to the purpose.

"As tups are always hired in Lincolnshire by the breeders, the lambs may be said to be purchased before they are born; as a year's credit, however, is given on this occasion, they are not paid for till the actual value can be fairly estimated; if, therefore, any one who has hired a tup at a considerable price, finds the lambs he has got not sufficiently above the ordinary sort to pay him the difference, with interest, he complains to the tup-man, who gererally views the lambs with him, and makes a fair abatement, which is generally settled in the price of the hire of the next years' tup; this regulates the price of letting, and makes the tup-men a most useful set of people. The great mass of breeders in Lincolnshire sell their beeder-lambs about Old Michaelmas time, or a little after; a succession of fairs for that purpose are held in a village called Partney. These lambs are re-sold in the spring at Lincoln fair, under the name of hogs: at Midsummer their owners clip, and then winter them; the succeeding spring they are carried to Boston, where, in a long succession of markets, they are sold to the graziers, with their wool on, under the name of shearlings, and

 imme-

immediately turned into the marsh to fatten ; the graziers take their fleeces, and having wintered them, get the kindliest to Smithfield in the course of the succeeding spring ; those that do not fat so easily, yield the grazier a fleece at Midsummer, and are got off the ground in the course of the next autumn. Here you see a combined system of sheep agriculture, for as the animals are eternally either changing hands, or yielding fleeces, they make a return of some kind or other to their owners nearly half-yearly, from the time of their birth to that of their final dissolution at Smithfield."

Estimate by Mr. Parkinson.

Sheep in 1781, 2, 3, 4, 5. An acre of land, worth 20*s*.

1st, An acre keeps two ewes, and produce two lambs, 12*s*.	£.1 4 0	
Two fleeces, four to tod, 10*s*.	0 5 0	
		£.1 9 0
2d, Two lamb hogs bought in 18*s*. kept one year, sold 26*s*.	0 16 0	
Two fleeces, three to tod, 14*s*.	0 9 6	
		1 5 6
3d, Graziers buy said shearlings at 26*s*. sold at 28*s*. two of them ; profit by carcass	0 4 0	
Four fleeces, or one tod and a half wool, at 12*s*.	0 18 0	
		1 2 0
		£.3 16 6

Profit

Profit by beasts and horses nearly the same as below; to be bought in April, grazed the summer months, and sold out in the autumn	£.1 5 6

Sheep, 1794, 5, 6, 7, now worth 30*s*. per acre.

One acre of land, of the best average pasture in the county of Lincoln, will keep and produce as follows, according to the prices of 1796 and 1797:

1st, An acre keeps two ewes, produce two lambs, at 24*s*.	£.2 8 0	
Sell at Michaelmas and two fleeces, at the rate of four to a tod	0 9 0	
		£.2 17 0
2d, Two lamb hogs bought in at 34*s*. kept one year, sell out again, shearlings at 50*s*. profit 16*s*. makes	1 12 0	
Two fleeces, 7*s*. each, suppose three to tod	0 14 0	
		2 6 0

N. B. If clipped again before sold, would be 14*s*. more.

3d, Buy said shearlings at 50*s*.; sold three shearlings out again, about 56*s*. profit of two sheep	£.0 12 0	
Four fleeces of wool about one tod and a half, 19*s*.	1 8 6	
		£.2 0 6

N.B. Every

N. B. Every two acres of this sort of land is supposed to fatten a small heifer and leave a net profit of about 50*s*. in each acre, 25*s*. added to the mean of

Sheep profits	£.2	17	0	£.7	3	6	= to	2	7	6
	2	6	0							
	2	0	6							
Besides extra summer keeps for horses, &c.								£.2	12	6

N. B. It is always understood in Lincolnshire, that all sorts of grazing occupations should pay two years' rent, and rabbit-warrens the same. But arable farms ought to produce three years' rent.

An

An Estimate of the probable Gain that may arise by Grazing a Farm. By Mr. Parkinson.

The Rent. — *Dr.*

Grazing Land.	A.	R.	P.	Val.p.Ac.	£.	s.	d.	Acr.
1. To land for keeping the breeding ewes - - -	160	0	0	16	128	0	0	160
1 To ditto for keeping the tups -	15	0	0	30	22	10	0	15
1. To ditto for the she hogs -	58	0	0	16	46	8	0	58
1. To ditto for the he hogs -	55	0	0	25	68	15	0	55
2. To ditto for the shearlings -	55	0	0	25	68	15	0	55
3. To ditto for the two-shear -	55	0	0	25	68	15	0	55
4. To ditto for the three-shear -	45	0	0	36	81	0	0	45
1. To ditto for the drape ewes -	50	0	0	30	75	0	0	50
Total - - -	493	0	0		559	3	0	493

Profit. — *Cr.*

Breeding ewes	Loss.	Net.		Tods.		£.	s.	d.
300	37	263	Half 4 to a tod; Half 3 to a tod	76½				
Tups 30		30	Half 2 to a tod; Half 3 to a tod	12½				
She lambs 131	16	115	Half 2 to a tod; Half 4 to a tod	33				
			Hoe lambs the same	33				
Two-shear sheep 105	10	95	At three to a tod	31½				
Three-shear 95	5	90	Half 3 to a tod; Half 2 to a tod	37				
Drape ewes 120	20	100	At three to a tod	33				
			Total -	256½	at 20*s.* per tod	256	10	0

			£. s. d.	£.	s.	d.
30	1	Tups lett at the average price of 4*l.* each - -		120	0	0
116		He lambs at six months old, at 21*s.* -	121 16 0			
110	1	Hogs at ditto, at 30*s.* - - -	165 0 0			
105	2	Shearlings at ditto, at 40*s.* - -	210 0 0			
95	3	Two-shear at ditto, at 50*s.* - -	237 10 0			
90	4	Three-shear at ditto, at 60*s.* - - - -		270	0	0
700	1	Drape ewes at ditto, at 30*s.* - - - -		150	0	0
		Total profits, Cr. - - -		796	10	0
		Deduct rent, Dr. - - -		559	3	0
		Net gain by sheep - - -		237	7	0

The same quantity of Sheep.	Profits. £.	s.	d.	Rent. £.	s.	d.	Gain. £.	s.	d.
1. By selling hogs 12 months old -	590	0	0	363	13	8	226	0	0
2. By selling shearlings - -	668	0	0	409	8	0	258	12	0
3. By selling two-shears - -	727	0	0	478	3	0	248	17	0
4. By selling three-shears - -	796	10	0	559	3	0	237	7	0

Remains to be accounted for in the farmer's profit, the feeding of beasts in the pastures with sheep; and it may be observed in an arable farm, the fallows of 15 acres in turnips will supply the winter keeping of 55 acres of grass, to winter the lamb hogs.

Mr. Thomas Tannard, of Frampton, near Boston, is one of the greatest graziers in Lincolnshire; he feeds above 100 oxen, and clips 1400 sheep: his growth is 600 tod of wool; but in 1797, 1852 fleeces gave 768 tod; and his capital per acre may be estimated at 30*l.*; some years it will be less. His opinion is decidedly in favour of the true Lincoln sheep, which he sells at three-shear at 3*l.* 10*s.* and to 4*l.* a-head. He has about three sheep per acre in summer, and two in winter, on his land. One superiority of the Lincoln breed which he remarked, was, that they travel much better to London; and as to keeping more Leicesters than Lincolns on the same land, he observes that he has had both, and keeps as many of one as of the other.

Mr. Tannard favoured me with some particulars of the progress of prices, which well deserve minuting. He has a manuscript note of the year 1716, which runs thus: "In the year 1716 my father sold 366 tod of wool to John Aggs, at 22*s.* 9*d.* per tod; and in 1717, 367 tods, at 27*s.* and one guinea over; and in 1718, 373 tods, at 27*s.* and a guinea." This was by Mr. John Fotheringham, of Holbeach: it is curious; let the attentive reader consider the advance which has taken place in mutton, and in every product of the earth, wool alone excepted, in manufactures, and in all other objects of consumption or export, and then ask, why a *fall* has been experienced in this only article; what can be the cause? It is answered in a moment; wool is the only object of export restricted by a system of impolitic laws, which fetter it in a manner unknown to any other raw material in this kingdom.

In 1782 Mr. Tannard bought wethers at 15*s.*; in 1796, at 46*s.* the weight equal. In 1782, drapes at 8*s.* 6*d.*

6*d*. and wool, 452 fleeces 177 tod, at 8*s*. In 1797, 120 fleeces, 50 tod, at 20*s*.

The late Mr. Berridge, brother to the Rev. Mr. Berridge, of Alderchurch, stated an experiment comparing the two breeds of sheep, the Lincoln and New Leicester, which deserves minuting; Mr. Linton also recited the circumstances. He drew off twenty of each breed, the late Mr. Codd, of Ranby, choosing ten Leicesters from a lot, against ten Lincolns; they were directly weighed alive, put into the same pasture, and killed at the same time; were of the same age; being shearlings the difference in weight at that time very little; the 4th of May they were weighed again, and the increase nearly equal; one of each was killed. At Michaelmas again, the best and worst killed, when the Lincoln had a little advantage. The 11th December two more were killed, when the Lincoln had gained more upon the Leicester. That time twelvemonth, in December, the increase of the Lincoln was far more considerable; the expression used to me was, "beat the Leicester hollow." This experiment deserves attention, though the written minutes of it were not to be produced; it was known by many gentlemen from the commencement to the end, and by several present when this account was given me.

Mr. Loft, of Marsh Chapel.—The late Mr. Codd, of Ranby, about sixteen years ago, having been possessed of a very fine flock of Old Lincoln sheep, made the change to New Leicesters, by going to Mr. Bakewell, and continued with him till he changed the mode of letting, to make the hirers bid; he then went to Mr. Stone, and thus has bred from very capital stock for many years. The flock at present consists of 450 breeding ewes. Clips 1800, as he buys for marsh land.

Sells

Sells the wethers three-shear, beginning a week after Old Lady-day, and all gone by the end of July, 1797, at 3*l.* each; in 1796 the same; in 1795 lower. In 1782 Mr. Loft sold his own at 25*s.* in 1783, 28*s.*; in 1784, 31*s* 6*d.*; 1785, at 34*s.*; in 1786, at 37*s.*; then 40*s.* 42*s.* 45*s.* and 52*s.* 6*d.* to 55*s.*; in 1796, at 54*s.*

Mr. Codd's at present,

Lamb at 6 months, 25*s.*
12 months, 30*s.* in the wool; 9½ lb.
18 months, 38*s.*
24 months, 48*s.* in the wool; 12 lb.
30 months, 50*s.*
36 months, 60*s.* naked; wool 14 lb. at 8*d.* or 9*s.* 4*d.*

Breeding ewes, clip two fours to one three.

Will rear, to Michaelmas 100 lambs from 100 ewes.

This weight of wool may appear great; let it be observed, that Mr. Loft and Co. have sold 1100 tod of wool from 2400 acres of all sorts of land, &c. included, which shews how productive these sheep are in wool. In running them on the land, he thinks, as breeding, they are thicker on the land than Lincolns, in the proportion of five to four; but in feeding, stocked the same as the others on grass. But the Leicesters are off in July, and the Lincolns on the same land, will not on an average be gone till October; thus the difference may be estimated at three months, and yet not make more money, nor so much mutton, sinking in price after many of the Leicesters are gone. In respect to health and distempers, the two breeds are the same; but if an accident happens, the Leicesters being fat, and the Lincolns not, the loss is greater with the latter. In respect of hardiness, Mr. Loft finds his

his breed as hardy as any in the county can be, and have never failed in any respect; nor has he ever put them in jackets, though it might be useful to any sheep. The great losses are in hogs from six months to fifteen months, and principally by the *respe*.

Mr. Loft prefers Leicester with a great weight and good quality of wool, to such as have lighter fleeces: and his reason is, that the wool will be heavier than from finer Leicesters; but no other motive. At the same time he also observes, that with the weight of wool comes a little addition of bone, which is a disadvantage.

Mr. Corrington, of Horncastle, partner with Mr. Loft in the farm at Ranby, informed me, that at Boston mart (1796) Mr. Ingram, a butcher there, killed five three-shear sheep, which were shewn as very extraordinary ones, of the Lincoln breed, which produced 17 lb. of wool the last fleece; grazed by Mr. John Bartholomew, of Freiston, and by Mr. Thacker, of Langrike-ferry; the former having bought them lambs at Lincoln fair, and sold them to Mr. Thacker, who fatted them. They were very fine, but Mr. Corrington has proof, that they were got by a tup of Mr. Codd, of Ranby.

Mentioning to Mr. Loft the objections I had heard from some very considerable graziers, to the New Leicesters, he remarked, that there is always a distinction to be made between men who buy and those who breed; to buy cheap is a great object, but it is not to be concluded that the best breed are to be bought cheapest. The true knowledge of a breed is only to be had from those who fatten the sheep they breed. There is something in this, but not enough to be conclusive.

After Mr. Loft had been ten years in the Leicester breed, he sold a sheep at three-shear, that had given

19*s*.

19*s*. 7½*d*. in one fleece of wool; but Mr. Kelk, of Postland, grew a Lincoln fleece that sold for 22*s*. weighing above a tod.

Mr. Cunliff, of Lancaster, a very considerable wool buyer, I met at Ranby, thinks that the average of the fleeces of all Lincolnshire, is about 9 lb. He remarked, that Mr. Chester, of Toïnton, grew beautiful wool; and Mr. Ostler, of Alesby, the same. Kirkby very fine, but that of Revesby uncommonly fine, better perhaps than any.

Mr. Blythe, senior, of Louth, is a friend to the New Leicester breed of sheep, and made a curious observation on increasing the wool by fresh crosses, after getting into that breed. If you add 2 lb. of wool, you lose 2 lb. a quarter in the carcass; for much wool will have a thick skin, and takes more feeding than a well made carcass. I read this note to him after I had written it, and he assented to the accuracy; it was at a moment when I could not prolong the conversation, or he would probably have explained himself to mean, that the loss *in general* would amount to that in profit, but not in any particular sheep; as the long-woolled ones are of a larger size, upon the whole, than the Leicesters. He has been forty years in the wool-stapling trade, buying 20,000 tods annually, and thinks that one-fourth of all the sheep clipt in all the county are threes; and three-fourths fours; and he thinks that all such parts of the county as he is acquainted with yields, on an average of all sorts of land, one fleece and a half per acre.

Mr. Smith, of South Elkington,

Breeding ewes	800
Clips	1600

Upon 1600 acres, 200 of which marsh.

Sells

Sells the wethers at two-shear; some fat, some lean to those who fatten on turnips.

The fat two-shear at 44*s.* in October.

Run all together, ewes and all, four to a tod, 29 lb. Has got a cross from Ranby, because he thinks that he shall get them fatter at the same age; and expects to run one in ten more on the same land. Whether he will lose in wool he does not know yet, but expects finer wool. In hardiness and distemper supposes the same; but expects fewer losses in lambing.

Rev. Mr. Allington, of Swinop.

Losses from May-day. 1793, to May-day, 1794, 165 sheep out of 1466.

From May-day, 1794, to May-day, 1795, lost 166 out of 1600.

From June, 1795, to June, 1796, lost 168 out of 1256. From June, 1796, to June 1797, lost 131 out of 1364, the number in June, 1796: the total numbers include lambs, and counting stock at the commencement of the years thus dated: of the lost sheep, by killing many as soon as taken ill, they have turned to one-third or one-fourth of their value.

Flock, July 4th, 1797	584 ewes,
	645 lambs,
	233 ewe hogs.
Clipped 817	1462

The wether hogs sold at Boston 4th of May, in their wool.

Sale.

Sale.—240 wether hogs.

	£	s.	d.	£	s.	d.
150 at 40s.				£.300	0	0
90, 70 at 25s. 87*l.* 10s.; 20 at 20*l.*				107	10	0
90 drapes at 30s.				135	0	0
Wool, the hogs *threes*, Ewes *fours*, } 220 tod, at 20s.				220	0	0
Locks, 26 stone 6s.				7	16	0
131 lost, of which 87 were hogs						
70 ewes sold, 60 for 36s.	£.108	0	0			
10 at 36s.	18	0	0			
				126	0	0
16 at 28s.				22	8	0
Stock in July, 1797, losses deducted	1462					
Stock in June, 1796	1364					
Increase	98					
Valued at 21s.				104	18	0
131 lost, of which 87 were hogs, made 5s.				32	15	0
Total				£.1056	7	0
The 150 sold at 40s. were joisted at Boston two weeks, at 6*d.* a-head	£.7	10	0			
Deduct 4s. keeping on 98 lambs from June to October, when valued at 21s.	19	12	0			
				27	2	0
Remains				£.1029	5	0

Or 35s. 3*d.* on the breeding ewes.

Go over of corn, seeds, turnips, and grass, 1300 acres, of which corn 350; but there are 37 farm-horses, and 40 others; and 16 draught oxen, 14 cows, 15 one and

and two years, 10 calves; the whole 1400 acres, including 50 gorse, and 50 meadow, of which sheep have nothing; would have lett five years ago, when Mr. Allington took it, at 420*l.* This flock has no hay; they are winter-fed on turnips; the hogs put on the beginning of October, and kept on them till sold in the spring, the ewes two months or ten weeks, according to quantity to spare. He sows about two-sevenths of his arable land, or near 300 acres; and three-sevenths of seeds, deducting generally one field of 30 or 40 acres. Thirty or forty yearlings, and two year old beasts run on them a good deal in summer, and afterwards some horses.

The wool of the Wolds, in a line from Barton to Gersby, is of a very fine quality. Mr. Holdgate, of Thoresway, informed me, that he, in 1797, sold at 22*s.* the tod of 28 lb., while I have seen much sold at 20*s.* the tod of 29 lb. He thinks the true Lincoln most saleable, and most profitable therefore to breed.

Mr. Johnson, of Kermond, had the goodness to shew me his shearlings, two, three, and four-shear tups, which he assured me are pure Lincoln, without the least *touch* of Leicester, and I am glad to observe that they are very fine; large in the carcass, and heavy woolled. He clips from 15 lb. to 21 lb. from his tups. Sells his lean shearling wethers 38*s.* to 44*s.* Clips above 1000. His father thirty years ago gave ten guineas for a ram. His tups are very high fed indeed; they had plenty of cabbages in a full bite of good grass, but no corn or cake.

Mr. Ellison, of Sudbrook, has practised giving cake to sheep for eight years. He fats shearling wethers both on grass and turnips; begins between Martinmas and Christmas, for eight or nine weeks; in that time they

they will be as fat as the weight will pay for. Hains the grass from beginning of September, so as to support the sheep well, and not depend entirely on cakes: by this means can keep four an acre, keeping them two weeks at first without cake; to tempt them mixes bran or oats, or puts some sheep among them that have been used to this feeding; generally gives a ton to a score of sheep, at from *7l.* to *9l.* a ton. Cake at *8l.* a ton is as cheap as turnips at *4l.* an acre. If cakes were *11l.* or *12l.* a ton, he would still use them in this application. By the nearest calculation, he estimates that they will pay *3s.* a-head for their grass, after having paid for the cake; or at four per acre, *12s.* an acre for the grass, cake being at *8l.* a ton; always supposing that other food would rise with cake; and that, if that were *12l.* a ton, turnips would rise proportionably. Without cake they would take sixteen weeks to fatten, and then not be so fat as the cake fed in eight or nine. This calculation of *3s.* is at the lowest, because in many cases it has run much higher; in one particular instance *20s.* a-head. Five years ago he bought in shearlings at *32s.*; in April summer-grazed them, taking the wool, and then put them on hained grass, and kept them on it till the end of November; then began cake, and held it till March, eating *10s.* a-head in cake; then sold half at *3l.* *8s.* and the other half at *3l.* *12s.* Clipped *7s.* or *8s.* a-head. They were the pure Lincoln sort.

In 1795 he put 61 of his own bred hogs (New Leicester cross, one-third that blood) to cole about Old Michaelmas, kept them till Christmas, then to grass which had been hained for them, giving cake as soon as to grass; kept them till the middle of February, and sold 60 at *3l.* *15s.* each, being only shearlings.

lings. They weighed upon an average 26 lb. a quarter; the fleece was worth 8*s.*; they tallowed well. Breaks the cake at first to the size of beans, afterwards of walnuts, but takes care the troughs are covered, as rain makes the cake pasty, and it is then wasted. The effect of feeding thus, to the land, is very great indeed; he has advanced grass from 12*s.* an acre to be worth 27*s.* by six years' feeding in the manner and time above-mentioned, four to an acre. The troughs are kept moving; best to do this every morning.

Mr. Ellison has been seven years in the Leicester cross, which he much approves of; he thinks he can run one-third more in number upon the same land. Upon this I particularly questioned the bailiff, and he persisted in the fact. He can get them fat upon a certainty half a year sooner. The wool is better by 2*s.* 6*d.* a tod. He sold this year (half hog) at 22*s.* 6*d.*; and the neighbours sold Lincoln one-third hog at 18*s.* 6*d.* and one-half hog at 19*s.* 6*d.* In hardiness and health equal; but perhaps on wet land the lighter fleece and thinner pelt may be rather against them.

Mr. Ellison's flock: breeding ewes	300
Tups	3
Lambs	300
Clipped last year	550
Next year	600

Sells his fat wethers before the second clipping; last year, sold drapes at 28*s.* lean: 550 gave about 150 tod.

The wether lambs would sell in September at 1*l.* 1*s.* each, on an average.

Meeting Mr. Thorpe, of Owersby, at Mr. Moody's, at Riseholm, and discoursing on the two breeds, he remarked

marked that the Boston graziers were not fair judges, for they could not get good Leicesters, as the breeders are able to fat them themselves, which they were in many cases unable to do the Lincolns; those graziers compare such Leicesters as they can get (bad ones), with the best Lincolns, which is not a fair trial; and then appealed to his and Mr. Lloyd's offer for a fair experiment*.

Mr. Moody, of Riseholm, has been some years in the New Leicester. I had been informed, that he had repeatedly given very high prices for tups in Leicestershire, in order to breed wethers; but I found this erroneous; his conduct has been much more measured.—His object was not wethers, but ewes; and he has not started as a tup-man, till by gaining a good race of ewes, he could use high-priced rams to a direct advantage. Now he speaks a different language, and means to tread that field in which so many hard battles have been fought. He was for some years in the Lincoln breed, when he sold fat drapes at 21*s*. mutton being at 3*d*. and three-shear fat wethers at 26*s*. mutton at 3½*d*. Shearling Leicesters he sold in March, 1796, in the wool, at 53*s*. at London; and in 1795, at Wakefield, the last week in April, clipped, at 56*s*. the wool 7 lb.

---

* Lincoln ram show, 1797 (Friday after New Michaelmas Day). Mr. Thorpe, of Owersby, and Mr. Lloyd, of Belesby, offer to any breeder of Old Lincoln sheep, to stock with New Leicester hogs, the half of a field any where in Lincolnshire; if any Lincoln breeder will stock with Lincoln hogs the other half; to be weighed in alive, and to remain not less than a year; then to be killed, and that breed which pays the most for the food shall be admitted to be best. No other food than the grass of the pasture to be given in the winter to either lot. Messrs. Lloyd and Thorpe not to put in less live weight than the Lincolns amount to.—Let it be on the worst or on the best land.

Witness, ARTHUR YOUNG.

at

at 20*s*. a tod; not a few; the whole lot being nine or eleven score; and drapes fat at 45*s*. at Michaelmas.

The average of all his fleeces, ewes, hogs, and wethers, *fours*.

He is clear that the Leicesters run one-fourth thicker on the land than Lincolns; that is, four ewes and lambs per acre on seeds, to three ditto Lincolns.

One breed he thinks as hardy as the other; but is of opinion, that from the age of six to twelve months, they are rather tenderer than the Lincolns. Mr. Hall, of Yorkshire, who was present, remarked ten months as the most tender age; that is to say, in the pinch of the winter. *Respe* the same with both.

Which will bear travelling best to London, Mr. Moody? Why, a Lincoln not fat (and I have never seen them so) may travel better than a fat Leicester; but let them be equally fat, and Leicester will inevitably beat them.

Mr. Moody clips a sheep an acre on all the land that sheep ever go on,—upon a corn farm.

Mr. Daniel Hebb, of Claypool, has been near thirty years in the New Leicester breed; but has had many Lincolns, so as to know well what that breed is; the former get as fat at one-shear as the latter at two, with less trouble. Sells his shearlings at 40*s*. out of the wool, which is 8 lb. to 10 lb. a fleece; at the Michaelmas following has sold at 50*s*. and can run them one-tenth thicker on the ground. He clips above 1000. His farm being cold clay ground, he has no turnips, but buys in Nottinghamshire; never gives any hay to his sheep except in snow, or to hogs, and to these, not so much as formerly. On his worst land he winters one sheep an acre; upon his best two on an average; some more, some less. In summer two an acre, and

 on

on some land three or four, besides cattle. He remarks that the New Leicester cut a bad figure as store sheep, but get by fatting to a large size, and very fat; and on wet land in winter will do as well as the Lincolns, keeping their mutton better. They lamb much easier. He has a neighbour who once lost twelve in sixty of the Old Lincolns, when a great head and large bone were reckoned beauties. Mr. Hebb letts about sixty in a year, from five to forty guineas. Selling shearlings at 40*s*. he thus divides the price:

At 6 months	18*s*. to 20*s*.
At 12 ditto	28*s*.
At 18 ditto	28*s*. to 30*s*.
At 24 ditto	40*s*.

Mr. Hebb shewed me some of his tups.

Mr. Dalby, of Marston, was in the New Leicester breed before Mr. Bakewell's sale in 1777, at which he bought a tup, and at that time Mr. Bakewell told him that Lincolnshire would, some time or other, be the best of markets for the Leicester tup-men, which Mr. Dalby did not at all credit; but the fact is proving itself every day.

Mr. Dalby gives the preference entirely to the New Leicester breed, and for the reason so often repeated, their coming sooner to market; and he thinks they may on the same land be run one-sixth thicker. He tods fours.

Mr. Walker, of Woolsthorpe, thinks that the deficiencies which want remedying in Lincoln sheep are these: it seemed to be an animal that had been formed with few other ideas than the production of wool; and till this object was attained, they appeared for a long time to regard nothing but the weight of wool per fleece.

fleece. It had a long, crooked, lean back, flat ribs, deep belly, dock large, forward loose shoulders, heavy neck, great head, and large bones, with a sinking dewlap; a pelt that appeared too large for the animal, wide in his hind legs, inclined to be poor upon moderate keep, but when forced in the marshes, laid on a quantity of loose coarse-grained mutton; the fleece generally of hogs and wethers well maintained 14 lb.; and ewes the same, 8 lb. to 10 lb. If there was a part in them superior to the rest, it was in the loin, and points of the rump, which were much better than the chine and ribs.

Progress of the New Leicester breed:

Mr. Bakewell for many years selected the best formed sheep wherever he could find them: he had some from near Sleaford early in the pursuit, others from near Melton Mowbray; some from near Grantham: that there is some Lincoln blood in the origin of the present Dishley breed, cannot be doubted; hence Mr. Walker conceives the singular propriety of Lincoln going back to that selection of her own stock (partially), which was formed by the best judge that ever existed.

It is therefore evident, that such a breed must be greatly improved by the introduction of tups which exhibit a back straight and short, for a long back is rarely good; but the whole length not short, as it is made up in the length of the quarters; with shoulders that lie back at top, joining the ribs imperceptibly; and the hind quarters so corresponding, with a springing rib, as to form an oval; with the intestines so small, and contained under the ribs, as to prevent depth of belly; with the top of the neck and the throat so light as to appear to be merely a passage to the stomach; but with a bosom round and fat; brisket wide and

and fat, but not deep; for no deep breasted sheep has a good chine; with a small long face, and a prominent eye; the ear so thin as not to indicate a thick pelt; no dewlap, nor superfluity of pelt; the gambrels of the hind legs rather inclining inwards, and the twist fat, and well filled; outside of the thigh light, being a sympton of fine flesh; dock small; the rump points narrow, to form their share in the oval above-mentioned, and fat; whether clefted deep or not, immaterial, for the very best sheep have not been clefted at all in the chine, though they were upon the rump as far as the hip; small bones; an inclination to be fat. It is necessary only to describe such points; any animal that has them will be fat, whether sheep, ox, horse, hog, dog, or cat.

In respect to size and wool. Of the first it must be observed, that though the frame of these sheep seem much smaller to the eye, they are not so in the scales, for it is not very uncommon for two-shear wethers to come to 40 lb. a quarter at Michaelmas; as to wool, it ought to be reckoned per acre, and not per fleece, and then the inferiority may not be so great as some imagine: per fleece they may be reckoned one-third inferior, of a quality rather preferable.

As to health and number brought up: suppose in 100 ewes put to tup, ten barren, five may miscarry in lambing, and in all fifteen per cent.; but conceives that the Lincoln will not have so many barren: this he attributes to not keeping the ewes and tups down enough in fat, for then this circumstance happens.

Another very material circumstance, is the value of the ewes when culled for the butcher; Mr. Walker has many

many customers that will sell all their drapes to the butcher at 2*l*. 12*s*. 6*d*. each, and he presumes that this is not to be equalled in the Lincoln breed.

He remarks, that Mr. Wilson, of Hungerton, has had tups from him, for four years only, on land of 7*s*. an acre, and if any person of fortune should be inclined to make an experiment on fatting wethers of this breed against any other, he has no doubt but the sheep bred by this gentleman, and others I found him ready to name, would prove satisfactory specimens for trials of that sort. In such cases let it be observed, that wethers for the purpose are ready in plenty.

Mr. Walker thinks that wethers from 28 to 30 lb. a quarter, is as large in a general way as it is desirable they should be at two-shear, killed at Michaelmas; but the breed comes up to 50 lb. a quarter; and some shearlings have been seen at fifteen months old, that weighed 30 lb. a quarter. But he regards size in sheep, as an object very inferior to blood and delicacy; as he is sure, from long practice, that if he keeps steady to these, he shall preserve the high degree of merit in disposition to fatten, which is a point of much more importance than a great frame, or a heavy fleece; and in point of food, he is of opinion that all live stock will eat a weight of food nearly in proportion to their own weight, every other circumstance being equal, as breed, age, health, &c. consequently a sheep of 25 lb. a quarter is as profitable as one of 50 lb. a quarter. He has this year kept four tups an acre of 35 lb. a quarter, on ten acres of clover, from the first of May till the 10th of October, besides mowing fifteen loads of hay from it. This Mr. Walker conceives to be heavy stocking; however, the field is the best he has.

This

This breed bears travelling better than any that are equally fat.

	s.	
Good sheep well managed, will be at 6 months	25	
12 ditto	35	wool 8 lb.
18 ditto	50	
24 ditto	60	wool 8 lb.
30 ditto	72	

Mr. Walker will bet, that he finds a score of wethers two years and a half old, in one man's hands, that weigh 36 lb. a quarter, and the same number that will weigh 30 lb. a quarter, at two years old.

In all the country west of the north road, this breed has greatly increased, and are increasing still.

The common breed here is a bastard Lincoln, very rough, bad woolled, small, and perhaps as bad as can be seen any where; and it is a curious fact, that in seven years Mr. Walker has lett only one tup in the whole lordship.

Amongst Mr. Walker's sheep, those I most admired for their apparent blood, were got by his own H, being the son of G; and G by a son of the Dishley old G. The ewes bred by himself and father for thirty-five years, *in and in*, all of the Dishley blood. One ram lamb, which I noted particularly for fineness, pelt, bone, flesh, &c. he then christened A. Y. I wish my namesake success. Examining this lamb, Mr. Walker remarked, that having caught his eye often for his extreme delicacy, he had some suspicion (afterwards negatived by fact), that he would prove imperfect, where perfection is most essential; as he had before found this to be the case with similar forms. I caught at this observation, and mentioned the reproach under

under which some of the best of this breed of sheep laboured, of being deficient in vigour; and that if an extreme degree of fineness and delicacy proved a sign of this circumstance, it should seem, that constantly attending to such a *ewish* form as a perfection, might gradually entail the greatest of evils. His answer was, that such instances as this had occurred (he shewed me two) in which the delicacy was not the cause of the imperfection, but the imperfection the cause of the delicacy: which may be true; but the objection is not thence removed: and it remains a question, whether, in a given number of rams, bred fine, and an equal number coarser, there will not be a greater number imperfect in the former than in the latter: and the objection extends yet further; it has been contended by some, that the New Leicester breed, though not *imperfect*, are yet *deficient* in vigour, and many ewes are found barren. Does not this fact unite with the preceding; and shew that these circumstances are really combined; and that you may *fine* a breed till you produce a beautiful animal, deficient, though not quite imperfect, in generative power?

That Mr. Walker is very deep in Dishley blood will appear, not only from the above circumstances, but also from these: in 1780, such was the effect of the American war, that there was but one ram lett at Dishley so high as ten guineas, and two persons joined for him; yet that year Mr. Walker gave five guineas for one, which was of considerable note. They had however been high; for about 1770, a ram made 100 guineas at Dishley. In 1774, his father gave there forty guineas for the covering of twenty ewes. In 1782, Mr. Walker gave twenty-five guineas for a shearling. In 1786, he hired there three shearlings for 150 guineas; and

and those three Mr. Bakewell lett the year following for 1000 guineas. About the year 1787, Mr. Walker joined with Mr. Buckley in giving 400 guineas for a ram. From that time the prices rose rapidly.

The Duke of Ancaster, at Grimsthorpe, clips 1500 wethers and hogs. Buys in the spring, at Grantham, lamb hogs; keeps on the poorest land till autumn; but as the two-shears are sent off, these are brought in to take their places. In November, on the best land; no turnips; but in blasts, some hay at stacks; no eddish, except to follow beasts, it being the winter growth that supports them; two to an acre in winter. Begins to send to market in May, and thence till November. Buys in from 24*s.* to 32*s.* for the lamb hogs; since prices have been high; about 1782, from 16*s.* to 22*s.* Sold in 1796 at 45*s.* or 46*s.* on an average; in 1797 something less; and the year before the same. Thus 18*s.* a-head profit, and two fleeces of wool, 18 lb. or 12*s.*; in all 30*s.* As to losses, they amount to about five in 100.

The breed Mr. Parker fixes on to choose, is the cross between Lincoln and Leicester, which he thinks preferable to either wholly; too much attention is paid to wool on poor land, as he thinks they should on such have more Leicester blood than they commonly have: he would wish to have not more than 9 or 10 lb. of wool; if they have more than that, he cannot make them fat without difficulty. Many graziers in this neighbourhood, who have gone to Boston to buy heavy woolled sheep, have found it so to their loss. Mr. Parker has the two sorts running at the same time on the same land, and he is clear in the superiority of the Leicester cross. He thinks the Leicester will travel best to Smithfield. Scarcely ever has a sheep dropt. Prefers them also in

respect

respect of healthiness. On breeding farms there is a great advantage in the fall of the lambs, the Lincoln coming large, the Leicester small. The difference of loss in lambing will be very considerable. He has bred many himself; he has more Leicester than Lincoln, and if he had still more, it would, he thinks, be better, but does not like giving up wool too much; and in stocking land with the two breeds distinct, he thinks 500 Lincolns would demand a third more land than 500 Leicesters. However, the Lincolns, he admits, will give more wool per acre than the *New* Leicesters. And of the sorts of Leicester, he thinks that the *finer* they are bred, the better they are for fatting: and he would not avoid any degree of fineness, except for the object of wool, which must not be abandoned.

There are many breeding flocks in the vicinity of Grimsthorpe, and generally a cross of the New Leicester. On the level beyond Bourn, they are more in the Lincoln; the greatest part of them having cole on their farms, by which they can make that breed fat.

To draw this great variety of miscellaneous information into some degree of order, upon the heads which are most interesting, is not an easy task; and I shall not attempt it, without cautioning the reader against passing over the minutes themselves, and looking only at the following extracts, which will contain merely the most prominent features of certain objects. When a question of comparison is so warmly agitated as that of the New Leicester with the Lincoln breed of sheep in this county, the private interest, prejudice, and habits of mankind, are strongly in the way of pure and genuine authority. The careful reader, who examines with a view only to truth, cannot be too much on his guard.

Price

Price of Sheep.

Place.	Age bought in.	Price in 1796, or 1797, lean.		General Price.	Price fat, 1, 2, and 3-shear.		Breed.
		s.	d.	s.	s.	d.	
Sutton	Shearl.	50	0	39	60	0	Linc.
Spalding	ditto	—		35	45	0	ditto
Weston	—	—		—	60	0	ditto
Boston	—	—		—	60	0	ditto
Holland Fen	—	—		—	52	6	ditto
Swineshead	ditto	42	6	32	55	0	ditto
Ewerby	ditto	30	0	—	—		Leic.
Berthorpe	ditto	27	0	—	60	0	ditto
Belton	ditto	20	0	—	—		ditto
Leadenham	—	—		—	47	6	ditto
Blankney	ditto	36	0	34	60	0	ditto
Hackthorne	ditto	38	0	—	—		Linc.
Norton	ditto	40	0	—	—		Leic.
Knaith	—	—		—	49	0	ditto
Alkborough	—	—		—	45	0	ditto
Barton	—	—		—	38	0	ditto
Barrow	—	—		—	40	0	ditto
Brocklesby	—	—		—	46	0	ditto
Cadney	—	—		—	42	0	Linc.
Belesby	—	—		—	45	0	Leic.
Tathwell	—	—		—	60	0	Linc.
Dalby	—	—		—	51	8	ditto
Driby	—	—		—	46	0	mixed
Skirbeck	—	—		—	55	0	Linc.
Stainsby	—	—		—	60	0	ditto
Keal	—	—		—	65	0	Leic.
Frampton	—	—		—	72	0	Linc.
Elkington	—	—		—	44	0	ditto
Swinop	—	—		—	40	0	ditto
Riseholm	—	—		—	55	0	Leic.
Woolsthorpe	—	—		—	72	0	ditto
Grimsthorpe	—	—		—	45	0	mixed
	—	—		—			
Average	—	—		—	35	6	

This average goes to the county feeding in general, and concerns not the question of the breeds. It shews the size and fatness of the wethers, and the fertility of the soil that feeds them.

Wool.

Wool.

Place.	Lincoln Fleece.	Breed.	Leicester Fleece.	Mixed.
	lb.		lb.	
Spalding	—	½ Linc. ½ Leic.	—	10
Boston	14	Linc.	—	—
Holland Fen	12	ditto	—	—
Wolds	9½	ditto	—	—
Swineshead	1st, 9	ditto	—	—
	2d, 11	—	—	—
	3d, 9	—	—	—
Ewerby	—	Leic.	8½	—
Hackington	9¾	Linc.	—	—
	—	Leic.	8	—
Belton	1st,	ditto	8	—
	2d,	—	8	—
	3d,	—	7	—
Norton	—	ditto	8	—
Barton	—	ditto	6½	—
Barrow	—	ditto	7	—
Lumber	9½	Linc.	—	—
	—	Leic.	6½	—
Belesby	7¼	Linc.	—	—
	—	Leic.	7¼	—
Alesby	—	ditto	7	—
	8	Linc.	—	—
Humberston	9	ditto	—	—
Tathwell	10	ditto	—	—
Cookswold	—	Leic.	7	—
	10	Linc.	—	—
Haffham	14	ditto	—	—
Gayton	8	ditto	—	—
Tathwell	8	ditto	—	—
Dalby	—	mixed	—	11
Partney	11½	Linc.	—	—
Driby	—	mixed	—	8
Carry forward	169¼	—	88¼	29

Brought

Place.	Lincoln Fleece.	Breed.	Leicester Fleece.	Mixed.
	lb.	—	lb.	
Brought forward	169¼	—	88¾	29
Spilsby	—	Leic.	9½	—
Skirbeck	8	Linc.	—	—
Stainsby	12	ditto		1160 tods of wool from 2400 acres of all sorts, or 14 lb. an acre.
Keal	—	Leic.	9	
Ranby	—	ditto	11	
Frampton	12	Linc.		
Mr. Cunliff	Average of the whole county 9 lb.			
Mr. Blythe	Average of the whole county 8 lb. And a fleece and a half, or 12 lb. per acre, the produce of the whole county.			
Riseholm	—	Leic.	7½ clip a sheep an acre on a corn farm.	
Claypool	—	ditto	9	—
Woolsthorpe	—	ditto	8	—
Grimsthorpe	—	mixed	—	9
	201¼	—	142¾	38
Average	10	—	7⅘	9½

The probability therefore is, that the average of the county may be as stated above, 9 lb.

Upon the very remarkable facts, that the whole county carries a sheep and a half per acre, at 9 lb. per fleece, I may observe, that if this is true, or near the truth, it is probably stocked far beyond any other in the kingdom: instead of 1,848,000 acres, let us call it 1,600,000, allowing 248,000 acres for lands that do not probably come into the account at all; at a sheep and a half, there are then 2,400,000 sheep in the county; producing 21,610,000 lb. of wool, which at only 9*d.* per pound, or 810,000*l.* amounts to 10*s.* an acre over the

the whole. Such an account, or any thing near it, is not to be produced in any other district probably in the world. This fact shews the immense consequence to Lincolnshire of a fair price of wool: the manufacturers, in their evidence given before Parliament, on the Wool Bill, stated what they called the rivalry of French fabrics of long wool, by means of smuggling it from England; supposing the fact (which was directly the reverse), it has now certainly ceased, for the French manufactures have ceased; add to this, that our woollen fabrics, as appears by their registers, and by the custom-house exports, are far more prosperous, yet the price of Lincoln wool was 1*s.* and it is now only 9*d.*; contrary to every thing that ought in such cases to take place. At a fair price, the wool of this county would sell for 1080,000*l.* a year: the difference is a very material loss indeed!

Circumstances of Comparison.

Boston. Lincoln better than Leicester on general experience, and particular experiment.

Brothertoft. In experiment very little difference.

Ewerby. Leicester tenderer than Lincoln.

Lincoln pay best for keeping to three-shear.

Hackington. Last year of Lincolns pay best.

Ewerby. Old sheep stand the winter better, and pay better than young.

Owersby. Shearling Leicesters have, at Wakefield, sold as high as two-shear Lincolns.

Difference of wool has been as eight to sixteen.

Leicesters run thicker, one in five.

Leicesters tenderer in winter.

Normanby.

Normanby. Lincoln fleece 2 lb. heavier than Leicester.

Leicester off-shearlings; Lincolns two or three-shear, but the latter pay well if kept to three-shear.

Leicesters finer grained mutton.

Leicesters rather thicker on the land, but Lincolns considerably larger.

As much wool per acre from Leicesters as Lincolns.

Walcot. Leicester fleeces, though not so heavy as Lincoln, sold in one instance for as much money.

Barton. Leicester not tenderer in winter than Lincoln.

Old breed of Lincoln used to go lean at two years old.

Now, Leicesters fat at the same age.

No difference in number on the same land.

Wool the same.

Bonby. Leicesters come to sale sooner, but will not bear cold wet land in winter so well, nor heat or cold after shearing, as the Lincoln.

Barrow. Five Leicesters where four Lincolns; and Leicesters have resisted hardships on the worst land better.

Brocklesby. Lincoln more profitable than Leicester.

Lumber. Where a man can keep, by means of marsh, to three-shear, Lincoln most profitable, but not otherwise. Not more Leicesters kept on the same land. Leicester wool 1*s.* a tod more than Lincoln.

Lincoln. Leicester more liable to the fly.

Cadney. Leicester will feed a little faster, and run a little thicker.

Belesby. Leicester one in six more on the same land, but both go at the same age. Leicesters hardier, and have less offal. Tallow equal; wool higher priced. Gives corn to Leicesters, but did not to Lincolns.

Alesby. Leicesters feed quicker, and have less offal; wethers and hogs less wool, but ewes equal, and on the whole more per acre; hardier, and bear driving better. Go off at the same age, but Leicesters fatter. Five kept instead of four. Lamb easier; necessary to give corn.

Humberston. More pride than profit in the new sort. Leicesters 2 lb. less wool than Lincolns, and not better; but run one in ten thicker.

Louth. Leicesters feed quicker, and have lighter offals. No difference in hardiness. Lincoln best.

Tathwell. Lincolns and Leicesters being put together into the Marsh, and sent thence at same time to Smithfield; the former yielded 4*s*. a-head more, and 5*s*. a-head more wool.

Cookswold. Marsh graziers all prefer Lincoln. No difference in number kept.

Tathwell. Lincoln wool 4 lb. heavier than Leicester. At two-shear, Lincoln heavier by by 2 lb. a quarter; at three-shear 5 lb. In tallow, 6 lb. at three-shear, in favour of Lincoln. In number per acre, no difference. In hardiness, Lincoln best. Leicesters less wool and less mutton per acre.

Driby. No difference in number kept.

Spilsby. Leicesters as fat at Lady-day, coming two-shear, as Lincolns at Lammas. Same number per acre. No difference in hardiness; Leicesters have corn.

Horncastle. Three-shear better than two, as sure to find more tallow.

Asgarby. Leicesters bred too fine; fine headed ones do not yield wool enough.

Frampton. As many of one as the other per acre. Lincolns travel best, and pay best.

Ranby. Leicesters thicker on land, as five to four.

Alderkirk. In an experiment of the two breeds on the same land, of the same weight and age, the Lincolns considerably superior.

Thoresway. True Lincolns most saleable, and most profitable to breed.

Sudbrook. One-third more Leicesters on the same land.

Riseholm. Boston graziers not judges, for they can get good Lincolns, but not Leicesters, as the breeders of these can fat them themselves. Leicesters run one-fourth thicker on the land. From six to twelve months old, rather tenderer than Lincolns; Leicesters travel best.

Claypool. Leicesters as fat at one year as Lincolns at

at two, and with less trouble, and one-tenth thicker. Do as well as Lincolns in winter on wet land.

Marston. Leicesters best, and run one-sixth thicker.

Woolsthorpe. Leicesters by far the best; but more apt to be barren than Lincolns. Drape ewes far more valuable.

Grimsthorpe. Leicesters travel best, and are the best; and much less loss in lambing; run one-third thicker.

I am very unwilling to add any thing here in my own person; the table is not long, and a little attention to it will enable any reader to draw his conclusions without material error. A clear distinction is to be drawn between the rich south eastern district and inferior soils; for upon the former the information is strong in favour of Lincoln.

In general I should observe, that the New Leicesters are spreading very rapidly over the county, probably faster than they have done in any other, one or two only excepted, which may be attributed to the general goodness of the soil; for this breed makes a much more respectable figure than it has done in various trials made in countries inferior to it in soil; and the breed driving out the Lincoln so much as it has done in the poorer parts of this county, is a fact that unites with this circumstance. The true Lincoln is a larger sheep, and with a longer wool, and therefore demands better pasturage; where it finds such, *there* the old breed remains; subject, perhaps, to little more change than *fashion* may cause. Upon inferior land the Leicester establishes itself; and upon land still inferior in other

other counties, experiments prove unsuccessful for the same reason; that of the necessity of having a smaller size and shorter wool.

In these notes are many points upon which it would be easy to expatiate: I wish there had been more experiments, and fewer assertions. I leave the Lincoln gentlemen to speak for themselves.

Feeding.

Knaith. 1 lb. of oil-cake a day per wether, with turnips, more profitable than the latter alone.

Tathwell. 450 acres, including corn, &c. &c. support 400 Lincoln ewes and 360 lambs.

Nothing makes wool grow so fast as feeding upon oil-cake.

Dalby. 2400 clipped on 1400 acres, grass and arable.

Asgarby. The food being weighed to two sheep of 34 lb. a quarter, and to two of 24 lb. a quarter, the difference eaten was not near to the proportion of weight; the largest ate least proportionably.

Sudbrook. After-grass with oil-cake, five acres and a ton of cake 20 wethers. Cake at 8*l.* as cheap as turnips at 4*l.* Grass thus advanced from 12*s.* an acre to 27*s.*

Swinop. 1462 sheep go over 1300 acres, including every thing.

Such particulars are interesting wherever found; and by being combined and contrasted with similar ones in other counties, will furnish materials equally valuable to the cultivator and the political arithmetician.

Age

Age at which sold.

	Worth at 6 Months.	at 12 Months.	at 18 Months.	at 24 Months.	At 30 Months.	At 36 Months.
	s.	s.	s.	s.	s.	s.
Ewerby	17	30	35	45	45	55
Berthorpe	17	27	32	40	43	—
Belton	12	20	25	35	35	35
Belesby	14	22	28	35	45	50
Dalby	20	30	33	46	—	—
Spilsby	28	35	40	48	56	60
Ranby	25	30	38	48	50	60
Claypool	19	28	29	40	—	—
Average	17	25	29	37	39	52
Add wool	0	7	0	7	0	7
Together	17	32	29	44	39	59
Increase by each six months	17	4	4	14	2	19
Ditto by each year	31		18		21	

It is sufficiently evident from this table, that to keep breeding ewes, where the lambs will sell at 17*s.* is more profitable than any other sheep system, supposing the land to be proper for the stock; 7*s.* for the ewe's fleece makes this 24*s.* per head for half the flock, the other half producing ewe lambs, do not pay equally; but let the average be reduced to 20*s.* still it is far better than any other system here noted, as admitting the 19*s.* for the last column, yet it is not to be attained without passing through the periods which answer so much worse than any others; and though both ewe and lamb are to be well kept for six months, yet the ewe is kept at a moderate expense the other six; whereas fatting sheep must be favoured in food.

Folding.

Folding.

This is dispatched in few words.—I never saw a fold in the county, except in a few open fields near Stamford, nor heard of its having been practised, except in a trial made by Mr. Wright, of Riseholm, near Lincoln, who had a very nice flock of the country sheep, that had been collected with care; but having seen and heard much of the effect in some other county, was convinced of the propriety; changed his stock, and got a flock of Hertfords, which he folded; the result, however, was so very unfavourable on the general account, though partially beneficial, that after a few years he gave it up, convinced by positive experience of the great loss attending it. A great experiment, though quickly described.

Mr. Hebb, of Claypool, assured me, that before 1771, when that and other lordships were open, the Old Lincoln sheep were regularly folded, and bore it well; but since the enclosure, nothing of it has been heard of.

In the open fields near Stamford, there are yet some folds remaining; but the sheep are miserably bad; in wool eight or nine to a tod.

Distempers.

Respe.—In hoggets; when dead, the flesh all rotten and putrid; it arises from being forced on cole.

In the marsh land at Weston, in 1797, vast numbers of sheep had the foot-halt: pare, and dress with butter of antimony: it arises from plenty of grass by the luxuriance of the year.

Mr. Cartwright has found, by many observations, by means of his engine for weighing live animals, that the

the least ailment, a little of the foot-halt, or a fly-struck sheep, loses weight greatly and immediately, and also that upon recovering, they thrive much faster than any other sheep. This is a point that deserves much attention in all comparative experiments, and also to have a constant eye to such sheep, to prevent these evils.

Upon Wildmore Fen the thistles are in such enormous quantity, that a common complaint is sore noses, with such a prevention of feeding, that numbers die: they run matter, and there is an idea that it becomes an infection; but this is probably erroneous.

In Holland Fen the *respe* is a fatal malady among sheep fed on cole; the loss has often amounted to fifteen per cent. and particularly in very luxuriant crops, on fresh land; the best sheep die first. To prevent it, they drive them in the night, and some for a few hours in the middle of the day, to another field. Mr. Cartwright, after losing many, tried this, and lost no more. It is good when this is not done, to *raise* them in the night; the shepherd goes into the field to disturb, and make them stale; the cole supposed to have a narcotic quality. All sorts and ages subject to this distemper. No losses but in cole; the grass lands quite healthy.

September 20th, 1796, observation by Mr. Gentle Brown, of Lincoln—that putting a large lot of lambs upon cole, was told he should have great loss; but by bleeding in the roof of the mouth before they went in, and once every three weeks afterwards, giving a large wine glass of strong salt and water, he escaped without losing a single lamb. The cole was upon his fen land, which he described to be of a black peaty quality.

The rickets have done great mischief at Leadenham: Mr. Betsal there, who had been at some expense in breeding

breeding New Leicesters, was forced to change his stock entirely, by which he hopes to escape this disorder; and some others in the neighbourhood have done the same. No rickets at Blankney; but they had it some years ago.

The *respe* has also made considerable ravages; Mr. Graburn has prevented it by giving, while on turnips, clover or sainfoin hay, which has prevented it; turnips alone are too watery, and dry food is useful. The gid kills one in forty; no cure; they have attempted to trepan, but no success.

About Louth, the loss in feeding rape by the *respe* is very great, and no attention, it is said, will entirely prevent it; some farmers thought they lost ten per cent. on all turned in; others not so many.

The foot-halt troublesome about Saltfleet; tar and salt wrapped in a strong canvas, the best remedy. They are certain that it is infectious.

The Rev. Mr. Allington, of Swinop, has suffered very much by losing sheep turnip-fed, by the red water; and upon being opened in the presence of a skilful surgeon, he was of opinion, that the distemper was simply a dropsy, as the kidneys had ceased to act. He has known no cure or prevention that is effective; has heard of salt, driving about, &c. but not found them effective.

The *respe* not particularly fatal at Sudbrook, rather the contrary; in 1796, in 300 lost only five.

Mr. Hall, from Yorkshire, has been informed, that antimony and brimstone in equal quantities, mixed up with treacle, is a preservative from the *respe*.

Mr. Dalby, of Marston, informed me, that the red sand of that vicinity has a quality in the seeds which he cannot account for, that of killing lambs at about ten days old; they die of the *skit*, or souring;

and

and it is particularly experienced in new enclosures; clay soil is free from it, and old meadow and pasture land; and the more the sands are improved, the more they have this effect; and it is remarkable, that the lambs which come for the first fortnight or three weeks, escape, it usually beginning about Old Lady-day, or a week before; it should seem from this, as if it arose from the first spring of the herbage.

He also informed me, that they lose many lambs of *the yellows*, from August to the middle of September, on fresh clover: they are putrid, as in the *respe*, but quite yellow.

SECT. III.—HORSES.

KEPT remarkably cheap in Deeping Fen, on rich commons in the summer, and in straw-yard in winter. Many never have any oats: cannot amount to 5*l.* a head; chiefly mares, and so nothing at all in fact.

Every farmer in Holland Fen keeps mares for breeding, and the numbers are very great; a very good four-year old cart-horse sells at 30*l.* and is a common price; 25*l.* for a very good three-year old. Mr. Thacker, of Langrike-ferry, buys in Yorkshire at three years old in autumn, winters on straw, works a little in spring, and sells at Horncastle fair in August; one of the greatest fairs in the kingdom. A good judge makes money in this way. Oxen are no where worked in common; Mr. Cartwright has used, and approves them.

Mr. Cartwright has found that the common groundsel, given plentifully to horses in the stable, will cure greasy heels. It is always of importance to know the

uses

uses to which weeds may be applied. The expense of keeping horses may be thus stated in Holland Fen:

	£.	s.	d.
20 weeks summer food, joisting price 4*s*.	£.4	0	0
32 weeks, 7*s*. a week, allowing a horse 18 lb. of hay, and half a peck of oats	11	4	0
(Shoeing) go barefoot behind, except in frosty weather	0	10	0
Farrier	0	10	0
Decline of value:			
Improve till eight years, and then are sold to stage-waggons; decline after, and some sooner; begin to work at two, for exercise; increase at three, and at four ditto full work	1	0	0
	£.17	4	0

These are for Mr. Cartwright's horses, which are harder worked by woad than farmers.

About Folkingham:

	£.	s.	d.
Two quarters two bushels of beans, 24*s*.	£.2	14	0
Hay twenty weeks, at 2*s*. 6*d*. cwt.	4	10	0
Chaff from barns			
Summer, 32 weeks, 4*s*.	6	8	0
Farrier	0	5	0
Shoeing by contract	0	5	0
	£.14	2	0

No decline of value, as they all breed, and rather make a profit than a loss.

About Grantham many oxen have been worked, but all left off; once they were seen all the way from Grantham

tham to Lincoln, now scarcely any; a pair of mares, and one man, will do as much work as four oxen, and two men.

The first signs I saw of working oxen were the yokes and bows at the farm of Mr. Thorpe, at Kirton; he uses them for ox-harrowing, and also for carting. The same farmer keeps his team-horses loose, in a well enclosed warm yard, littered, with the racks and mangers under an open shed: an excellent system for health. But on the Wolds, most farmers have some oxen for working.

About Normanby, Burton, &c. many bred, both for saddle and coach; sell at two, three, and four years old; get from eighty guineas, at four years old, a hunter, down to 7*l*. or 8*l*. A good coach-horse, at four years old, 30*l*. to 40*l*. Howden, in Yorkshire, is the fair, and one of the greatest in the kingdom; also many to Horncastle. Yearlings, and two year olds, all to Howden. Summergate, for a horse on the best marshes, 3*l*. from May-day to Michaelmas. Expense of farm-horses, 10*l*. per head; but few give corn, unless hard-worked. All black mares for breeding, and sell the colts at two years old, at 12*l*. to 20*l*.

Mr. Graburn, of Barton, shod his oxen with horseshoes reversed in putting on, that is, the heels of the shoe before; and they walked on stones perfectly well; but left off the practice, because the shoes came off, like common ones.

They use oxen at Wintringham in carting; and the proportion will be seen by the stock on Mr. Cust's farm, which is fourteen horses, four to six oxen, six colts, four cows.

They are also used moderately for carting, all the way

way from Barton by Grimsby to Louth; many bred about Louth.

Horses are bred in the marshes about Saltfleet, cart mares being chiefly kept; ten mares are found to one horse. Did sell Michaelmas foals at 10*l.* but in 1797 much lower; if not foals, at two, three, and four years old; at three or four years old, when high, at 30*l.*; but in 1797 not much more than half.

Mr. Bourne, of Dalby, breeds none, but buys foals from four to six months old, at six to sixteen guineas. He thinks the expense of keeping a farm working horse 15*l.* a year; no decline of value, as he never keeps longer than five or six years old; on the contrary, he thinks that all he keeps pays him, on an average, something*; perhaps nearly as much as other sorts of stock: observing, that those horses which do not work, and are two-thirds of the number, are kept at a more reasonable rate than the working ones; so that if he did not keep those horses, he should keep but few more cattle.

Mr. Neve, of North Sommercots, instead of giving his horses cooling, opening physic, feeds them for three weeks or a month with oats, malted in sea-water, and finds it highly conducive to their health.

Mr. Wright's horse from Dishley covers at Spilsby twenty black mares a year: sells at two and three years old; thirty guineas each; since, 25, &c. Has sold as high as 36*l.* and even 40*l.*

* The finest and best horses in the kingdom, chiefly of what are called the blood kind, are bred upon the Wolds; a greater attention is paid to that species of horse by the Wold graziers than even in Yorkshire or Durham, that formerly were so famous for their breed of hunting horses.—*MS. of the Board.*

Mr.

Mr. Smith, of South Elkington, like all his neighbours, works oxen for leading manure, and corn, and hay. They never have corn nor hay, except a little when they are in work; are at other times wintered on straw; and thinks that he can keep two oxen for the expense of one horse; but that the horse will not draw so much as the two oxen. He is of opinion, that there would be no such thing as ploughing with them, they move so slow.

SECT. IV.—HOGS.

THE hogs common in Holland Fen, about Boston, &c. are mongrel sorts of no merit; but others have been introduced which have made great improvement in this stock. Mr. Cartwright has a Berkshire boar, that is a capital one for size, weight, breadth, and length; many have been bred from him at 10*s*. 6*d*. a sow; a sure proof that he is well approved in the country. A sow came sixty miles to him, and two or three from Holbeach. At Brothertoft there are also some good ones of the black breed.

Mr. Hoyte, of Osbornby, has the breed of Mr. Buckley; white, small bone, short nose, full in the fore-quarters, level, and feeding in disposition; also a very excellent race of the black Chinese: these pigs have much merit. The common breed of the country is the lop-eared, long-haired, coarse, but improved by the black; which cross has been very profitable, for the size is not lost, but the feeding quality improved.

Mr. Fisher, of Kirby, has a good breed of black pigs. Mr. Thorpe, at Owersby, has a very good contrivance for feeding his pigs, so that every pig may have

have a hole for his head, without incommoding or driving away his neighbour. He has raised brick arches over a brick or stone trough, just sufficient to admit the pig's head in. He fattens his hogs on the same food as his bullocks, boiled lintseed mixed with barley-meal, and finds it answers well.

Mr. Lloyd, at Belesby, has a very good breed of pigs, on comparison with any I have seen in a long course of country through North Lincoln, where they have in general a very ill made hog, which ought to be improved.

Mr. Linton, of Freiston, has a great opinion of the profit of hogs; he breeds many, and has sold a year's produce of three sows for 65*l.* from which may be deducted about 7*l.* for the corn they ate, having nothing but the barn door, grass, and a few refuse potatoes. He does not grow above 130 acres of corn.

Mr. Johnson, of Kermond, has an excellent breed of large hogs, the black and sandy, thick, heavy, and light offals.

SECT. V.—RABBITS.

At Blankney, Mr. Richard Piers holds a warren under Charles Chaplin, Esq. who gave the following particulars.

On 1000 acres it is fair to kill 2000 couple, which are sold by the hundred; six score couple are a hundred of rabbits, which have sold at 10*l.* on an average of ten years; in 1796, 13*l.*

Killing and looking after, 60*l.* for 1000 acres.

They are fed in winter with ash boughs, gorse, oat straw, sainfoin, and clover-hay.

On

On the warrens between Gayton and Tathwell, silver skins have been from 15*s*. even to 21*s*. a dozen; but the common grey rabbit is so much hardier, that if a warren be stocked with both, there will, in a few years, be nothing but greys. A rabbit goes to buck the day she brings forth her young, as well known. She goes thirty-one days with young, which are eleven days blind after being born, and eleven more before they appear above ground. She suckles them twice a day for about twenty-two days.

A buck serves 100 does.

Stock upon a good acre, 200 couple.

Winter food—ash boughs, gorse, hay, turnips.

From Louth to Caistor, eighteen miles, ten of it are warrens, chiefly silvers; rent 2*s*. to 3*s*. an acre.

They plough a part every year for corn and turnips, and laying down again with seeds, let down the fences for the rabbits to enter. Warrens are reckoned profitable, so that some fortunes have been made on them.

In point of skins, those bred about May-day undergo no change from their white colour, but from a *white rack* become a whole skin. Bred at Lady-day, become black. In June, white. In July, black. In November, white again; then in full season, as the carcasses are also. The skins ought to have those colours on the inside when flead.

From 250 acres of land that was sainfoin worn out, and planted with rabbits, the following was the account many years ago; but all prices, rent, &c. &c. are calculated at the present rates; and it is to be noted, that the ground being thus new to rabbits, was much more productive than old warren land is found to be, as they breed much better on such new than on old land. Used to kill about 2000 couple; stock left about 700 couple.

Sod

Sod banks cost thirty-five years ago, 1*s*. 2*d*. a rood of seven yards, would now cost 2*s*. ; furz faggots were 7*s*. a hundred, that is, 5*s*. for the furz, and 2*s*. 6*d*. kidding; now doubled. Banks will last about seven years in a midling way ; from 3 to 20 : want facing once in seven years, at half the first expense ; want capping in three years with the furz. Laying on or capping 3*d*. a rood now. It was then reckoned that 250 acres would clear 100*l*. besides rent, which then was 1*s*. an acre. Fencing annually half a mile, 800 yards, 133 rood at 1*s*., 6*l*. 13*s*. for facing: furz, a kidd will do a yard; two miles and a half kidding, at a kidd a yard, 4400 yards and kidds, at 15*s*. now, for 120, or 27*l*. 10*s*. or per annum 9*l*. 3*s*. 4*d*. ; add 6*l*. 13*s*. it is 15*l*. 16*s*. 4*d*. per annum. A warrener 35*l*. a cow, fuel, and house ; in all 40*l*. Extra labour killing 18*s*. a week for sixteen weeks, 14*l*. 8*s*. Also for a month 18*s*. a week, 3*l*. 12*s* ; in all 18*l*.

Nets and thread 12 at 60 yards each ; last six or seven years ; would cost 1*l*. 11*s*. 6*d*. Traps 5*s*. a year. The men who kill will carry. Four horses for six weeks, 1*l*. 4*s*. a week, 7*l*. 4*s*. Charcoal for drying skins 5*s*. A person to order the skins, that is, clear from fat, and drying five weeks ; a useful woman will do it, 1*l*. Winter food, for after three days snow they must be served, cannot be less than 10*l*. a year on 250 acres.

Recapitulation.

	Per Acre.					
Rent now	£.0	6	0	£.87	10	0
Tithe	0	0	0			
Rates	0	1	0			
Fencing	0	1	3	15	16	4
Carry forward	£.0	8	3	£.103	6	4

Brought

	Per Acre.					
Brought forward	£.0	8	3	£.103	6	4
Warrener	0	3	2	40	0	0
Extra labour	0	1	6	19	0	0
Nets and traps, and charcoal	0	0	2	2	1	6
Horses	0	0	6¼	7	4	0
Winter food	0	0	0	10	0	0
	£.0	13	7¾			
Poison, powder and shot, and sundries; fox skins 1*s*. each				2	0	0
				£.183	11	10

Produce.

2000 couple, at 9*d*.	£.75	0	0
Skins, 9*d*. to 1*s*. 3*d*.; average 1*s*.	200	0	0
	£.275	0	0
Expenses	183	11	10
Profit	£.91	8	2

But notwithstanding this, he says, that if he had a warren of his own, he would plough it up for corn, &c. thinking tillage now more profitable than rabbits.

At Partney-fair, meeting with Mr. Grant, of Withgul, and discoursing with him upon warrens, he informed me, that a common stock in winter was three couple per acre, and the produce five or six couple killed; that killing, carrying, &c. might amount to something more than 1*s*. an acre; the sort *silver sprig*, which will not do well in other counties, where they have been tried. He has now 1000 acres of warren.

Upon 1000 acres, the stock 2600 couple, and kill 5000

5000 couple annually. New land is the most productive. On such a warren the rabbits must have two loads of hay a day in a storm; or two or three large waggon-loads a day of turnips. The warrener has 20*l.* a year, and two cows; the killers 8*s.* or 9*s.* a week, and board for ten weeks. Silver skins in 1797 were 10*s.* a dozen; have been 14*s.* or 15*s.* Fences 60*l.* a year; no cross ones; no buildings. The immense occupation of Mr. Grant and his sons, being much the most considerable in the county; with the circumstance of making an ample fortune, made me desirous of seeing him. I called at Oxcomb, but unfortunately for me he was absent.

In 1777, Driby had a warren of 12 or 1300 acres; and the rent of the farm including it 300*l.* a year, which rent has been doubled by ploughing. Mr. Kershaw observed, that the community received next to nothing from warrens.

Mr. Parkinson.—Calculation of a warren of 700 acres under rabbits, rent 5*s.*; standing stock 2000 couple of silver hair, valued to the incoming tenant at 2*s.* 6*d.* a couple ten years ago; and demanding a capital of 1400*l.*; and carefully *typed* to catch all extra bucks, so as to leave only one-fourth of the total number of bucks.

	£.	s.	d.
Produce 3000 couples for sale, worth, on an average of seven years past, 15*l.* a hundred	450	0	0
But as some are greys, the price 10*l.*	300	0	0
	£.750	0	0

Take the average of the two, that is, silver hair of the Wolds, and greys of Lincoln Heath, it will be on a medium 375*l.* or about 10*s.* 10*d.* per acre.

Add

Add to this 350 sheep, kept by a course of tillage, that is, ploughing up fifty acres annually for paring and burning for turnips, then spring corn and seeds, which seeds sheep-fed one year, and thrown out to rabbits; the sheep at 2*d*. a week for twenty-five weeks, will amount to 72*l*. 10*s*. this is inferior to the common produce of sheep; but the rabbits will demand hay, &c. to the amount of the difference; and also a team of horses must be kept for the cultivation of 100 acres of land, and carrying the rabbits to market.

The fifty acres of corn will be consumed by the horses, and master's and warrener's cows, &c. 447*l*. 10*s*.

A Rabbit-Warren Farm.

Dr.	£.	s.	d.	£.	s.	d.
To rent 700 acres land, 5*s.* per acre				175	0	0
To tithe, one-ninth				19	8	10
To town charges				21	17	4
To master and mistress's board, and clothing	£. 52	0	0			
To four children, 10*l.* per year	40	0	0			
To four servants, 10*l.* ditto, viz. three men and one maid	40	0	0			
To extra labourers, carpenters, and other workmen	30	0	0			
Total housekeeping ..	———			162	0	0
To Husbandry.						
A warrener, with house and two cows	£. 26	0	0			
To three extra labourers mowing corn and hay, repairing, fencing, assisting in killing rabbits, &c.	72	0	0			
To blacksmith's bill £. 15; Carpenter's ditto . 22	37	0	0			
Extra turnip-hoers, and hay-makers, in summer	20	0	0			
	———			155	0	0
				533	6	2

Per Contra. Cr.		£.	s.	d.
By slaughter of 3000 couple of rabbits 15*l.*		450	0	0
By 300 fleeces of wool, four and five to tod, about 65 tod, 20*s.* per tod		65	0	0
(viz. 200 ewes, and 100 hogs.)				
Sell about 80 he hogs from turnips, 24*s.*		96	0	0
And about 50 drape ewes, 21*s.*		52	10	0
By 50 acres barley, 3 qrs. per acre, and oats	£. 150			
Deduct seed and horse corn	70			
	———			
Remains 80 qrs. at 21*s.*		84	0	0
By 20 beasts, to sell about five to graziers, 8*l.* per head		40	0	0
By swine, poultry, &c.		20	0	0
Profit in breeding foals		20	0	0
Total		627	10	0
Expenses		533	6	2
Net gain		94	3	10

N. B. As the family is maintained out of the farm, the interest of the capital of about 1400*l.* is not charged, because the interest would be only 70*l.* per year, when they are maintained out of the farm with a profit of 94*l.* 3*s.* 10*d.*

Mr.

Mr. Parkinson informed me, that ploughing rabbit-warrens near the Green Man on Lincoln Heath, had answered so little to Mr. King, that though he had subdivided it in small enclosures for tillage, yet he afterwards was induced to lett the rabbits in again, as it did not answer. Such is the fact; but perhaps he might look to corn as the principal object of his tillage: in such case, I am not surprised; for on poor lands, sheep, not corn, should be the great object.

The warren of North Ormsby, occupied by the late Mr. Ansell, is supposed to be one of the best managed in the county.

The rabbits chiefly consist of silver greys, the land of the yearly value, from 2*s*. 6*d*. to 8*s*. and some little of it 10*s*. the statute acre.

Mr. Ansell was of opinion, that lately his warren lands would have paid him better had they been applied to the purpose of growing corn, and grass-seeds for keeping sheep. The rabbit produce he supposed to be from 8*s*. to 10*s*.; in some particular years they have paid from 15*s*. to 21*s*. an acre; but to obtain any extraordinary profit, very great care must be taken in killing the many different kinds of vermin which depredate, and without the utmost vigilance will quite depopulate, the warrens. A considerable expense also attends the necessity there is for night-watchers to protect them from the infinitely worse vermin, the poachers.

The silver grey skins have been sold from 8½*d*. to 15*d*. and 16*d*. per skin; the last two years they have only brought from 10*d*. to 11*d*. per skin; but to obtain even these prices, they must be what is called full seasoned whole skins, and of the choicest colours, with respect to which the fashion varies very greatly. The

carcasses

carcasses of late years have not averaged, net into pocket, more than 4*d*. per couple, after paying the expense of drying them, and by means of light diligence carts, having them carried to markets, thirty, and sometimes more than sixty miles, to obtain even that sum. This inconvenience is occasioned by the increased* number of rabbits kept on the high wold lands in this part of the county of Lincoln, and its being necessary to kill eight or ten parts of a year's slaughter in so short a time as between the second week in November and Christmas, on account of their skins being then only in full prime, and as they are also very soon subject to become putrid (much more so than hares), and their being obliged to be packed close together, very greatly increases the mischief.

Turnips, clover, and sainfoin, are the most proper kinds of winter food for rabbits, as also thrashed oats or barley, when corn is tolerably cheap, may be given them with great propriety; the two latter need only to be allowed when the ground is covered with snow, and when it does not blow about so as to cover the corn when laid down; but in severe storms turnips are the most proper food, as they can find them by their scent, and will scratch the snow off when covered. Three large cart loads of turnips a day will fodder 1000 or 1100 couples of rabbits, which are about a proper quantity to be left as breeding stock on 500 acres of en closed warren land. When the rabbits are enclosed in a warren, they very seldom breed more than twice in a year, and in some seasons numbers of them only once, and many of them not at all. After every exertion, it

* This reason is by no means admissible, for rabbits have *decreased*.

is

is very probable, that one year in three there will be a failure in the increase, and then consequently it will prove a very unprofitable season.

In heavy snows, a great deal of money must be expended in clearing the snow from tue warren walls, in order to keep as much as possible the rabbits within their bounds.

The skin of the silver grey is not so generally esteemed for the hatter's business as that of the common rabbit; the former are therefore dressed for the China market; which, for various reasons, fluctuates so much as to render this branch of rural economy a very precarious business. It is necessary to observe, that every year there are a great quantity of what are called half skins, quarter ditto, and racks, sixteen of which are only allowed for as one whole skin.

These particulars were communicated by Mr. William Allison, jun.

Swinop.—The warrens here are found chiefly in the parishes of Binbrook, Towes, Irford, Thoresway, Thorganby (which will soon be destroyed), Croxby, and Rothwell. Of these, Thoresway is the largest; the rent is very dicffiult to ascertain, as they are lett with farms in the gross; but in a general way, is supposed to be from 5*s.* to 7*s.* Perhaps the whole of Rothwell, *at present* (in 1797) is not above 5*s.* Thorganby, Croxby, Rothwell, and Binbrook, belong to Mr. Willoughby. The soil is either a loose deep mold on chalk-stone, or in some places marl; the natural grass *shar*. The annual sale per acre may be estimated from three couple to eight: but this will depend on being well wintered; a good manager will, by feeding well, in the opinion of Mr. Allington, but who has no warren himself, carry the product to 10*s.* and even 12*s.* upon new land.

and. The price in 1793 was 16*d.* a skin; in 1796 not above 9*d.*; probably 1*s.* average; the carcass sells at 10*d.* a couple. For expenses we must estimate a rood of banking at 14*d.* to 20*d.* including the coping, whether of gorse or deals. To surround a square mile of 640 acres, there are 914 roods, at 1*s.* 6*d.*, which is 68*l.* 11*s.*

A circumstance which makes any account complex, is, that upon many warrens here, as well as elsewhere, they take in annually a certain portion of the warren to break up by paring and burning, if the turf admits it, for turnips, and then corn, in a short rotation, and throw it out after seeds, taking care not to let in the rabbits the first year, or they destroy the seeds. If the turnips are good, the corn is so; but Mr. Allington, from breaking up a warren without paring and burning, is of opinion, that the land is not improved by rabbits, further than time making a turf which enables the farmer to pare and burn; a mode of breaking up he highly approves.

In adverting to any profit that may result from warrens to the occupier, Mr. Allington remarks, that they are a horrid nuisance to the neighbours' corn, new seeds, turnips, and above all, to the quicks, which they presently destroy; and killing what they can of such depredators, is a very small compensation for the evil. In this respect, the laws are deficient, by protecting the rabbits as private property, and leaving no resource but killing them when astray. This observation is peculiarly applicable to such warrens as are not enclosed; but it is found even with the best fences.

Ride through the estate of Thoresway, 3000 acres, a warren farm. Mr. Holdgate, the tenant, had the goodness to favour me with many interesting particulars

culars on this branch of husbandry, which is so little known in printed agriculture. He states the expenses of 1700 acres under rabbits, the silver sort, thus:

	£.	s.	d.
Labour, three regular warreners, with extra assistance at killing	£.85	0	0
Fences	42	10	0
Winter food	42	10	0
Nets, traps, &c. &c.	14	3	4
Delivery	21	5	0
Rent is said to be 7*s*. an acre	595	0	0
	£.800	8	4
The capital employed is that sum, with the addition of stock paid for; suppose this, as stated by Mr. Grant, three couple an acre, at 2*s*. 4*d*.	595	0	0
	1395	8	4
Interest of that sum one year, 5 per cent.	69	5	0
	£.1464	13	4

Annual Account.

	£.	s.	d.
Expenses as above	800	8	4
Interest	69	5	0
	869	13	4
Produce 10,000 couple, at 2*s*. 4*d*.	1166	13	4
Expenses	869	13	4
Profit	£.297	0	0

or 24*l*. per cent. (the five per cent. included) on capital employed. This is very great, reckoned on the capital,

pital, but small reckoned by rent, as it amounts to only half a rent. But *suppose* the gross produce 1500*l.* which I take to be nearer the fact, then the account would stand thus:

Produce	£.1500	0	0
Expenses	869	0	0
Profit	£.631	0	0

or 47*l.* per cent. on the capital.

Take it how you will, it explains the reason for so many of these nuisances remaining. The investment of a small capital yields an interest that nothing else will; and thus the occupier will be sure never to convert them to better uses. But what says the public interest? Here are only 200*l.* expenses to 600*l.* rent what is the population, the industry, the improvement! the landlord gets the lowest of rents, the tenant makes a good profit; they divide all, and the rest of the world are little the better for them.

Mr. Holdgate being an excellent farmer, the rest of this great tract of land is as well managed as the warren allows it to be; but it is to the eye a melancholy scene, more of desolation than culture, the remains only of old fences: no wonder; what fences can be preserved on a warren? These circumstances are the sure concomitants of this execrable stock.

I am glad, however, to observe, that there is something better on this noble farm of 3000 acres than rabbits; under that animal there are,

Acres

Acres	1700
Corn	350
Grass, turnips, and seeds	950
	3000

And 700 sheep are kept, with a herd of cattle.

In the many journies I have taken through this kingdom, and the numerous inquiries I have made concerning warrens, I have found more difficulty in gaining intelligence upon this, than upon any other subject. Of the preceding particulars, some, as the articles of Blankney and Ormsby, I *suspect* the correctness; Mr. Parkinson has taken data too complex; but Mr. Holdgate gave me his particulars in a conversation, the colour and circumstances of which induce me to give much credit to it; but the rent and capital employed are supplied. The article of Dalby is correct also, and on good authority. Upon the whole, I trust this branch of husbandry may be pretty well analyzed from these particulars.

SECT. VI.—POULTRY.

Geese plucked five times a year; at Pinchbeck it is at Lady-day, Midsummer, Lammas, Michaelmas, and Martinmas. The feathers of a dead goose worth 6*d.* three giving a pound. But plucking alive does not yield more than 3*d.* a head per annum. Some wing them only every quarter, taking ten feathers from each goose, which sell at 5*s.* a thousand. Plucked geese pay in feathers 1*s.* a head in Wildmore Fen.

Inquiring of Sir Joseph Banks's boatman on East Fen,

Fen, the profits of keeping geese on that watery desart, he gave me the following account of what he did himself:—his stock was eight score; and in 1797, which was not a good year, he reared 500; in a good year 700, eight the average brood: they sell this year at 2*s.* which is higher than ever; has sold at 1*s.* Plucks four times, at 4*d.* each time (some folks five times), because he thinks more hurts the old ones. His expense in corn is from 20*l.* in fine winters, to 50*l.* in bad ones. He plucks the young twice or thrice, and gets ten quills from each goose, at 6*d.* per 120.

Average produce 1*s.* 3*d.* goose; 1*s.* 3*d.* feathers; 600 at 2*s.* 6*d.*	£.75	0	0
Corn	35	0	0
Profit	£.40	0	0

His wife and children do all the labour they demand.

As much conversation of late has passed about enclosure, such accounts are now to be suspected of exggeration.

SECT. VII.—FISH.

It has been observed by some authors, that the plenty of fresh water fish will depend somewhat on the seasons. I do not know either that the fact is ascertained, or that, were it ascertained, it would lead to the means of remedying bad seasons; however, as facts are very rare, and future combinations possible, I shall here enter the minutes of an annual fishing party held by Sir Joseph Banks in the river Witham; which, if it does not produce

produce any thing of importance in the natural history of fish, merits a note in the register of rural hospitality; for I found these fishing parties, which lasted four days, spoken of by many persons with great pleasure. Miss Banks has kept a particular journal of these piscatory excursions, which is decorated with many drawings: she had the goodness to favour me with the following totals.

	lbs. Wt. of Fish.
In 1788, a carp of $5\frac{1}{4}$ lb.	1764
1789, a pike of $15\frac{1}{4}$ lb.	693
1790,	1711
1791,	842
1792, a salmon of 10 lb.	1410
A burbolt of $3\frac{1}{2}$ lb. being 22 inches long, and eleven in circumference.	
1793,	2644
1794, a perch 2 lb.	1366
1795, a tench of $2\frac{1}{4}$ lb.	2567
1796,	1562

In Sir Joseph Banks's kitchen is the picture of a pike that wighed 31 lb. which was thirteen years old; he increased therefore about two pound and a half annually.

CHAP.

CHAP. XIV.

RURAL ECONOMY.

SECT. I.—LABOUR.

AT Long Sutton from 17*s.* to 21*s.* an acre for reaping, yet a vast number of labourers have come on account of the employment the enclosed common has yielded.

At Spalding, in winter, 10*s.* 6*d.* a week, summer 15*s.*; in harvest 7*s.* 8*s.*; and in 1796 up to 10*s.* 6*d.* a day. Reaping 12*s.* to 20*s.* an acre.

At Brothertoft, labour, in winter, 1*s.* 6*d.* the lowest; 10*s.* a week the average. Hay 12*s.* for a month. Harvest 5*s.* a day for six weeks, then winter price. Occasional instances, when there is a scarcity of men, and corn ripens, up to 10*s.* 6*d.* a day; and all prices under; an acre of reaping 25*s.* by contract has been known. A head farmer's servant 16*l.* 16*s.*; common one 14*l.* 14*s.*; a hog-boy 6*l.*; a dairy-maid 5*l.* 5*s.*; a carpenter, wet and dry, 2*s.* 6*d.*; a mason 3*s.*; his labourer 2*s.*; beer to none of these prices. Thatching 3*s.* a square for houses; 6*d.* to 9*d.* a yard for stacks, running measure*.

About

* In the Fens, from the end of harvest till Christmas, in dry autumns especially, the labourer earns, by ditching, &c. at least 2*s.* per day, nor is less than 18*d.* given to a day-labourer. From the quantity of public works now carrying on from the war, the price of labour is on the increase.

About Folkingham, in winter 2*s*. a day; keep on till hay, then 2*s*. 6*d*. for five weeks: for harvest 9*s*. a week, and board, which is worth 7*s*. more, till Michaelmas; then winter; reaping an acre of wheat 11*s*.; mowing an acre of grass 3*s*.; hoeing turnips twice 6*s*. and beer; a woman, in hay, 10*s*.

About Grantham, in winter 2*s*.; summer and har-

---

increase. From Christmas to Lady-day from 1*s*. 3*d*. to 1*s*. 6*d*. is given; from thence to hay time 18*d*. from hay to harvest 2*s*. and in harvest from 3*s*. 6*d*. to 7*s*. per day; but 4*s*. 6*d*. or 5*s*. per day is the average price of a reaper from 1794 to 1797. This increase of the price of labour is owing in some measure to the scarcity of hands, but more still to the sudden ripening of the corn, which brought the harvest fit together in every part of the kingdom.

The consequences of such high prices are very baneful; the workmen get drunk; work not above four days out of the six; dissipate their money, hurt their constitutions, contract indolent and vicious dispositions, and are lost to the community for at least one-third of their time in this important crisis. It is a pity but the legislature could interfere.

It may be wondered at, and reprobated by persons not acquainted with the Fen country, that so much of the corn should be reaped, whereby such an extraordinary quantity of hands are required. In wet seasons it is impossible to mow the grain, it being laid in every direction: and in drier ones, when it can be mowed, it must then be bound up out of the swarth (for to cock it, the barns and stack-yards would be filled with lumber), requires much more barn or stack room, brings with it a great deal of foulness, which would be left out by shearing, and costs more by one-third in thrashing. The price of reaped corn to be thrashed is pretty generally ascertained; oats at 5*s*. per last; beans and barley at 10*s*. 6*d*.; and wheat at 1*s*. per coomb. Women have not that general employment they ought to have; but besides weeding and hay-making, they are employed in collecting the sods from off breach land, picking up twitch to burn, knocking about muck, spudding of thistles, and gathering, spreading, and turning of flax; for twitching and weeding, they have, upon an average, 9*d*. per day; for hay-making 1*s*.; and about flax they have from 15*d*. to 18*d*. per day. In harvest but few women reap who are natives of these parts; they earn more for themselves by gleaning.—*MS. of the Board*.

vest

vest *3s.*; but most by contract. To mow an acre of grass *3s.*; to reap, *9s.*

At Leadenham, and the villages in its vicinity; in winter 1*s.* 6*d.*; hay 10*s.* 6*d.* a week; harvest 14*s.* for six weeks; reaping 6*s.* to 10*s.*; mowing corn 2*s.*; mowing grass 2*s.* 6*d.*

At Blankney, 1*s.* 6*d.* in winter; 2*s.* and beer in hay and harvest; reaping oats in the Fen 15*s.*; this year 18*s.* and two quarts of ale a day; but the crops quite down.

At Hackthorne, in winter, 1*s.* 4*d.* to 1*s.* 6*d.*; in summer 2*s.*; that is, from Midsummer to Michaelmas, mowing grass 2*s.*; mowing corn 1*s.* 6*d.* reaping wheat 6*s.* to 8*s.*; three bushels of malt to each man in summer.

At Norton, in 1777, 6*s.* for one half of the year, and 8*s.* for the other; now 9*s.* in winter half year, and for summer half year 12*s.* and in harvest 18*s.* but some less. A woman, in hay, 8*d.* and 9*d.*; harvest 10*d.* and 1*s.* Head man, thirteen or fourteen guineas. Reaping 6*s.* to 8*s.*; grass 2*s.* 6*d.*

At Knaith, &c. all the year, except harvest, 10*s.* 6*d.* a week; harvest 2*s.* 6*d.* a day. Reaping 10*s.* 6*d.* an acre; woman, in hay, 1*s.* 3*d.*

In Axholm, winter 1*s.* 4*d.* to 1*s.* 6*d.*; summer 1*s.* 6*d.* to 1*s.* 8*d.*; harvest 2*s.* 6*d.*; reaping white corn 7*s.* to 8*s.*; beans 10*s.*; mowing grass 2*s.* and beer; corn the same: wages, head man, 13*l.*

About Normanby, Burton, &c. in winter 1*s.* 3*d.* that is, from Michaelmas to Lady-day; from thence to hay time, about 1*s.* 6*d.*; in hay 2*s.* 6*d.*; in corn harvest 3*s.* to 3*s.* 6*d.*

	s.	d.
26 weeks, at	1	3
10 at	1	6
9 at	2	6
7 at	3	3
Rise in four years, winter	1	0
Spring	1	3
Hay	1	6
Corn	2	6
Twenty years ago, winter	0	10
Spring	1	0
Hay	1	6
Corn	2	0

The women are not industrious; for though by spinning flax they might earn 4*d.* a day, they content themselves with 3*d.*; but many not 2*d.*

At Wintringham, in winter and hay 2*s.*; in harvest 3*s.* 6*d.* Women 1*s.*; some 1*s.* 6*d.* and in harvest 2*s.* 6*d.* Reaping oats 15*s.*; wheat 11*s.*; mowing barley 2*s.* 6*d.* ditto grass 2*s.* to 2*s.* 6*d.* Hoeing turnips 5*s.* to 6*s.* Head man's wages 15*l.* 15*s.*; some more; ploughman 12*l.* 12*s.*

Labour at Barton:

Winter 10*s.* a week Michaelmas to May-day.
12*s.* May-day to harvest.
3*s.* a day, harvest.

Mr. Graburn, mow and sheaf, 5*s.* 6*d.*

At Humberston, in winter and till hay 2*s.* Hay 2*s.* 6*d.* 3*s.* Harvest 4*s.*; that is, 3*s.* and food. Wages of a head man fifteen or sixteen guineas. A woman in hay time, &c. 1*s.*

At Tathwell, and its vicinity near Louth, in winter till May-day, 10*s.* 6*d.* a week; then to hay 13*s.*; in hay 18*s.* harvest, and to Old Michaelmas 24*s.*; ale included

cluded in all. Reaping 12*s*. to 20*s*.; average 15*s*. Mowing grass and corn 3*s*. 6*d*. Hoeing turnips 5*s*.; and they run over an acre a day. Thrash wheat 3*s*. 6*d*. a quarter; spring corn 1*s*. 6*d*. Woman in hay 1*s*. 3*d*.; ditto reaping 3*s*. 6*d* ; and hands not to be got at any price; much work left undone that would be executed, but hands not to be got. Carpenter 10*s*. 6*d*. a week, bed and board ; mason 2*s*. 6*d*. and board, or 4*s*. without; thatcher 10*s*. 6*d*. a week, and board; man servant 15*l*. 15*s*.; lad 9*l*. or 10*l*.; hog-boy 4*l*. 4*s*. ; all washed for.

Labour about Saltfleet in winter 1*s*. 6*d*.; in spring, 2*s*. Women in hay, 1*s*. 2*d*.; in harvest 3*s*. 6*d*. a day for July, August, and September. The inhabitants have not much to do; yet there is now ten times as much arable as there was in Mr. Neve's memory.

About Spilsby, &c. winter, 1*s*. 6*d*.; in spring, 10*s*. 6*d*. a week; in hay, 15*s*.; in harvsst, 18*s*. Woman in hay 1*s*.; a woman for reaping 2*s*. Reaping by the acre 7*s*. to 21*s*. Mowing spring corn, 2*s*. 6*d*. a day; ditto grass, 3*s*. 6*d*.

Through the hundred of Skirbeck 9*s*. a week, for five months; 10*s*. 6*d*. for four months; and 17*s*. for three months. Reaping wheat 10*s*. to 20*s*.; ditto oats, 10*s*. to 18*s*.; beans 9*s*. 6*d*.; mowing spring corn 3*s*.; mowing grass 4*s*. Hoe turnips 6*s*. Woman a day in hay 1*s*. 4*d*.; in harvest 2*s*. 8*d*. A carpenter 2*s*. 8*d*. A mason and server 5*s*. 2*d*. together. From 1767 to 1777, 1*s*. a day for six months; 1*s*. 2*d*. for three months; and 2*s*. 2*d*. a day for three months.

At Swinop, in winter, not regular labourers 1*s*. 8*d*.; in spring 2*s*.; in harvest 2*s*. and meat. A woman in hay 1*s*.

At Sudbrook, in winter 1*s*. 6*d* ; in the spring 2*s*.; in

in hay and harvest 2*s*. 6*d*. and beer or 6*d*.; but very little done by the day. To reap an acre of wheat 7*s*. to 10*s*.; to mow an acre spring corn 2*s*. 6*d*.; hay the same. To hoe turnips once 4*s*. to 5*s*. To thrash wheat, 2*s* 6*d*. a quarter to 3*s*. 6*d*. in summer; barley 2*s*. to 2*s*. 2*d*.; oats 1*s*. Wages 16*l*. 16*s*.; others 14*l*.; lads 9*l*. or 10*l*.; a muck boy 6*l*.

Labour about Grimsthorpe 1*s*. 6*d*. in winter, from Michaelmas to Lady-day; then to hay 2*s*.; in harvest 3*s*.; and in the Fen to 5*s*. Reaping 10*s*. 6*d*.; mowing corn 2*s*.; mowing grass 3*s*. Thrash wheat 3*s*. a quarter; in 1796 2*s*. 3*d*. to 2*s*. 6*d*.; barley 20*d*.; oats 1*s*. beans 1*s*. 3*d*. Hoeing turnips 6*s*. loose.

At Brocklesby, in winter, from Martinmas to Lady-day, 1*s*. 6*d*.; thence to mowing 1*s*. 8*d*. to 1*s*. 10*d*.; in hay 2*s*.; in harvest 12*s*. 6*d*. a week, and meat. Head team-man, wages 15*l*. 15*s*.; next 12*l*. 12*s*.; lads 10*l*. Reaping wheat 6*s*. to 13*s*. 6*d*.; average 9*s*. 6*d*. Mowing grass and spring corn 2*s*. Woman in hay or harvest 1*s*.

At Swinop, with labourers who have cottages, a cow and a pig kept for 5*l*. 5*s*. a year. To mow corn and hay 1*s*. 6*d*.; to thrash wheat 2*s*. 6*d*.; barley 1*s*. 2*d*.; oats 1*s*. In winter 1*s*. 6*d*. a day; at Midsummer 2*s*.; in harvest 2*s*. and meat. Hoeing turnips 5*s*. 6*d*.

Recapitulation.

Places.	Winter, per Week.		Spring, per Week.		Summer, per Week.		Harvest, per Week.		Reaping per Acre.		Women, Sum.	
	s.	*d.*	*s.*	*d.*	*s.*	*d.*	*s.*	*d.*	*s.*	*d.*	*s.*	*d.*
Long Sutton	—		—		—		—		19	0	—	
Spalding	10	6	—		15	0	42	0	16	0	—	
Brothertoft ..	10	0	—		12	0	30	0	18	0	—	
Folkingham ..	12	0	12	0	15	0	16	0	11	0	5	0
Grantham ..	12	0	12	0	18	0	18	0	9	0	—	
Leadenham ..	9	0	10	6	10	6	14	0	9	0	—	
Blankney	9	0	9	0	12	0	12	0	15	0	—	
Hackthorne ..	8	6	8	6	12	0	12	0	8	0	—	
Norton	9	0	9	0	12	0	18	0	8	0	5	0
Knaith	10	6	10	6	10	6	15	0	10	6	7	6
Axholm	7	6	10	0	10	0	15	0	7	6	—	
Normanby ..	7	6	9	0	15	0	19	6	—		—	
Wintringham	12	0	12	0	12	0	15	0	11	0	—	
Barton	10	0	10	0	12	0	18	0	—		—	
Humberston	12	0	12	0	16	0	24	0	—		6	0
Tathwell	10	6	12	0	18	0	24	0	15	0	8	0
Saltfleet	9	0	12	0	14	0	21	0	—		7	0
Spilsby	9	0	10	6	15	0	18	0	14	0	7	6
Skirbeck	9	0	10	6	17	0	17	0	15	0	10	0
Swinop	10	0	12	0	12	0	24	0	—		6	0
Sudbrook ..	9	0	12	0	15	0	18	0	8	6	—	
Grimsthorpe	9	0	12	0	12	0	18	0	10	6	—	
Average ..	10	0	10	9	13	6	20	0	12	0	6	9

In order to see the amount of the year's earnings, we must call the winter twenty-six weeks, spring nine, summer nine, and harvest eight, which not uncommonly in price lasts till Michaelmas.

		£.		
26 weeks	at 10*s.*	13	0	0
9 ——	at 10*s.* 9*d.*	4	17	7
9 ——	at 13*s.* 6*d.*	6	1	6
8 ——	at 20*s.*	8	0	0
		£.31	19	1

Which

Which is near 12*s*. 6*d*. a week the year round.

And this I take to be under the truth, were it to be correctly known. Hence we may determine, that labour is probably higher than in any other county in the kingdom.

SECT. II.—PROVISIONS.

BOSTON; price of mutton 6*d*.; beef 5½*d*.; butter 1*s*.; cheese 6*d*. Coals 27*s*. and in winter 30*s*. and 32*s*. per chaldron.

Price at Folkingham; mutton 6*d*.; beef 6½*d*.; butter 10*d*.; cheese 7*d*. Coals 11½*d*. per cwt. At Norton, coals 20*s*. a chaldron, 48 bushels or strikes, at the barge; butter 20*d*. a cake, of 2 lb.

The Trent furnishes Gainsborough, &c. with some sorts of fish in great plenty. Salmon, which rises to 46 lb. at 1*s*. a pound; pike, up to 17 lb. at 6*d*.; perch, to 5 lb. at 6*d*.; tench, to 4 lb. at 1*s*.; carp to 10 lb. at 1*s*.; eels plentiful; but carp and tench rare. Butter 10*d*. per pound; the poor buy at 8½*d*.; and twenty years ago at 2½*d*. Wild ducks 3*s*. to 3*s*. 6*d*. a brace; teal 1*s*. 6*d*. a couple; grey plover 1*s*. 6*d*. Coals, 17*s*. for 48 bushels.

At Haxey, in Axholm, coals 16*s*. a ton, laid in.

At Burton, Normanby, &c. the chaldron 48 bushels, in summer on the river side, 20*s*. Butter 10*d*.; mutton 6*d*.; beef 6*s*. 6*d*. a stone, veal 6*d*.; pork in winter 5*s*. a stone; potatoes 3*s*. a sack; salmon 1*s*.

At Barton, coals come from near Wakefield; the sloops that carry corn and wool bring back coals, and many go on purpose; the best Flocton 20*s*. a chaldron of of 48 bushels: other sorts so low as 16*s.* and 18*s.* Mutton 6*d.*; beef 6*s.* 6*d.* a stone; pork in winter 7*d.*; butter 9*d.*; in winter 1*s.* In winter, cod 3*d.* a pound; salmon caught there, 1*s.* to 1*s.* 6*d.* a pound.

At Spilsby; mutton 6*d.*; beef 6*s.* a stone; butter 9*d.* which eight years ago was 3*d.*

At Louth; butter 9*d.* has been accidentally 1*s.* 3*d.* I heard of a pleasant story of the Corporation ordaining that all butter not eighteen ounces to the pound, be taken away: I wonder (if the fact be so) who made these gentlemen legislators? In 1759 it was 3*d.*; geese 3*s.* 3*d.*, or 4*d.* per pound; turkeys 6*d.* per pound, or 4*s.* 6*d.* to 6*s.*; beef in harvest, in 1786, 2½*d.*

CHAP.

CHAP. XV.

POLITICAL ECONOMY.

SECT. I.—ROADS.

UPON its being proposed some time ago to make a turnpike to join the Spilsby road from Tattershall, the proposition was rejected, without throwing the expense by tolls on the public; and the issue shews, that without a very general public spirit, and proprietors being of ample fortune, or great spirit of exertion, such schemes rarely succeed: here the business has been well and effectually done through Revesby; but I understood, that for a large extent of it the road is still much neglected.

In the hundred of Skirbeck to Boston, and thence to Wisbeach, they are generally made with silt, or old sea-sand, deposited under various parts of the country ages ago, and when moderately wet are very good; but dreadfully dusty and heavy in dry weather; and also on a thaw they are like mortar.

Take the county in general, and they must be esteemed below par.

SECT. II.—CANALS.

THERE is an inland navigation from Boston, by Brothertoft farm on the Witham, cut to Lincoln, and then

then by the Fossdyke canal to the Trent, and thence to all parts of Yorkshire, Lancashire, &c. Rotherham having been, in good times for the manufacture, a great market for cattle and sheep, Mr. Cartwright executed a boat for taking sheep. It will carry 80 in two parcels, one in the hold, and the other on the deck; the latter secured by netting, supported by stancheons. The deck is of moveable hatches, covered with tarpauling to keep free of urine; to give air below a line of hatches along the centre moveable; and the upper manger around that aperture. By this means they can be conveyed very commodiously, and saving the loss of 3*s.* a-head by driving. (*See the annexed Plate*).

At Sleaford, a new canal made from the Witham to Boston, finished in 1796, and has but lately begun to operate.

Another, the Grantham canal, from Grantham, and goes into the Trent near Holm Pierepoint.

The Ankhom cut extends, and is navigable from Bishop Bridge to the Humber, at Ferraby Sluice.

Also from Horncastle to the river Witham, at Dogdyke near Tattershall; but not yet completed.

Another from Louth to the sea at Tetney.

At Grimsby, they have raised 20,000*l.* by subscription, to improve the haven, by a new cut, to bring ships of 700 tons to the town; but in the execution of the work they have managed so as to waste much money; and have now applied to Mr. Rennie for his advice how to proceed. Much of the earth, for want of precaution, has sunk in again. They have fine speculations, if they succeed, of rivalling Hull, as the great entrepôt of the Humber.

The conduct of engineers is complained of as a great obstacle

obstacle to navigations; for after giving their plans, they leave you to yourselves; and then difficulties arise in which the people are ignorant, and upon application to them, and ready to pay, cannot have their attention. Horncastle to the Witham below Tattershall, act passed, and money raised; and every thing has been ill done, for want of that attention which engineers ought to give; thus many thousand pounds were very ill spent.—Subscriptions 15,000*l.* and 6000*l.* more borrowed.—Tolls last year brought 250*l.*

The act for the navigation from Boston to the Trent was passed, and the work executed in 1798, to the benefit of Lincoln, as well as all the country.

From Grantham to Nottingham, thirty-three miles, there is a very fine canal, completed in 1796, which cost 100,000*l.*, and from which very great returns are expected. It passes near some fine beds of plaster, which will probably be productive; and lime is already brought in large quantities from Criche, in Derbyshire.

SECT. III.—MANUFACTURES.

Mr. Smith, at Gainsborough, has (1797) a ship of seven hundred tons on the stocks there; she will cost 3800*l.*: he builds many. A pretty considerable fabric for brushes there; also coarse hemp sacking.

About Normanby, Burton, &c. there is a good deal of flax spun, and woven into linen; do not earn above 3*d.* a day at it; but owing to indolence.

To establish a woollen manufacture at Louth, was a favourite

favourite scheme in the county some years ago. To build a mill for spinning long and short wool, 1792, the subscription 1540*l.*: the man broke; great difficulties; at last ended in a small establishment.

Mr. Chaplin established a machine at Raithby, near Louth, a *Big Ben* for combing wool, invented by Mr. Edmund Cartwright; he lost a great deal of money; a fire-engine there for it; all now gone and done with.

A lee of woollen yarn measures in length eighty yards. A hank of ditto, by the custom of Norwich, consists of seven lees.

	Yards.	*Miles.*
24 hanks in the pound is esteemed good spinning in the schools	13,440	8
70 hanks in the pound is esteemed superfine spinning at Norwich	39,200	22
150 hanks in the pound were spun in 1754, by Mary Powley, of East Dereham, in Norfolk; and this was thought so extraordinary, that an account of it is entered on the registers of the Royal Society	84,000	48
300 hanks in the pound have already been spun by Miss Ives, of Spalding; and though this young lady has carried the art of spinning combed wool to so great a degree of perfection, she does not despair of improving it still farther	168,000	95

The manufacturers of Norwich, zealous to encourage Miss Ives's ingenuity, are desirous of improving their looms in such a manner as will enable them to weave her delicate yarn. Mr. Harvey of that place has already manufactured some that is very fine; and he is at present

sent (1797) engaged in weaving her finest sort into a shawl, the texture of which is expected to equal that of the very best that have hitherto been brought from India.

SECT. IV.—POOR.

THE women in Holland Fen spin flax: the price for spinning is the price of the flax; when 8*d.* per pound, 8*d.* for spinning; now 10½*d.* and the same spinning. Earn about 6*d.* a day. In general, they are all to be considered as well off; no where better: constant employment at high wages. Rent of a cottage with a garden 1*l.* 11*s.* 6*d.* to 3*l.*; in common 1*l.* 11*s.* 6*d.* to 2*l.* 12*s.* 6*d.*

Major Cartwright remarks on the principle and the policy of the English poor laws. "Dr. Franklin, in his letter published at London, I believe reasoned well; but it might now be found impracticable wholly to change the system. The error of those laws, however, if an error it be, might gradually be corrected; to the advantage and comfort of the poor themselves, and to the relief of the rest of the community, on whom the poor's-rates are now so burthensome. To interweave *universally* with the laws for maintenance of the poor, the simple, natural, and admirable principle of the friendly societies; so as necessarily to induce, in a way not to be avoided, the rational practice of making, during health and abundance, some provision for a time of sickness, seems to be in every view of it, a measure of the greatest wisdom and humanity; and calculated to have a happy effect on the moral character of the poor. If their earnings would not admit of it, their wages ought to be raised; but that their condition

dition does admit of it, is proved by the numerous societies which exist in all parts of the kingdom. What the sober and provident do voluntarily, the idle and dissolute ought to be compelled to do. But in touching on this subject, I had principally in view to point out a very material defect, which runs very generally, I fear, through the rules of such societies: it is the defect of not making any provision for medical assistance when a member is ill. He is allowed out of the box sick pay, merely for his subsistence; but how to cure him of his disease, or obtain him the medical assistance of which he stands in need? He has the parish, it is true, to apply to, but in such cases, the poor man's application is seldom made till he thinks himself dying, and even then seldom complied with so soon as the case requires. Those who have any experience amongst the country poor, must know that their sufferings are great, from these causes; that the lives of many are sacrificed, and that many others languish for years with ruined health; when with timely aid, and a pennyworth of medicine, they might have enjoyed health and strength; the support and comfort of their families, and adding to the prosperity of their country. As the best remedy which, in the pesent state of things, I can suggest, I beg leave to mention what is practised in every considerable fishing harbour of Newfoundland; a skilful surgeon is encouraged by the merchants to settle in the place; and the fishermen and artificers, by a small contribution each, make him a competent salary. For this contribution every subscriber is entitled to attendance and medicine; and as it is the surgeon's interest to keep his subscribers in good health, he is early in the administration of medicine and regimen; and even anticipates applica-

tion,

tion, when he reads the approach of disease in a pale countenance or a languid gait. It is on this principle, that I have drawn up a plan for the benefit of the poor of this township, and others in my employment; which is likewise open to such other poor as choose to become members of our society. Having met with an active surgeon, who accepts of such a subscription as we can raise, I hope the last hand will be put to the design in a few days."

About Folkingham, the women spin flax and hemp that grows in Holland Fen, and earn 6*d.* a day at it. Rent of a cottage and garden 40*s.* and if land for a cow, 20*s.* an acre: they have three acres for a cow; and in the new enclosures, find great comfort in having it.

The management of Charles Chaplin, Esq. at Blankney, and in the other lordships which he possesses, cannot be too much commended: he assigns in each a large pasture, sufficient to feed a cow for every cottager in the place; besides which he letts them a small croft for mowing hay, to keep their cow in winter, which, with the assistance of a pig and a garden, are found to be of the greatest comfort to them. Upon inquiring what were poor's-rates—8*d.* in the pound! In another parish, 15*d.* nominal rent. Men are apt to complain heavily of poor's-rates in many counties, yet take no steps to remedy them. Here is an instance which strongly unites with those which Lord Winchilsea has so ably explained, to prove one great means of keeping rates down, by increasing benevolently the comforts of the poor. They all get cows here without difficulty; "lett them but land, and they will be sure to find stock for it," was the answer.

At Hackthorn, rent of a cottage 20*s.*; if a cow, 3*l.* 10*s.*;

10*s*.; have enough for winter and summer food; not one-fourth have them; but in some towns a good many. If land could be got, all would have cows; if a cow dies, they get collections for it. The women here spin flax; a quarter of a pound of twelvepenny, or 3*d*. is a day's work; but earn rather more by coarse work.

In the new enclosure of Glentworth, on Lincoln-heath, I saw some large pieces under various crops, that were in a most slovenly and wretched condition, run out, and almost waste; and on inquiry found they were allotments to cottagers, who, each knowing his own piece, cultivated in severalty within a ring-fence: it is a strong instance to prove that their shares ought always to be given in grass; they are unequal to any other tillage than that of a garden. At Kirton, in the new enclosure, there is in the vale twenty-eight acres of grass in one close, and twenty-two in another; one for the cottagers' cows in summer, and the other for hay; fifty in all: this is good, though not equal to every man having his own separate. None here find difficulty in getting cows, if they can but get land. By the proportion, twenty-eight acres meadow, near one acre and a half each cow, which yields two loads of hay for each gate. This fifty acres is worth 50*l*. rent for sixteen cows for the whole year; but they pay 4*l*. 4*s*. or 28*s*. an acre; thus the land letts better by 8*s*. an acre, at the same time a great benefit to them.

It is singular that the labouring poor, with the extraordinary high price of labour at Norton, Kirton, &c. consume very little meat, except the stoutest labourers at task-work, who earn 3*s*. a day: these have for dinner some meat in a pye; all consume a good many potatoes.

Upon

Upon Sir John Sheffield's estate of twenty square miles of country, the rents of the cottages have never been raised, and to prevent all oppression, they have been taken out of the hands of the farmers, and made tenants to the landlord; they pay little or nothing, or rather less than nothing, for the cottage, as the land is worth more than they pay for both. For a comfortable habitation, a garden for potatoes, of a rood or half an acre, called a *garth*, with summering and wintering of two cows, which enables them to keep two or three very fine pigs (but never any poultry), they pay 40*s*. This great indulgence has no ill effect; they are very clean in every thing; remarkably well clothed; no children in rags; their beds and furniture good; are very sober, and attentive to church; but not equally so in educating their children to be industrious. Let me, however, note, that in the great extent of this estate, there is but one public-house; a remarkable instance, that speaks strongly upon a point of infinite importance to the national manners and prosperity. In the parishes of Flixborough and Burton, the principal of the estate, poor's-rates are, at the highest, 1*s*. 10*d*. and this owing to militia laws, and some contested settlements. Upon Mr. Goulton's estate, where nearly a similar system takes place, the rates are only 1*s*. The cottagers are very numerous on Sir John's estate, therefore if a different system was embraced, and their habitations, gardens, and cow-grounds, were raised to as much as might be, 200*l*. a year might be added to the rents. This sum would equal 1*s*. in the pound on the poor's-rates of these parishes. This is a very singular fact, which deserves great attention; for it may be fairly concluded, that more than 200*l*. a year is saved

by

by this uncommon system of benevolence, from which it has arisen. At this valuation of 200*l*. a year, they would still be on a par with others. They live in them from father to son, and even leave their cottages through confidence that no child or widow will ever be turned out, unless for offences that do not occur; and the effect is so great, that there is a reliance on the attachment of the poor which nothing else can affect. Population increases so, that pigs and children fill every quarter. And at Burton, &c. no cottages have been pulled down, but several new ones built; in the last twenty years the baptisms at Burton have exceeded the burials by 136; and though some have certainly emigrated from the parish, yet by no means in any thing like that proportion, as is visible in every circumstance that can be recurred to.

The women are very lazy; I have noted their indolence in spinning; Mr. Goulton's expresion was, "they do nothing but bring children, and eat cake;" nay, the men milk their cows for them; but the men very sober and industrious.

At Alkborough, 9*d*. in the pound.

Mr. Elwes's cottagers at Roxby, have also each two cows, and very good houses.

In all this country, the common-gate for a cottager's cow is two acres for winter, and one and a half for summer.

At Winıringham, upon Lord Carrington buying the estate, he made all the cottagers tenants to himself, and all have cows and gardens.

Lord Yarborough's cottagers have all cows and a garden.

Mr. Lloyd, of Alesby, has no labourers that have not cows; and it is the same with those of Mr. Skipwith

at

at Alesby. The custom seems general through all the country.

At Humberston, Lord Carrington has paid the same attention to them as at Wintringham. The whole of the parish, near Grimsby, in Lincolnshire, is his property; in that parish there are thirteen cottagers, every one of whom has conveniences for the keeping of one cow, and some for the keeping of two cows. The land on which the cottages stand, with the little paddocks and gardens adjoining them, is in all about sixteen acres. Besides which, at a distance of a quarter of a mile from the town, about sixty acres of land are appropriated to the use of the cottagers. This land is divided into two plats, one of which is a pasture for the cows of the cottagers in summer, and the other is kept as meadow land, to provide hay for them in the winter. Each cottager knows his own little piece of meadow land, and he lays upon it all the manure which he can obtain, in order that he may have the more hay.

When one of the two plats of land has been mown for two or three years, it will be converted into a summer pasture, and the other plat will become meadow land, so that no part of the land in the occupation of the cottagers will be injured by constant mowing.

The cottagers are totally independent of the larger farmers, as they hold their cottages and lands directly of Lord Carrington, and not as sub-tenants. This gives them a degree of respectability which they would not otherwise enjoy; and their situation is the more desirable, as the rent they pay is less than the rent paid by the farmers in general. But it is certain that, in numberless places in the kingdom, many a poor cottager would

would rejoice to give the utmost value for as much land as would keep a cow, if he could obtain it.

Lord Carrington is the patron of the living of Humberston; and in addition to the comforts which have been bestowed on the poor of the town, in the way which I have mentioned, his Lordship has been careful to give the living to a most respectable, conscientious clergyman, who has much at heart the religious and moral improvement of his parishioners. The labours of the clergyman have produced great good; the cottagers are sober and industrious; and it is not known that any man in the parish lives in habitual immorality. Soon after the clergyman was presented to the living, he was assisted by Lord Carrington to establish a school, much for the benefit of the youth of the parish.

The poor's-rates in the parish of Humberston have never amounted to more that 9*d.* or 10*d.* per pound on rental, and sometimes not to more than 6*d.* This is undoubtedly to be attributed to the attention which has been paid to the poor in various ways, and particularly to the support which they have derived from the small quantities of land which they have occupied.

At Tathwell, &c. near Louth. all the labourers on Mr. Chaplin's estate have two cows, two pigs, and a few sheep, all for 4*l.* a year.

At Saltfleet, &c. most of the poor have cows. It is a general rule for every grazier and farmer to keep cows for his regular labourers, at a low joist; and on the Wolds it is universal, one or two cows, and a pig or two, with a few sheep. In the Marshes the poor eat a great deal of bacon; very few but what kill a pig, and some two, feeding them much with potatoes, and some barley-meal; and few are without their piece

piece of potatoe ground for their families, and pigs; in general living very well. Shepherds here, who have two or three hundred acres to look after, live very well indeed.

About Spilsby, Dalby, &c. the generality have cows, excepting those who are maintained by the parish; and are upon the whole extremely well off.

Hundred of Skirbeck.—Mr. Linton at Freiston. Poor's-rates having gradually increased, it is conceived that one means of preventing the continuance of that evil might be effected, by allotting so much land to cottages as will enable the labourer living in them to keep a cow, a pig, and a very few sheep; chiefly raised cade lambs. About four acres of tolerably good land would answer this purpose. It is upon this idea, that Mr. Linton's grandfather and father continued allotments of this sort to several of their cottages, which Mr. Linton himself has also continued, and formed others. In general, they have from two to seven acres at the rent of the country, paying about 40*s*. for the cottage, exclusive of the value of the land. By means of this they keep from one to two cows, a pig or two, but some only sows, kept for one litter, and then fattened. Their sheep system is to keep on the ground in winter as many ewes or hogs as the land will support, buying lambs in the spring to be reared as cades, for which they give 3*s*. each, which they sell either in the ensuing autumn, or the succeeding spring, at upwards of 17*s*. in the former season, and to 24*s*. in the spring. Thus a man who has four acres, will keep a cow, a pig, and five breeding ewes, and be able to raise five cade lambs in the spring. Fencing and digging the garden, he does himself in mornings and evenings;

 all

all other attention by his wife and family. He fattens the calf and sells it to the butcher. He sells some butter, except when the lambs are rearing; but this varies of course with circumstances. Mr. Linton has not observed, that having land in this manner has any effect in taking them from their work, saving a day or two for their hay; and that the system tends to bring up their families in habits of industry; and he scarcely knows an instance of families thus provided, applying to the parish for assistance; and he is well convinced that he loses nothing by this application of the land. He thinks that there are not many difficulties in their procuring money for thus establishing themselves, as, with a view to it, servants take care to save money enough for this object before they marry. And a widow is rarely such long, from the eagerness there is to get into cottages thus circumstanced.

It is remarkable, that friendly societies do not flourish at all in the hundred of Skirbeck. There was one in Freiston, and another in Leak, and both are broken up; because the fund increasing much, they divided their money, and when demands came upon them, they were bankrupts through inability to pay. In the hundred of Kirton there are some.

At Swinop, Mr. Allington's regular labourers (and it is the same all through the country) have cows. If they are rich enough to buy themselves, they do it; if not, the landlord finds them cows, but in that case he has the calf gratis every year; but they like best to have their own cows, and they generally manage to get the money. Two labourers are now building cottages on leases of twenty-one years, at an expense of not less than 30*l*. each. The way the cows are fed, is with the farmer's own, both in summer and winter;

winter; the value of keeping a cow is estimated at 5*l.* at least, for they eat two tons of hay, besides straw. A cottage and garden is reckoned to be worth 40*s.* to 50*s.* None have sheep, but all a pig, which they fatten with gleaned corn; at other times run also with the farmer's pigs.

Many of the cottagers about Sudbrook have cows, a pig, and two or three cade lambs; but it is not universal. Mr. Ellison's bailiff informed me, that there are instances which shew, that the benefit of the practice depends much on the substance and management of the man; he has known a family with a cow, &c. very poor, and in uncomfortable circumstances, and when they have had their cow no longer, to have been much better off; and this he attributes to their sometimes depending too much on their live stock, neglecting their regular labour, and getting bad habits from it: but it is quite contrary with the sober and industrious, who are much more comfortable from having cows. All have from half an acre to an acre of land for potatoes, &c. They pay for a cottage and an acre, from 40*s.* to 3*l.*

It is much to the credit of Lincoln, that I can rank the card assemblies of that place, as a distinguished means of charity; it is not a mere accidental circumstance that now and then operates; for there is no year that passes, which does not produce very many cases of necessity and misfortune thus relieved: a gentleman of that place said, he had known forty instances in a short period of time.

At Marston, which is a populous village, I remarked that every cottage has a small field of half an acre or an acre, with a garden, and a little hay-stack; and each has four or five acres besides for their cow in summer.

mer. They have, besides, a pig or two, and some a few sheep; and as the land here does not always suit to remain in meadow, they plough and lay it down again, and their crops are good, and pay them well. This only in the small piece by the cottage. The whole was a sight that pleased me much.

Upon the Duke of Ancaster's estate, they have from three acres to eight, and some fourteen or fifteen, upon which they keep a couple of cows, a few ewes, and always a pig or two, for which they pay from 10*s*. to 20*s*. an acre. It is found a very great benefit to them, and at the same time they are enabled to bring up their families without the aid of the parish. Not a cottager on the Duke's estate that ever demands the aid of the parish, unless very great sickness befalls them; and they have ideas which spurn the aid, unless circumstances force them to it. They pay for a cottage and garden 20*s*. to 40*s*. and in general the land for their cows joins the house; and in consequence this does not make them bad labourers, but on the contrary, they are remarkable for being orderly, decent, church-going men, who behave themselves well. Poor-rates at Grimsthorpe *by the acre* not 1*s*. for every thing; but in Sunstead 5*s*. last year; owing to the mechanics and other little tradesmen having taken many apprentices before the enclosure; now it is expected they will reduce them by a different system.

Upon the new enclosures they have not pulled down houses, but built new ones.

Upon clay and mould soils, which do for grazing, enclosure changes arable to grass; but upon creech continued arable.

It is impossible to speak too highly in praise of the cottage system of Lincolnshire, where land, gardens, cows,

cows, and pigs, are so general in the hands of the poor. Upon views only of humanity and benevolence, it is gratifying to every honest heart to see that class of the people comfortable, upon which all others depend. This motive alone ought to operate sufficiently to make the practice universal through the kingdom. But there are also others that should speak powerfully to the feelings even of the most selfish. Wherever this system is found, poor's-rates are low; upon an average of the county, they do not amount to one-third of what is paid in Suffolk; and another object yet more important, is the attachment which men must inevitably feel to their country, when they partake thus in the property of it. It would be easy to expatiate on such topics, and indeed they can hardly be dwelt upon too much. But the great object which ought to employ every heart and hand, is to devise the means of rendering the system universal. This comes with peculiar propriety within the scope of the Board of Agriculture; nor do I see the use of surveying the whole kingdom, and attempting to discover every local circumstance that merits attention, if measures are not founded on the knowledge thus gained; if the Board does not follow such clues, or sift such subjects to the bottom, nor ascertain the best means of rendering universal, systems which have so much to recommend them. Well adapted premiums would here do much, probably in animating landlords to the work of benevolence, certainly in procuring still larger and more varied information, which is wanting, and particularly on the best means of carrying the practice into effect on poorer soils, where difficulties principally occur. By attaining such knowledge as is within the power of so respectable a body, when its energy is thus brought into play,

play, the right means of legislative interference would probably be discovered, and the Board would find itself in a position respectable, because unquestionably useful, between Administration on one hand, and the People on the other : an office of intelligence gleaned from the whole kingdom, and of ready application to many great measures of political economy. This is but one, though an important instance; many others might be named, were this a proper place.

SECT. V.—POPULATION.

I FOUND ideas afloat, that the country, in some districts, was not so populous as it had been; chiefly founded on the militia lists : one man is now taken in seven or eight, and once it was only one in twelve or thirteen; and vast numbers have enlisted in the army, which is singular in a country where wages are so high. But it was well observed on this by Mr. Chaplin, of Blankney, that perhaps this circumstance was the cause; such wages enabled them to get drunk and acquire idle habits; and then playing the fool was not surprising.

In Gainsborough, something above 1200 houses.

I wished to procure, while in the county, the births and burials of many parishes, but was unable to effect it; a few I was favoured with; some of which will shew in what manner enclosure has operated to diminish or increase the people.

Wintringham was enclosed in 1764; the Rev. Mr. Knight favoured me with the

Births

Births from 1732 to 1763, both inclusive, being 32 years	413
Ditto from 1765 to 1796, both inclusive, being 32 years	607
Increase since the enclosure	194

Deaths from 1732 to 1736	354
——— 1765 to 1796	398
Increase	44

Difference between the births and burials, 1732 to 1763	59
Ditto, 1765 to 1796	209

The comparison in this parish is therefore striking in every point of view, and proves that a vast increase of population has taken place since the enclosure.

Horbling was enclosed in 1764; I owe the account to the Rev. Mr. Shinglar.

Births in 33 years before the enclosure	385
Ditto in 33 years* since the enclosure	350
Diminution	35

Deaths in 33 years before the enclosure	390
Ditto in 33 years since	348
Diminution	42

In this parish, therefore, births have lessened.

Billingborough was enclosed in 1771; the same gentleman favoured me with this also.

* The year of enclosure included.

Births

Births in 26 years before the enclosure	360
Ditto in 26 years since the enclosure	444
Increase	84

Deaths in 26 years before the enclosure	390
Ditto in 26 years since	475
Increase	85

Here, births are increased considerably.

The Rev. Mr. Allington favoured me with the account of Swinop.

	Births.		*Burials.*
Births and burials in ten years, from 1704 to 1713	9	....	6
Ditto in ten years, from 1714 to 1723	10	....	8
Ditto in ten years, from 1724 to 1733	9	....	13
Ditto from 1734 to 1743	17	....	7
Ditto from 1744 to 1753	10	....	3
Ditto from 1754 to 1763	12	....	9
Ditto from 1764 to 1773	15	....	5
Ditto from 1774 to 1783	13	....	0
Ditto from 1784 to 1793	23	....	6

Population seems here to have been almost on a regular increase, but especially for the last thirty years. There are some circumstances in the statistical progress of this parish that are curious.

Account of the estate of Swinop in 1728, by Mr. Amcotts, of Harrington, written to Mr. Allington's uncle.

"Mr. Field the tenant makes as follows;

Letts

	£.	s.	d.
Letts off to cottagers about, per annum ..	£. 15	0	0
Sold 100 quarters of oats, at 13*s*.	65	0	0
Sold about 70 quarters of barley, at 24*s*. ..	84	0	0
N.B. Corn gives a high price.			
Wool, about seven to the tod, at 14*s*. about 60 tod	42	0	0
N.B. Wool very low, and they have great losses in their sheep through the poor keeping.			
Three-shear wethers, sold 40*s*.	25	0	0
Ten oxen sold	40	0	0
Swine, horses, drape ewes, and old cows, raised about	32	0	0
	£. 303	0	0

"I find he pays Mr. Remington 24*l*. tithe of the land he occupies, which is 6*s*. in the pound, for his rent is but 80*l*. as he letts to cottagers 15*l*.

"His outgoings,

	£.	s.	d.
Rent	£. 95	0	0
Tithe	24	0	0
Town charges about	4	0	0

Servants wages, labour, wear and tear, repairs, I cannot judge of.

"He keeps two draughts, and adds one in spring for the sowing time; generally plough for oats 100 acres, and for barley 60. Gathers two quarters from each acre, and sows half a quarter on each. He lives very carefully and providently; keeps little company, and bears a good character, as a justice, for not promoting business. Orford is on the west of Swinop, where Lord William Poulett's tenant sows turnips, and has after them good barley."

Mr.

Mr. Allington remarks on this account, that the quantity under gorse must have been very considerable; and from no mention being made of it among the products, it is probable that nothing was made of it. Also that bad as it thus appears to have been in 1728, he has reason to conclude, from the very great marl-pits on the estate, and which are very ancient, that it was once better cultivated.

By a survey of the estate in the latter part of the reign of Queen Elizabeth, it appears that the meadows, 47 acres, were divided into four pieces; and 280 acres of pasture were 25 pieces, some so small as one rood and five perches.

This estate, which in 1728 lett at 95*l.* cottages included, would now lett at 12*s.* an acre round, tithe-free, which, for 1600 acres, the measure then, is 960*l.* supposing the enclosure finished, which Mr. Allington has a power of doing, and buildings for two farms raised.

It lett in 1762 at 230*l.* for 21 years, by Mr. Allington's father. In 1779, for 300*l.* for fourteen years, sinking four years of the former lease; this ran on till 1793, when the present Mr. Allington took it.

Prices at Swinop.

1752. Wheat, two quarters and a sack, 4*l.*; 32*s.* a quarter.

1753. A fat hog 3*s.* 6*d.* a stone.

Sainfoin 20*s.* a quarter.

Three pair of six year old oxen, 14*l.* 15*s.* a pair.

A pair of five year old beasts, and two heifers two year old, 21*l.* 5*s.*

Eighty

Eighty wethers at Caistor, 12*s*. 9*d*. each.
Forty old ewes, at 6*s*. each.

1753. Twenty-seven culled wethers, 14*l*. 3*s*. 6*d*.
Wool 15*s*. 6*d*. a tod, and locks at 3*s*.
Slaughter of rabbits, sold at 7*s*. 6*d*. a dozen.
Bought 23 two-shear wethers at 10*s*. 9*d*, in May.
——— 21 one-sheared ditto, at 10*s*. 3*d*. in May.
Five gelt ewes, at 8*s*. 6*d*. in June.
Ten hog sheep, at 9*s*.
Bought a sow and nine pigs, 3*l*. 5*s*.
Bought two tups, 4*l*. 4*s*.
Sold a cow and calf, 4*l*. 7*s*. 6*d*.
Wintering fourteen steers, at 8*d*. a head per week.

1754. Fat hog 3*s*. 6*d*. a stone

1755. Oats 12*s*. a quarter.
Pirky wheat 23*s*. a quarter.

1758. Two six year old beasts bought at Caistor fair, 12*l*. 14*s*.
Three yearling calves bought at ditto, at 2*l*. 2*s*. each.
Four Yorkshire steers bought at ditto, 15*l*.
One four year old steer ditto, 4*l*. 4*s*.
A Welsh bull 2*l*. 15*s*.
Twelve Welsh heifers 2*l*. 17*s*. each, two year old.
Thrashing *bullimon*, 7*d*. a quarter.
——— barley, 1*s*. a quarter.

The progress of things in this parish seems to have been a picture of the kingdom at large. In the Chapter of Sheep, it appears that Mr. Allington keeps on this farm 1460 which produce above 1000*l*. In 1728 there were 420 on it, which yielded from 60*l*. to 70*l*.; it it was then nearly all sheep-walk, but now a scene of cultivation! What a change! Our politicians wonder at the ideas of those days, that England could bear no greater national debt than 100 millions. Proportionably to this parish, she could better bear a thousand millions now, than fifty in 1728. For want of searching in old family papers, we know little of the miserable state of this kingdom sixty or seventy years ago, a few counties near London, excepted: the great flight has been taken in the last forty years, and much, very much, has been done in thirty, since the period of my Tours; and curious it is to me now to travel, and see the marvellous change.

State

State of Population at Horncastle, in Lincolnshire, for the last Fifty Years; taken from the Parish Register, beginning January 1, 1740, and ending December 31, 1789, inclusive.

Anno Domini.	Births.	Deaths.	Increase by Births.	Diminution by Deaths.
Jan. 1, 1740, to Dec. 31, inc.	52	43	9	—
1741	39	49	—	10
1742	41	32	9	—
1743	49	33	16	—
1744	41	24	17	—
1745	46	34	12	—
1746	37	33	4	—
1747	50	58	—	8
1748	50	49	1	—
1749	39	35	4	—
1750	44	21	23	—
1751	38	13	25	—
1752	42	36	6	—
1753	51	40	11	—
1754	43	32	11	—
1755	50	34	16	—
1756	50	32	18	—
1757	40	21	19	—
1758	41	22	19	—
1759	39	43	—	4
1760	48	58	—	10
1761	54	69	—	15
1762	48	34	14	—
1763	58	40	18	—
1764	44	30	14	—
1765	62	29	33	—
1766	56	53	3	—
1767	51	36	15	—
1768	44	49	—	5
1769	40	47	—	7
1770	59	21	38	—
1771	43	35	8	—

Anno

Anno Domini.	Births.	Deaths.	Increase by Births.	Diminution by Deaths.
Jan. 1, 1772, to Dec. 31, inc.	42	44	—	2
1773	47	47	21	—
1774	58	31	—	—
1775	42	44	—	2
1776	62	38	24	—
1777	59	47	12	—
1778	60	40	20	—
1779	48	45	3	—
1780	59	52	7	—
1781	51	47	4	—
1782	55	34	21	—
1783	64	60	4	—
1784	55	64	—	9
1785	55	47	8	—
1786	61	47	14	—
1787	54	44	10	—
1788	72	33	39	—
1789	83	39	44	—
1790	66	53	13	—

The former Statement divided into periods of five years.

1740 to 1744 incl.	222	181	41
1745 1749 —	222	209	13
1750 1754 —	218	142	76
1755 1759 —	220	152	68
1760 1764 —	252	231	21
1765 1769 —	253	214	39
1770 1774 —	249	184	65
1775 1779 —	271	214	57
1780 1784 —	284	257	27
1785 1789 —	325	210	115

From a MS. state of the diocese of Lincoln, taken in the year 1565, it appears that Horncastle then contained 164 families.

Burton

Burton parish:

Years.	Baptisms.	Burials.
1776	14	7
1777	15	6
1778	13	6
1779	20	6
1780	7	8
1781	9	3
1782	16	8
1783	14	10
1784	16	4
1785	11	6
	135	64
	64	
Increase	71	

Years.	Baptisms.	Burials.
1787	14	12
1788	14	9
1789	13	4
1790	13	6
1791	13	4
1792	13	7
1793	15	4
1794	9	7
1795	14	7
1796	11	6
	129	64
	64	
Increase	65	

In

In Freiston:

Years.	*Births.*	*Deaths.*
1775	22	17
1776	21	20
1777	20	18
1778	25	19
1779	21	26
1780	15	56
1781	23	26
1782	18	23
1783	23	12
1784	24	30
1785	26	18
	238	265
		238
	Decrease	27
1786	27	16
1787	23	28
1788	32	23
1789	18	29
1790	23	23
1791	19	13
1792	17	9
1793	20	23
1794	19	16
1795	23	23
1796	20	23
	241	226
	226	
Increase	15	

In

In this parish there are quite as many houses now, as there were 30 years ago; several new ones have been erected in the five years from 1792 to 1797; some have been built from an idea of the common being to be enclosed, on the sites of old ones that had gone to decay: this, with a view of claiming their common-rights. Farms remain as they were; there is not one in the parish of more than 280 acres, though there are 3094 acres in the parish; and the next in size does not exceed 140. Poor's-rates in 1796 were 360*l.* of which about 60*l.* the Navy, besides Militia. Rent about 3000*l.* Population remains nearly stagnant, though the difference in the burials more than balances that of the births.

CHAP. XVI.

OBSTACLES.

A VERY singular nuisance in Deeping Fen, from 1795 to 1797, has been mice; which have multiplied to such a degree in the pastures, as almost to starve the sheep. The land is alive with them. Mr. Greaves has, in a field of a few acres, killed eight or ten by his horse treading on them.

In the hundred of Skirbeck, the chief obstacle is the height of tithes; and, as there thought, the unwillingness of landlords permitting grass land to be ploughed up, which would pay much more under the plough than in grazing. In all the parishes that have been enclosed here, the ancient lands have been exonerated of tithe, as well as the new enclosure, which has removed the former in many instances.

About Kevesby, &c. a material obstacle also (in the opinion of my informant), is the unwillingness of landlords to permit the farmers to plough grass-land; but which is in part removing, by their now permitting parts to be ploughed for turnips and seeds, to support the sheep in winter, which formerly used to be done by mowing the best grass land for winter food.

But the greatest obstacle I know in the county, is the general practice of giving no leases.

CHAP. XVII.

MISCELLANEOUS.

SECT. I.—SOCIETIES.

FEBRUARY 29, 1796, there was established at Folkingham a society, very properly called the Lincolnshire Agricultural Society, being the first in the county. The purport seems to have been, to collect the practical farmers together, and to turn the conversation upon topics well adapted to promote improvements: this produced a disposition to turn desultory discourse into some more formal attempt to make a regular subject the object of disquisition, so that after a few meetings, questions of utility were regularly proposed for discussion, and resolutions come to upon such; this being but the infancy of the institution, it is not to be expected that any great progress has been made; however, the following circumstances will shew that this infant society have got into a very good train, and that in their future progress the greatest things may be expected from them, viz.

Query I. Whether is it right to reduce lands from their original state, viz. from curves into straight lines, or let them remain in their original state?

Resolved, by the members present, that reducing such lands to level and straight work is approved.

Query II. After reduced in the manner above-mentioned.

tioned, what sized lands are best adapted to farming to the greatest advantage?

Resolved, that from four to five yards are the best sized lands.

Query III. What is the cause of the halt in sheep; what produces it? Does it originate in the constitution of the animal?

Various opinions were held; but in general determined, that a general neatness in the pastures, and to keep the animal well pared in the spring months, are preventatives.

Query IV. What is the best method of producing food for sheep in the spring, after turnips are expended?

Resolved, as the general opinion, that tares are the properest, unless land be in a high state of cultivation, so as to admit sowing rye on light soils; which in such case might be fed in the spring, and afterwards left for a crop.

Query V. What is the best method of ensuring a crop of turnips? what manure best to lay on; whether straw manure, made in the yard previous to sowing, or that carted out the season before, termed spit manure?

Resolved, that straw manure is proper for heavy soils, and spit manure for light ones (but not generally determined); and to scale them in previous to sowing, and afterwards give them a second ploughing; or otherwise lay on the manure, and plough in, and sow immediately. Recommended by the members now present to try both methods, and report the result of their operations both ways.

Members

Members of the Society:

Thomas Rasor,	Thomas Harley,
Henry Burton,	William Wyan,
Stephen Oliver,	Edward Maples,
John Holderness,	John Newton,
Robert Newcomb,	John Summers,
William Dawson,	Henry Hoyte, Secretary.
John Cragg,	

SECT. II.—WEIGHTS AND MEASURES.

"In that rude state of society, while all exchange of commodities is by barter, weights and measures are useless; but as soon as they become necessary, they ought to be sacred. Every departure should be watched with a vigilant eye, and opposed with a vigorous hand. Even in the infancy of commercial intercourse, divers weights and measures have always been found an evil; but in the present maturity of British commerce, when the same person may have occasion to transact business at a vast variety of distant markets at the same time, an almost equal variety of weights and measures must prove extremely vexatious, and frequently the cause of imposition and loss. As such a diversity in the standards of exchange between man and man, can answer no other purpose than to render the simple, the illiterate, and the unsuspicious, more the dupes of the designing and dishonest than they are by nature; so it should seem, that a complete correction of the evil complained of, is a debt which Government owes to the country. With respect to that inequality which most affects the interests of agriculture, meaning, in the measure of corn,

corn, I hear it said, "you have statutes; let them be executed."—It may be answered, that at the time those statutes were enacted, it is probable the people did not properly interest themselves in the matter; so that for want of a self-enforcing principle in the statutes themselves, and of a disposition in the people to second the efforts of the legislature, the excellent provisions in those laws never, in fact, became generally established; and were, indeed, to the generality of the people, utterly unknown. The people, therefore, of this generation are not to blame; and in many instances where the public spirit, and zeal of individuals, have caused them to exert themselves in the business, it has been found impossible, without the renewed exertions of the legislature, to root out old custom, and combat the powers of interested opposition. But as the people have manifested that their attention is now awake to this necessary reform, and have in various parts of the kingdom shewn their disposition to second the legislature, now is the opportunity for rendering to the country this important service. To say that the legislature cannot effectually remove the evil, by an amendment of the law, would be a strange position. Perhaps the magnitude of the present penalties may prevent prosecutions. Perhaps applying the penalties to some *parochial* purpose, might have an admirable effect. I should recommend, that in every parish, he who should produce to the Justices at quarter-sessions, all his bushels and *other measures*, register their dimensions (agreeing with the standard), and declare upon oath that he would neither buy nor sell any other measure than such as the law prescribed; nor make any bargains whatever, wherein any allowances should

be

be made, either in money or in corn*, flour, &c.; for deliveries by measures not according to the standard, *should be exempt from all parochial assessments whatever, until three-fourths, at least, of the inhabitants had in like manner, so registered their measures, and taken the like oath;* and that such inhabitants, or occupiers of land, in the parish as should neglect such registry, and such oath, *should be liable to make good all deficiencies, occasioned by such exoneration of those who complied with the law;* and further, that all persons dealing in corn, &c. not so registering their bushels, and other measures, should by the clerk of the peace be reported to the collectors of taxes, whose duty it should be, *to levy on them double taxes on houses and windows."—By J. Cartwright, Esq.*

SECT. III.—RELIGION.

The prosperity of agriculture, as of every thing else, depending on the moral and religious habits of the people, too much attention cannot be paid to those circumstances which influence it. I found upon the Wolds a neglect of public worship, which ought to receive animadversion. It is not uncommon in many parishes to have divine service performed but once in three weeks or a month; in others, once a fortnight. Where this is the case, such a mischievous defect generates

* Here it would be necessary to guard against all evasions in deliveries, by the *quarter*, *loom*, *last*, &c. by declaring the Winchester bushel to be the *root* of all measures, whether larger or smaller than a bushel, and to give a table of the same, constituting a *legal standard* throughout the whole scale, from the *pint* to the *last*.

nerates inattention and carelessness whether or not it is performed at all. What right has the landlord to expect an honest farmer, and what farmer to expect an honest labourer, in a country where the worship of the Almighty is thus neglected? The livings are miserably poor: does not this shew the necessity of the Clergy being well provided for? If the stipends are so small, that four or five parishes can only support one clergyman, such must be the consequence; and the people, abandoned to Sundays of mere idleness, without religious instruction, necessarily resort to ale-houses, and become depraved and licentious. National prosperity depends on the industry of the common people; industry on good morals; and as good morals amongst the poor are nursed only by the Gospel being preached to them, it must be clear to every considerate mind, that the most important of the national interests must suffer by a neglect of public worship. Nothing tends more strongly (as Addison has well remarked) to civilize the lower classes, than the institution of a Sabbath; when their labours cease, and dressed in their best attire, they assemble at the parish church to worship the common Father of all. The omission of this motive, and opportunity of appearing clean, and mixed in a general assembly of the parish, entails dirt, slovenliness, and rags; drunkenness, idleness, and consequent profligacy, and would, if continued, tend more strongly than any other circumstance to render them savages. I know nothing better calculated to fill a country with barbarians ready for any mischief, than extensive commons, and divine service only once a month. I am not a judge of the means of remedying such an evil; but the Right Reverend Prelate, who presides ecclesiastically in this province, and

and whose abilities are well known, would, without doubt, have done it, had he possessed the power.

As I have thus the occasion to touch upon the subject of religion, I shall make one other remark. Labour is so extremely high in the fen part of this county, that I have many times heard it there regretted, that they could not work in harvest on Sundays, in ticklish seasons. My opinion is so much the reverse, and would be the same if I farmed in the county, that I must add one word on this pernicious idea, which seems to take it for granted, that saving a little corn is of more value to the farmer, than so much of a religious temper of mind amongst the poor, as depends on keeping holy the Sabbath day; and which, in fact, is the whole of the religion that is found amongst most of the poor. The Gospel is their *peculiar* privilege; and I know not a more abominable proposition than to attempt to bribe them to the neglect of it. People who think and speak thus carelessly, can have little notion of the providence of the Almighty, when they imagine the possibility of thriving by economy in corn purchased at the expense of His worship, whose bounty is the origin of all crops, and all possessions. *Would they not be as well employed, as in drinking at an ale-house?* I do not know that. They may be tempted of a Sunday to transgress; but it is not upon *design*, upon *system;* they are not hired by their masters to do it; they are not led astray there by superior ranks. But why is a bad habit on one part of the Lord's day to become a reason for misapplying the rest of it? If a labourer is tempted to the alehouse in the evening, can that be a reason for inducing him to neglect the worship of God in the morning? Can any accidental breaches of the Sabbath be a motive

tive for lessening his respect for that day of rest? And how is he to respect it, if he sees his betters abusing it? To the scandal of the kingdom, of the legislature, and the execution of the laws, therefore to the scandal of the magistracy, we see carriers' waggons, and stage-coaches, crowding the roads on Sunday: add to this, the fields full of workmen; and where soon would divine worship be found? Do French principles make so slow a progress that you should lend them such helping hands? No; far be it from any honest farmer to regret this day of sacred rest to his servants, his labourers, and his cattle; nor ever forget, that let him plough, and sow, and water, it is ANOTHER who giveth the increase; that great, and for ever to be adored Being, to whom we owe our ALL, who gives the rich the enjoyment of their wealth, and the poor and miserable the consolation of the SABBATH*.

* I believe in harvest as much is, in many cases, gained by resting on a Sunday, as in others is lost by it. In a ticklish season, after some days of rain, the common error is carrying too soon; at such times, being forced to lose a day, is, in fact, a gain.

THE END.

Printed by B. McMillan,
Bow Street, Covent Garden.